KILLER FICTION

BY

G.J. SCHAEFER

AS TOLD TO

SONDRA LONDON

FOREWORD BY COLIN WILSON

INTRODUCTION BY SONDRA LONDON

FERAL HOUSE

An earlier version of "The Serial Killer Who Loved Me"
was published in *Knockin' on Joe: Voices from Death Row*
Nemesis Books (London, England, 1993),
along with "My Ticket to the Society of Fiends," "Death House Screams,"
"Early Release," and "Nigger Jack."
"Nigger Jack" was published in *Loompanics Unlimited Main Catalog 1992*
and *Loompanics Golden Records 1993*.
"Early Release" was published in *Loompanics Golden Records 1993*.
"Spring Break" was published in *Brutarian*, Vol. 1 #2.
"Expecting Dinner" was published in *Boiled Angel* #7.

All photographs and illustrations
are provided courtesy of Sondra London.

This Special Edition of *Killer Fiction* is published
by
FERAL HOUSE
© 1997 by Sondra London & Feral House

First Printing

CONTENTS

ILLUSTRATIONS

HALITOSIS OF THE SOUL
by Colin Wilson

G erard John Schaefer was undoubtedly one of the nastiest serial killers of the twentieth century.

I am not speaking simply about his crimes — which were certainly bad enough — but about his mind. George Orwell said of Henry Miller that there must be millions of men who think and speak of sex just as crudely, but that the surprising thing is to see it written down. That comment could readily be applied Schaefer. American prisons must be full of men whose view of sex is as brutal and sadistic as Schaefer's; the astonishing thing is to see it presented in the form of literature.

Schaefer did his best to perpetuate that view. His stories, he said, were supposed to be shocking; their purpose was to make people see what real violence was all about. Many readers, I suspect, will fail to understand what purpose is served by printing them. Although I see their point, perhaps I can provide a meaningful rationale.

When I first read an account of Schaefer's crimes in *True Detective* magazine in 1974, and learned that the evidence that convicted him consisted of a number of sadistic stories that were found in the back of a closet, I felt considerable curiosity about the stories. Then finally in 1991, when I saw *Killer Fiction* advertised in the catalogue of New Jersey bookseller, I ordered it immediately.

I found that this collection of Schaefer's stories, edited by Sondra London, certainly provided an interesting insight into the mind of this most sadistic serial killer. Schaefer fantasizes repetitively about the same thing: picking up a "whore," taking her to some remote location, then stabbing or hanging her and defiling her lifeless corpse. So in fact, these early writings cannot be treated as literature, even of the most primitive order — they are too repetitive. The only possible reason to study them is for the insight they afford into the disordered mind of the sexual psychopath.

Technically speaking, based solely on his convictions, Schaefer could not be labeled a serial killer. He was sentenced to life imprisonment in 1973 for the murder of two girls, Georgia Jessup and Susan Place, whom he killed while he was out on a $15,000 bail for "kidnapping" and threatening two other young girls.

Fortunately, the mother of Susan Place had noted down the license number of Susan's date on the evening she disappeared. That license number, beginning with a 4, led the police to the obviously innocent owner of a car in Pinellas County, Florida.

Six months after her daughter's disappearance, Lucille Place happened to be driving through Martin County when she noticed that all the car license plates began with 42. She now re-checked the number she had noted down, substituting 42 for 4, and learned that this license belonged to Gerard John Schaefer. Learning

that Schaefer was now in jail for the abduction and assault of two girls, Mrs. Place went to look at Schaefer's picture, and recognized him as the man who had driven off with her daughter and Georgia Jessup. Georgia's purse was found in Schaefer's room, as were three cartons of papers containing the "killer fiction" that jurors cited in sending him to prison for two life terms. The police were fairly certain by then that Schaefer was responsible for at least twenty other dead or missing girls, and recent detective work has brought to light some tantalizing connections between the writings Schaefer bills as fiction and some very real victims.

Sondra London describes how, when she was 17, she met a handsome 18-year-old student then known as John Schaefer, who became her first lover. Bright, attractive and personable, she reports that he made quite a presentable escort for the greater part of a year. But in due course, his darker side emerged as he admit-

Susan Place,
Murdered in 1992
by G.J. Schaefer

ted that at times he was overwhelmed by the violent compulsions of his "inner demons." In fact, by his own admission (in "False Confessions") he had killed at least seven women before he ever had normal sex with a girl — who may well have been Sondra London.

One of the essays he wrote about the time he was dating Sondra concludes: "It is trying to fight the urge to relieve these terrible cravings. I am sure that there must be an answer somewhere, and some day I will be cured." Schaefer was tormented by his obsession with sexualized violence, and seems somewhat wistful as he tries to wish it all away.

Sondra states that she broke off her affair with the budding serial killer not because he harmed, abused or threatened her, but because she did not want to serve as his psychiatrist or mother confessor. They parted company after a year, and then nine years later, she learned that he had been convicted of murder. Finally, in 1989, twenty-five years after first meeting him, she wrote to her ex-lover in prison, inviting him to collaborate on a book about his life and crimes.

Most prisoners are glad to enter into a correspondence. Prison is a dreary and demoralizing place, and since human beings can only achieve personal evolution through self-expression, one of the most damaging things about imprisonment is that the convict's mind is condemned to stagnation. And so it was that after being isolated from intelligent companionship for the greater part of his adult life, Schaefer poured considerable energy into his correspondence with the woman who had once been his closest companion.

Although Schaefer's writing technique showed considerable improvement after being honed by college-level creative writing courses under the Southern Gothic novelist Harry Crews, his psyche remained fixated at the same coprophilic level revealed in the early writings seized by police in 1972.

In the spring of 1989, Schaefer began sending London not just repetitive, sadistic fantasies, but also some extremely interesting narratives that appear to be far more factual, with titles like "Flies in Her Eyes" and "False Confessions." It is typical of Schaefer that he modified "confessions" with "false," so that if challenged, he could claim that it was just a fantasy; he always tried to have it both ways.

I have to admit that Schaefer is a far nastier character than Danny Rolling, the Gainesville serial killer, to whose autobiography — under this same publisher's imprint — I have also written an introduction. What comes over clearly from Rolling's book is that, no matter what he has done, Rolling remains a fundamentally a decent human being who is as appalled by his heinous acts as his readers are.

Let me state before we go any further that I am not one of these "bleeding heart" liberals who insist that all criminals are created by their environment and upbringing, and therefore are not really to blame. I do not believe this and, frankly, neither do most criminals.

At St. Elizabeth's Hospital New York in 1961, two psychiatrists of that liberal persuasion, Samuel Yochelson and Stanton Samenow, began to study criminals and ended by doing a complete about-turn, finally concluding that criminals are adept self-deceivers whose conduct only changes when they face up to the fact that they are going to spend a lifetime in jail if they go on like this. They change by making a conscious choice to do so. But most of them, Yochelson and Samenow found, exhibit a "cutoff mechanism" that enables them to push inconvenient thoughts out of their consciousness. They would, for example, confess frankly at one meeting, then insist they had never said it at the next. Years of research brought Yochelson and

Georgia (Crystal) Jessup,
Murdered in 1992
by G.J. Schaefer

Samenow to the conclusion that the essential trait of the criminal mind is a sort of wishful thinking that Sartre called *mauvais foi*, or self-deception.

I am inclined to dismiss the usual excuses about why criminals commit crimes. Yet one thing is perfectly obvious. The criminal's background tends to be basically *purposeless*. Which means that he will usually allow himself to drift into situations. This helps to explain why youngsters like Elmer Wayne Henley and David Brooks, associates of the Houston mass-murderer Dean Corll, can become killers without giving it much thought. Most teenagers are bored out of their minds. And, given a bad family background and a few minor brushes with the law, it is not difficult for a young person to take those first steps toward becoming a hardened criminal. It seems to me that Rolling drifted unwittingly into patterns of criminal behavior in this fashion, but that Schaefer did it far more willfully and with less of a sense of self-division.

At this point, I must make an admission that may seem totally absurd. When I began to write a book called *The Occult* in 1969, I had no doubt that most of the phenomena reported were the product of nonsensical superstition. With continuous and careful study, however, I came to believe that what we call a "ghost" may be a kind of "tape recording," which might be the emotional counterpart of an unpleasant smell lingering around the scene of a tragedy. I was also initially inclined to believe that poltergeists — "banging ghosts" — are due to psychokinesis, or mind over matter, on the part of emotionally disturbed teenagers. But more than a decade of study has finally convinced me that ghosts might well represent the spirits of the dead, and that poltergeists, in most cases, are also disembodied spirits.

My research into thousands of reported cases also came to change my mind about so-called "possession." In the days when I was writing *The Occult*, I was confident that the phenomenon was simply the result of an overheated imagination fueled by sexual frustration. Two important books by psychiatrists disabused me of that interpretation: Adam Crabtree's *Multiple Man*, and Ralph Ellison's *Minds in Many Pieces*. I finally came to accept that there may be some highly unpleasant entities in the "psychic ether," that can freely gain access into minds that are already on the same "vibration" or wavelength. This, then, may be the real meaning behind the Devil's temptation of Faust and other similar legends.

Danny Rolling readily admits that his mind was already inclined towards negative vibrations, starting with his relationship with an irascible and domineering father, and later compounded by problems with his marriage. His first rape was committed in a state of rage, misery and self-pity when his wife divorced him, and from then on — as always in such cases — sex crime became steadily easier. Rolling's belief that, when he committed sex murders, he was taken over by a demonic entity, *may* be self-deception, but I am now willing to allow for the possibility that he could be correct.

And now, upon reconsidering *Killer Fiction*, I feel even more strongly that if ever a man "opened" himself to negative forces, it was Gerard John Schaefer.

On Feb. 28, 1989, before he started writing the new stories for *Killer Fiction,* he wrote a letter to Sondra London expressing this awareness, and then deliberately summoned up the very forces he identified as malignant:

> The unsettling thing about my fiction is that my most superlative pieces all centered around a violent theme and then it became a violent theme with sexual tones woven in. I became so accomplished at this violent theme that people would read it and believe it was *ME* rather than a creative exercise. But it ain't creative, it's destructive.
>
> I came to realize over the years that thought is energy and in the act of thinking and transcribing the thought to paper, I was creating an energy pattern of murderous violence. The energy pattern is *negative* and therefore attracts the unseen evil forces that feed off the violent thought.
>
> Since I've come to understand the matter, I've avoided writing murderous fiction. But then I started writing murderous fact.

Schaefer claims, in "False Confessions," that his first murder was accidental,

and that he was surprised to find that in "fooling around" with a garrote, he had killed a girl. If that is true, it was certainly appallingly bad luck — like the glimpse of a girl undressing that supposedly initiated Ted Bundy's lifetime interest in sex murder. Of course, Schaefer may be fabricating here; but I am inclined to think there is an element of truth in even his most perfervid ruminations; if not in a literal sense, certainly in a psychological sense.

The problem with young and healthy males is that most of them go around in a state of permanent sexual arousal. I speak quite candidly from my own personal experience, since during my own teens, from about the age of 13, I was thinking about sex more often than not. One advertisement along our school bus route, of a girl in bra and panties climbing onto a pair of scales (advertising a laxative) never failed to cause a violent stir in my loins; so did every shop window full of women's underwear, as well as every pair of knickers on a clothes line. I was in a continual state of sexual overstimulation, and often walked around exhausted from mastur-bation. But at least my powerful sexual impulses found their relief in fantasy and fetishism; there was never the slightest temptation to commit a sex attack. And when, at the age of 18, I was seduced by a 15 year old girl, and suddenly discov-ered that it was not difficult to persuade girls to make love, my sexual impulses found a "normal" channel — although the fetishism remained as strong as ever (as I suspect it does in a large percentage of "normal" men.) My sexual impulse, however, still tended to be about ten times as strong as convenient, and the mere sight of a girl bending over in a miniskirt was like a kick in the solar plexus that left me shattered and breathless.

So I find it perfectly easy to empathize with Rolling or Schaefer to a certain extent. I only have to assume that Schaefer was somehow "imprinted" with the idea of raping "whores" (in the same way that I was imprinted with instant arousal at the sight of a pair of panties — whether on or off a girl) to realize how easy it must have been to become a sex killer. In the young and oversexed male the de-light of sex seems infinitely sweet — this is, after all, the method by which nature deceives us into propagating the species — and most young men would walk a thousand miles to have sex with an attractive girl. Danny Rolling quotes a study in which male college students were asked whether they would rape a girl if they could get away with it, and 90% of them said yes. I personally could never have committed rape, because I was too sensitive to the feelings of other people. My equivalent was to commit symbolic rape on a pair of panties from a bathroom laundry basket. But if some genie could have been persuaded to present me with naked girls in a state of drugged sleep, I believe I would have found it easy enough.

So when I read "Gator Bait," with Schaefer's description of his sexual excite-ment as he spied on the woman sunbathing in her bikini, I can perfectly under-stand why he committed his first sex attack. But here I notice a significant differ-ence between Schaefer and my own teenage self. He wants to humiliate her, to call her a whore, to urinate on her, to pretend he was about to penetrate her anus with a knife. Like so many sex criminals, he finds the notion of sodomy more exciting than normal vaginal penetration, possibly because it is more "forbidden." And the whores fascinate him because, unlike "virtuous girls," he feels they are inviting degradation, rape, and ultimately murder by being "immoral." As a youth,

Schaefer's overdeveloped sexual urges were already focused on real girls, without the possibility of "symbolic rape." He had also become "imprinted," for some reason, on the idea of hanging women.

It seems clear that the double assault for which Schaefer received his original prison sentence was the enactment of a long-standing and often-rehearsed fantasy. We can see that, in spite of having committed a number of murders already, he did not reveal himself to be a particularly competent perpetrator in this case, as he allowed both girls to escape. Schaefer was not living in the real world, but rather in a world inside his own head, almost as if his crimes were happening in a book. And in a book like this one, we can see that for Schaefer, writing about a crime was almost as satisfying as committing it. Once he got a good fantasy going — like the idea of a black man who is allowed to wash and sodomize corpses after execution — he is perfectly satisfied.

I have to admit that I have never succeeded in reading *Killer Fiction* from beginning to end, and that I am forced to skip hastily through most of his stories. Schaefer suffers from a kind of halitosis of the soul, and the stench quickly induces disgust.

Again, I try to plumb the depths of his pathology by comparing it with my own. When I was about ten years old, a friend showed me how to catch a tiny winged insect like a small dragonflies, pull off the end of its body, then insert a tiny privet twig into it. Thrown into the air, it would buzz like a tiny airplane. Yet after doing this for a quarter of an hour or so, I suddenly felt sick. Although they were only insects, I had a distinct sense of doing something *wrong*, and I was never able to bring myself to do it again. I feel the same way as I read Schaefer. His moral ceiling is so low that I feel suffocated.

Why, then, do I write this introduction? Because it seems to me that if it comes down to a choice between understanding a serial killer and not understanding him, then I will choose the power of knowledge and understanding over the helpless vulnerability of ignorance. Schaefer's writing vividly depicts the appalling urges that drove him to kill, and it seems to me that understanding the etiology of these atrocities is better than being merely sickened and baffled by them. On the whole, I am somewhat nostalgic for the days when a book like this would be sold only to the medical profession, like the original edition of Krafft-Ebing's *Psychopathia Sexualis* in the 1880's; but since this is the twentieth century, I must accept that it will reach a wider audience.

Books like Wilton Earle's *Final Truth*, about the sadistic serial killer Pee Wee Gaskins, are in some ways more appalling than *Killer Fiction*, but they are generally available in a cheap paperback form. So, whether we like it or not, it seems that there is no middle course between suppressing this book altogether, and making it available to all who may wish to learn from it.

That leaves the question of Schaefer's perverse psychology. It is quite clear that his writing is a form of virtual exhibitionism. Regrettably, very little is known about his upbringing, so it cannot be determined whether anything in his family background gave him (as Jack the Ripper put it) a "down on whores." Sondra London, who was present in the household, reveals that "his father drank a lot, and abused his mother, whom he revered," so it sounds as if he shared certain contributing factors with Rolling.

Schaefer, however, as a Catholic, was steeped in the imagery of the Blessed Virgin and the martyred saints. He attended parochial school, attempted at one time to become a priest, and by his own account, attended daily mass throughout most of his youth. However, this still fails to explain his oddly moralistic position about "whores." In many cases, killers who are morbidly obsessed with prostitutes — like the Yorkshire Ripper Peter Sutcliffe — come from a fairly respectable (and often Catholic) background. They often find the idea of women "selling themselves" at once disgusting and exciting. It is a well-known fact that many sex killers characterize their victims as "whores," presumably providing a spurious sense of self-justification.

It may seem that someone as frankly sadistic as Schaefer would not bother to seek justification; but we only have to look at a story like "Early Release" to see that Schaefer wrote of his victims as a sadistic Nazi thug would write of Jews. "Danny cringed back against the wall, his delicate fag hands waving before him. Cowardly little AIDS-ridden queer…" The sexual psychopath *needs* to justify his own brutality by viewing his victims as evil or degenerate; thus deserving, to his way of thinking, extermination.

Schaefer's attitude towards publicity was also strangely ambivalent. He filed suit on me because I referred to him in *The Serial Killers* as a serial killer. Yet the case was thrown out of court, as I knew it would be, because the defense merely had to draw the judge's attention to Schaefer's own boasts of being the worst serial killer of all time.

It seems clear that, like so many serial killers, Schaefer was deeply lacking in self-esteem. His murders, then, were based on a fantasy of the power he felt by being "in control" of his victims. There is a sense in which we all wish we could be "in control" of the people in our lives. And, of course, as George Bernard Shaw has observed, we all bid for admiration with no intention of earning it. But most of us have the sense to realize that we cannot obtain such admiration without earning it.

Yet even "normal" people often give in to the temptation to obtain admiration or pity by telling lies. The tragedy of such deception becomes apparent in time, and fate takes its revenge as the wheel inevitably turns, placing the victimizer in the position of the victim.

I have just finished reading a remarkable biography by James Sloan of the writer Jerzy Kosinski, which tragically is not unlike that of the life of a serial killer.

When Kosinski came to America as a student in 1957, he began to tell acquaintances appalling tales of having spent the war alone, wandering around Poland; his tribulations included being hung up by his hands from the ceiling by a sadistic landlord, and being hurled into a cesspit by angry peasants because he had dropped the host during mass. Some of the people who were enthralled by his tales of suffering suggested he should write it all down; the result, *The Painted Bird*, was an immense literary success. But Kosinski now felt obliged to keep up the lies, and when his deception was finally exposed, he sank into the depression which ended in suicide.

Kosinski's story is also relevant here because his work is so full of sadism; even though happily married, he was literally a "sex maniac" who had to go out every

night in search of prostitutes, and it seems clear that he loved to humiliate women. This sadism is as basic a part of his deformed psyche as his habitual lying.

Such men are clearly victims of the "sexual illusion." Fetishism is the simplest example of how sex endows mundane matters with a kind of "magic" that produces desire. A girl knows that the panties covering her genitalia are merely a piece of cloth, no more intrinsically exciting than a tea towel. And the young male who experiences an erection when he sees the panties as she bends over also knows, intellectually speaking, that they are merely a garment. Yet something like "another being inside him" responds with excitement and desire.

The sexual illusion is obviously vital to the propagation of the human race, whether it takes the crude form of the sex urge, or the romantic form of the belief that a woman is a kind of goddess. Yet it is of vital importance to remain aware of this element of illusion, and to regard it with a kind of amused tolerance.

Gerard Schaefer seems to have become totally controlled by his own sexual illusions, until they virtually took possession of his soul. In *Killer Fiction*, Schaefer's intellectual capacity comes across as flashes of brilliance, but it is clear that he has surrendered so completely to the sexual illusion that little remains of his true humanity. Are such people *worth* studying? I would argue that they are — just as Kosinski is worth studying.

As to the contention that in publishing this book, Sondra London is merely revealing her own morbid obsession with crime, it seems clear to me that this cannot be sustained. In the preface to *Killer Fiction*, she describes how, in 1989, she was a technical writer who wanted to write something more interesting than computer manuals. The fact that her love life had started with an affair with a serial killer suggested a direction, and the result was the publication of *Killer Fiction* and *Knockin' on Joe*, which includes interviews with Danny Rolling and Henry Lee Lucas' partner in crime, Ottis Toole, and has gone on to become somewhat of a crime classic. It seems to me that with that one book alone, she was justified in abandoning technical writing. And I certainly believe that the autobiography she co-authored with Danny Rolling, *The Making of a Serial Killer,* is an important book, which will continue to be studied by criminologists for years to come.

Although *Killer Fiction* may be dismissed by the casual reader as gratuitously offensive, still it strikes me as a worthwhile addition to the literature of criminal psychology. Law enforcement and psychiatric professionals, as well as laymen who sincerely seek to understand the sick urges that result in the senseless slaughter of innocent strangers, cannot afford to ignore these confessions.

With this volume, the late Gerard John Schaefer, however we may judge him as a person, has certainly left his mark on the literature of true crime.

THE SERIAL KILLER WHO LOVED ME
by Sondra London

Rogue cop GJ Schaefer,
Lady-killer, baby-raper,
Fallen angel, voice from hell,
Found slaughtered in his cell.

Killer fiction, killer fact
Scripted his own final act.
Criminal justice took his life
By enigmatic bloody knife.

Infamy inscribed his name.
Thus inevitably slain
The killer victim on the floor
Will perpetrate — *nevermore.*

CRIMINAL JUSTICE

G erard John Schaefer was hacked to death in his cell at Florida State Prison on Sunday morning, December 3, 1995.

Found by guards an hour later, his blood-drenched body had sustained over 40 stab wounds, predominantly about the head and neck. Chaingang legend has it that one of his eyeballs was found on the yard, but a prison official who inspected the body after hearing the same story himself said that both eyes were still intact. Take your pick.

Vincent Rivera was charged with the murder on February 1, 1996, but a year later, the heavily-muscled 34-year-old confessed double murderer with a yen to die in the electric chair says they have the wrong man.

Psychiatrist Dr. Melvyn Gardner says Rivera has "the highest potential for homicide of any person I have ever examined." With 46 disciplinary infractions since his incarceration in 1991, Rivera regularly disobeys direct orders. Blood-stained clothes and a makeshift shank were taken into evidence, and bloody palmprints found at the scene were preserved pending further investigation.

The news of Schaefer's demise affected me as if a fetid miasma had drifted out the window of my life.

THE CLASSIC CASE

The term *serial killer* was coined by Robert Ressler, the retired FBI agent who helped form the world-renowned Behavioral Science Unit. In his book *Whoever Fights Monsters,* Ressler cites a classic case:

> In our road shows, when I used to display the slides and give the lecture about the organized offender Gerard John Schaefer, someone in my audience would accuse me of having taken the characteristics of that sort of offender right from the details of Schaefer's case. That's not so, but it is true that the patterns associated with the organized killer are starkly apparent in this instance.

Even though he uses Schaefer to exemplify the organized type of serial killer, in a private conversation with this author Ressler reviewed the technicalities involved in defining Schaefer's status:

> I cannot say Schaefer actually was a serial killer, as we go by the record. By my own definition, a serial killer commits at least four murders, in four separate events, precipitated by fantasy, and separated by an emotional cooling-down period. Now, by law, Schaefer had only been convicted of two murders which were done at the same time, so technically, he didn't fit the definition. But everything else did fit — the background, the fantasies, the psychological characteristics, the additional crimes he was suspected of — and so far as I'm concerned, the only thing that kept Schaefer from being labeled a serial killer was the inability of law enforcement to catch up with him.

Since no one knows a subject better than its originator, it is significant that out of thousands of cases, Ressler chose Schaefer to illustrate every salient feature of the organized serial killer. However, neither Ressler nor any other expert in serial murder knew Schaefer as well as I did, because they have never even met the man. I have gone much further than that.

A REAL LADY KILLER

At a high school dance in 1964, before my eyes materialized a dazzling young stranger — a tall, smiling blond, dressed to good advantage in a ruffled blue dress shirt that complemented his brilliant blue eyes and a white sports coat that set off his deepwater tan. Proverbially, he caught my eye across the crowded room and soon we were exchanging words over the punchbowl. So poised, so courteous, so articulate!

The handsome stranger was unable to get my number that night, but I did give him my full name, and the next day he hit the phone book, trying every phone number listed under that name until he found me and asked me out. I was flattered by the attention at the time, but looking back I realize that was an indication of

how thorough and persistent he could be when tracking down a female that excited him. It was the first time I knew what it was like to be pursued by a serial killer.

At 18, John Schaefer was one year older than I was. A bright, well-mannered Catholic boy whose family belonged to the local yacht club, he became my closest companion over the next year. We were in love. My parents were glad I had met such a *nice* boy, and invited him to go along with us on our summer vacation. I remember how we whiled away the hours out on my grandmother's old porch swing, shucking peas and shooting the breeze, good-ole-boy style. I can still see him holding up his hands for my grandmother to wind her knitting yarn, patiently listening to her long, rambling tales and laughing easily at her corny jokes. My aunts adored him, commenting openly on how pleasant and polite he was. Even my demanding father approved of him.

After supper we might ramble through an old graveyard, philosophizing about the ancient dead before making love amongst the tombstones. Those early days remain in my mind like a bubble memory — how well he treated me, how sensitive he was, and how sweetly we loved each other. Many times he held my life in his hands, as he took me into the tangled wilderness of the Everglades, or out on the high seas in his daddy's motorboat. But after a year, as young lovers will, we went our separate ways. I thought I'd never see him again.

Then in 1972 came the screaming headlines: "6 Dead, 28 May Be," and the ghoulish stories about the smiling cop turned sadistic killer and corpse-loving fiend, hoarding mementos of his mutilated victims, and writing it all up in feverish prose. *Absolutely unbelievable!* I was appalled that crimes like this could be committed by anyone, much less someone I had known intimately. Remember, those were the days before the term "serial killer" existed, before Ted Bundy, John Wayne Gacy, and Jeffrey Dahmer so irrevocably showed us what it meant. In those days, Schaefer's type of crime was not only unnamed, it was unheard-of.

Frightened by what had become of my baby-faced dream, I was haunted by questions with unthinkable answers. Did I lose my virginity to a *real* lady-killer? And *how* could it be possible for the sweet boy I had held in my arms to be a homicidal maniac?

As shocked as I was, I'd always wondered about my first lover. Gentle and sweet, bright and polite, he was unfailingly eager to please. There was nothing abnormal about our youthful affair; he was a sensitive and enthusiastic lover. Yet as I searched my mind for clues to the monstrous entity he had become, I recalled the signs of danger. I had been too inexperienced to realize what I was seeing when I was involved with him as a teenager, but once I heard about the murders, looking back I remembered how he had been haunted by violent urges and twisted emotions.

When I first met him, he told me his last girlfriend could only get off when he would play-rape her, rip her clothes off, talk dirty and force sex on her. I let him know I was not like that. He assured me he didn't get off on it either, he only did it to please her. He promised not to treat me that way, and to his credit, he never did. Perhaps I would have seen a different side of him from the beginning if I had responded differently.

According to the last few letters he sent me, he had been cultivating a secret life of sexual perversion and violence even while he was going steady with me. That would explain why his legitimate sex-life was apparently so free of deviance. Hiding the compulsive violence from friends, family members and coworkers is essential to maintaining the lifestyle of the serial killer.

I remember the day I pulled him off his father, who in his usual drunken haze, had called his mother a whore. In defense of his mother's honor, John went after his father with a golf club, cracking him soundly over the head, and the two men were locked in what could have easily been mortal combat as I followed them out of the kitchen and into the carport, begging John to stop. Another time under similar circumstances, he had given his father a concussion with a bottle of barbecue sauce.

Sondra London in 1964
While Dating Schaefer

I have no first-hand knowledge placing my young boyfriend at the scene of any murder. I never saw him kill anything but squirrels, birds and fish. But the murderous intent I saw in his eyes as we stood out in his front yard one summer's eve was unmistakable. He pointed out a certain window on an upstairs bedroom in a house two doors down. Cheeks flushed and eyes simmering with rage, he told me how a girl we both knew enjoyed flaunting her naked charms at him through that window. "What a slut!" he spat. His eyes narrowed as he vowed through clenched teeth, "I'll put a stop to *that*."

When Schaefer was arrested, among his collection of women's jewelry, teeth, and ID's was a dainty gold locket engraved in curly old-fashioned script with a single word that tells an eloquent tale to one who knows how to read it. The legend engraved on that gold locket says simply, "Leigh."

Her name was Leigh Hainline. I was not a close friend, but I did go to school with her. She was known as Leigh Bonadies when she turned up dead, and the address listed was across town, but it was the same girl Schaefer had been watching for years. His name did come up in the investigation, but prosecutors had been unable to find enough evidence to bring charges.

Ironically, only months before Schaefer's grim demise, Tim Bronson, Homicide Chief of the Ft. Lauderdale Police Department had re-opened the Hainline/Bonadies case, along with those of Belinda Hutchens and Carmen Hallock, two other women whose pitiful belongings had been found in Schaefer's possession. Bronson had hoped to conclusively link Schaefer to these murders.

Years later when I asked Schaefer what happened to Leigh, his laconic reply was both a confession and a threat: "When you fuck with the bull, you get the horn."

Schaefer was only nineteen years old when he told me how he struggled with the urge to kill another woman who lived on his street, whom he angrily accused

of flaunting herself at him as she sunbathed in her back yard. We were out on the beach right across from Bahia Mar one windy night in 1965 cuddled up close together under an old Army blanket as he wept with dismay describing how he had planned to murder the sunbather, whom he had already taken to calling a whore, although he knew the woman had a full-time job and kissed her dates good-bye at the front door when they brought her home. He knew that from hiding and watching in the darkness, stoking his rage and stroking his sex, as his fantasies coalesced into plans. He had all his supplies stashed in the back of his old green Ford station-wagon: the baseball bat, the blanket, the ropes, the chains, the gun, and the concrete blocks.

He was going to hit her over the head with a baseball bat and knock her out, quickly wrap her unconscious body in a blanket and tie her up with her rope, drive the wagon down to the dock at the end of the street, load the bundle onto his daddy's boat and run her out to the Everglades, where he would shoot her in the head and "she'd be gator bait by morning." He was sure he could get away with it. "No body, no crime," was the way he put it to me that night. The same phrases he uttered when was just nineteen would be repeated down through the years like a grim litany as the budding *fleurs du mal* blossomed into fullblown flowers of evil.

G.J. Schaefer in 1964
While Dating London

Although he never did kill his neighbor, a graphic account of the how he actually did sexually assault her later surfaced in a nasty little piece of work called "Gator Bait."

About this same time, he confided in Betty Owen, his creative writing teacher, tearfully telling the middle-aged woman that he was obsessed with the urge to kill one of the younger female teachers. She referred him to the school counselor, who told me years later that it was to his everlasting regret that he had recognized the homicidal tendencies in the youth, but had been powerless to help him.

Not long after my young boyfriend broke down in tormented tears over his murderous urges, I told him it was over, dropping him flat without turning back. I don't remember ever feeling afraid of him. I was just tired of being drafted into battle with his demons and I didn't want to be his therapist.

After I broke up with him, he sent me melodramatic poems with silly images like "the ships of hope that had no hulls," and told me he would hide and watch when I came home from dates with my new boyfriend. "I'll get you back," he promised. At the time I took his parting shot to mean he wanted me back as a girlfriend, but time has revealed the ominous undertones of that ambiguous phrase.

Eventually Schaefer moved on to other interests, and as the years passed I put him as far out of my mind as I could. But as hard as I tried, I could not escape the somber knowledge that I was alive while so many of the women who had known him were not.

I found myself scrutinizing the faces of rosy-cheeked blue-eyed strangers, wondering, "Is that him? Is that how he's changed over the years? Is he out of jail already? Has he come looking for me? Is he still mad at me for leaving him?" I'd be on edge until I could determine that the stranger didn't recognize me, because I knew that if it really were him, he'd know me instantly; I would see the flash of recognition in his eyes.

A Good Scare

It was a blistering hot Saturday in July of 1972, a good day for the beach, and Nancy Trotter, 17, and Paula Sue Wells, 18, had planned on catching some rays so they'd have something to show for their trip. Paula, better known as Sue, was from Texas and Nancy was from Illinois. They had been vacationing in Stuart, Florida for just two days. They were going to catch a ride to the beach with the smiling young sheriff's deputy they'd met the day before.

When Nancy and Sue first met Jerry Schaefer, the uniformed cop had been driving his squad car. He told them he'd give them a ride to the beach if they'd meet him at the bandshell at 9:30 A.M. the next day.

But when he pulled up to the bandshell in his battered baby-blue Datsun on Saturday, July 22, he was dressed in shorts and a sport shirt. He'd been switched to plainclothes duty, he explained, and was just doing observations. Because they knew he was a cop, they jumped right in his car, never stopping to wonder what he planned on observing.

Marion County Sheriff Richard Crowder was using his day off to mow the lawn, when his wife called him to the phone. It was Deputy Sheriff Jerry Schaefer, and he said it was important, as Sheriff Crowder described it to me one day in his office. "'I've done something terrible,' he said. 'You're really going to be mad at me this time.' I asked him, well, what was it, and he told me he had arrested a couple of girls and had tied them up but they had got away. So I told him to come on in and report to his shift captain, and I got in my car and went out looking for the girls. I found both of them still in handcuffs, one of them swimming across the river, and the other one walking along the road. Schaefer went on in and turned himself in. Now, he was convicted on that one, and he went to jail for it, but while he was out on bail, it looked like he got ahold of another couple of girls and this time, he killed them."

The day after the assault, Nancy and Sue, covered with bruises, scratches and insect bites, described their day at the beach with Officer Schaefer. In an interview with State's Investigator Littman, Nancy described how it all began.

"Well, he started driving towards Jensen beach, and he asked us if we wanted to see an old Spanish fort that was on the river, and we said OK, you know," said Nancy. "And so he was driving down, and then he pulled in this dirt road, that's when I started getting worried. He kept going back further and further…"

Sue continued, "I got worried, because he had told us the day before when he picked us up, not to tell anyone, you know, he emphasized it several times, not to tell anyone a policeman was taking us out there. I got worried when he turned down that road, because it seemed awfully suspicious."

Nancy described how Schaefer parked the car at the Spanish fort and they all got out. Schaefer thoughtfully sprayed the girls with insect repellent before escorting them around the fort. "Then we went to get back in the car and, uh, we just sat there, and then he looked at us and he said, 'Why did you girls lie to me yesterday?' you know, and we were shocked. And we said, 'About what?' and he started, "Well, I checked up on you in Juvenile Court," and he said he had called up there and that we were runaways."

After explaining to Investigator Littman that it wasn't true, Nancy continued, "We both started laughing, you know, runaways, it sounded kind of funny. And I told him, I said, 'I'm not a runaway, my mother knows where I am and I'm eighteen and it wouldn't matter anyways...'"

Sue picked up, "Then he asked us if we wanted a free ride home, and we said, 'We're not ready to go home, we want to stay another week.' And he said, 'Well, I'm sorry, but you have to go home anyway. Your parents are worried about you, and they want you to come home, and you're runaways. And if you resist, I'll put you under arrest.' And so we figured, well, we don't want to be put under arrest, you know, a free ride home, OK, you know? So then he said, 'Do you have any dope on you?' and we said 'No,' and he said, 'Get out of the car.'"

The girls described how he made them stand outside the car while he went through Nancy's purse. Then, Sue continued: "He asked me if I had anything on me, and I said I do, then he said, 'Well, what do you wear?' and I told him, and he said, 'Do you wear any underwear?' and I told him no. So he said, 'Well, I can't search you because that's illegal, but there's one thing I can do,' and he got in his car, and that's when he got the handcuffs out."

When he asked Nancy what she was wearing, she told him she had on a bathing suit underneath her clothes. "So he said, 'Well, I'm placing you two under arrest for runaways,' and he handcuffed us behind our backs."

Then Sue described how she told him, "'Well, may I laugh? This is really funny,' and he said, 'Sure, go ahead and laugh,' so we just started giggling and then he said, 'Y'all think this is a big joke, you just don't know how serious it really is.'"

But they were soon to find out. Schaefer put the girls back in the car, handcuffed behind their backs. They thought he was going to take them back to the police station, but he told them they were going to sit right there. He asked them numerous questions about the halfway house they'd given as an address, and he wanted to them to tell him all they knew about Stuart, with particular emphasis on where they were getting their dope. They told him they'd only been there two days and they didn't have any dope. For 45 minutes, they sat in the sweltering midsummer heat handcuffed in the back seat of Schaefer's dingy Datsun, listening to him rant about dope and related topics.

"And then he started talking about white slavery," said Sue.

"He asked us how we'd like to be sold into white slavery," explained Nancy. "He said it ought to be a nice experience, you could really see the world, go to South America or South Africa and be a white slave... then he said, 'Would you screw me for $150?' and I said, 'No, not for all the money in the world,' and he said 'If you were a white slave, you'd be doing it for free.' Then he goes, 'How would you like that, Sue? How would you like that?'

"So we just quit talking to him."

"Then he started estimating how much he could get for us," said Nancy. "And he started asking about our parents, if they knew where we were, and did we think they'd put up a ransom for us."

"And I told him my parents would try to scrape up the money, I mean, they're not that well-off, but…" Sue hesitated, then came back, "And then he started in about the white slavery again, and he kept saying he had a friend he could sell white girls to."

Then Nancy Trotter mentioned the same theory Schaefer had described to me seven years earlier. "He was telling us how people disappeared, and there's no crime without a victim, it's just a missing person when they don't have a body." How many other women heard Schaefer recite that sinister motto? And where are those women now?

Paula Sue Wells was still in shock, and her mind had already begun the healing process of suppressing as much of her ordeal as she could, but as she and Nancy relived it for Investigator Littman, it started to come back. "Yes, now I remember. I hadn't thought about it till now, but he said he'd kill us and bury us in a hole real deep and cover us up and nobody would ever find us."

"And all we'd be was a missing person," said Nancy. "I thought all this was to scare us into telling who had the dope in the city, but we were both confused. We couldn't see what it was all for." But the confusing chat in the car was drawing to a close. Now it was time for action.

"He had us get out of the car," Nancy said, "We were still handcuffed, and he got my blanket and made us go over in the field."

Sue continued, "He went to his car and got the key to his trunk, you know, and I saw everything then. He had a bunch of ropes and rags and stuff to tie us up with, and he said, 'We're going to go out in back here in the bushes, and y'all don't run away.' and, 'Can I trust you to stay here while I go get my friend?'"

"Yes, and he wanted us not to scream, too," interjected Nancy.

"So then he took us back in the bushes and laid the blanket down, and gagged both of us, and he told me to lay down on the blanket, but I didn't lay down. I just stood there. And then he tied my legs up and said he was going to separate us and tie us up in different places. And he told me not to try to get away because if I did he would kill me, he'd catch up with me and kill me. And then he told me not to scream, because he said if I screamed, he'd come back and wrap the gag around me so tight I would shit in my pants."

There you have it. Sue had mentioned Schaefer's signature. His fantasies consistently revolved around the moment when the female victim is so terrified she defecates. If she doesn't do it before her death, then she can always be made to produce this thrilling effect in the course of being murdered. His fantasies were predominantly scatological to the end, and the imagery of defecation was bound to surface in any crime he committed. In the parlance of law enforcement, this signature would be appear as Schaefer's "ritual," since that feature was employed solely for his own personal gratification. The pragmatic approach of qualifying his potential victims beforehand and then carefully disposing of their corpses afterwards would be his "M.O." because he did it in order to avoid apprehension.

Sue went on to describe how Schaefer had gagged and bound her hand and foot as she stood there handcuffed in the trees.

Meanwhile, Nancy had just been standing there gagged and cuffed. "Then he took me over to the river and had me stand up, and he tied my feet together with the rope, and then he redid my gag, cause it was falling off. And he had me stand on the root of a tree and he made a noose around my neck, put a rope around my neck, and hung it over a branch of the tree, and he tied the other end down onto a branch, a stub that was sticking out. Then he started, like you know, a scene. Like, please don't do it here, there's too many mosquitoes, and I was crying and he didn't do anything. And then he started, he pinched me, you know. And I got real disgusted, and I said 'Don't,' and he said, 'I could just take your pants off right here,' and he started..."

"Where was he pinching you?" asked Littman.

"On the butt," Nancy replied. "And then he started to go for my zipper, but I turned around. And he just laughed, and he didn't do anything. And I started to fall off this root. If I fell off this root I would have hung. I started falling off and choking, and he just, he pushed me back up and sat me on there, and he warned me not to scream. And then he left me."

Nancy described how she chewed the noose around her neck, then crawled up the root and untied the rope from the stump. After that she had to do a backbend to untie her legs, as she was still handcuffed, but she did manage to undo them undone and escape.

Meanwhile, Sue had maneuvered her way out of the ropes on her legs, but she still had the gag in her mouth when Schaefer came back. "He said, 'I'm going to tie you up to a tree now, so that if you try to get loose, you'll hang yourself,'" Then Schaefer helped her to her feet, and picked up the blanket. Carrying a long rope and the blanket he set off for the river. "I couldn't walk very fast cause of the stickers, and he kept saying, 'Hurry up, hurry up!' and I kept saying, 'Well, I have stickers in my feet, wait and let me try to get them out.'"

Apparently Schaefer couldn't wait, because he picked Sue up and threw her over his shoulder, carrying her to a tree, where he trussed her up much like he had Nancy, except this time it wasn't a root she stood on, it was a slope. "He tied my legs up, then he ran a rope up from behind, from my ankles up, and tied it to the handcuffs. And then I had to spit the gag out, and he said, 'How did you do that?' And he put it on real tight, and I felt like I was going to black out. So I said 'Loosen it, it's hurting me,' so he loosened it up a little, and he tied me to the tree and all, and then he said, 'Do you have VD?' And I said, 'No,' because I was afraid. I really thought he was going to sell us, and I was afraid if I told him I had VD, he wouldn't, and he'd have no use for me, so he'd kill me... Then he picked up my shirt and looked down my pants and he just laughed. Then he said, 'Don't scream, and don't try to run away cause I'm not going to be very far down the road, I'm just going down the road to meet that man that's going to buy you,' and I said, 'Why do you want to sell us?' and he said, 'For the money, I'd do anything for money,' and I said, 'Well, that's wrong,' you know. And I was going to talk to him, that's before he gagged me, when I was trying to talk to him. He said, 'Don't lecture me, sweetheart. I didn't bring you here for a lecture.' Then after that, he

*Assault Victim Nancy Trotter returned to Florida in 1973 to perform
a reinactment of the 1972 assault for police cameras.*

tied me up, and before he left he said, 'Don't try to run away,' and then he walked off, and I started getting loose. And I found Nancy walking down the road..."

Nancy cut in, "Yes, I had gotten loose, and..."

"He didn't come back to check on you then?" Littman asked Nancy.

"No," she explained. "I went up on back of that Spanish fort and I saw his car still there. So I ran back by the river and I saw Sue in the trees, and she was calling, 'Nancy, Nancy' but I thought he was there making her call me, I thought he saw I was gone. So I didn't say anything. I started going faster down by the river, and it sounded like someone was following me, so I started running, and I took up on land, and hid in this overgrowth for about a half an hour... I got eaten alive by mosquitoes..."

Nancy told of struggling through the underbrush and the woods, and then walking along the river until she saw a road on the other side. Handcuffed, she man-

The re-enactment was ordered and paid for by the state, but curiously, it was submitted into evidence on behalf of the defense.

aged to swim through the river to the other side, where Sheriff Crowder picked her up.

"After I saw Nancy, I was afraid to yell for her again," said Sue, "because I was afraid he had just left a couple of minutes ago, and I still had the noose on my neck and part of the rope on my feet." After she got free from the ropes, she ran through the woods and the river, still gagged and handcuffed, her arms bound with a scarf. "I found a dirt road, and I ran down it and I was crying, and this man stopped in a pickup truck and then the policeman came."

Robert Ressler analyzes Schaefer's crime:

> Before going further with the story, let me point out the attributes of the organized offender that are present so far in the narrative. The abductor personalized the victims by talking with them, used his own vehicle, and conned the women

into his car by means of his verbal skills. He brought his own threatening weapon to the scene and took it away with him, had a rape kit, and was plainly planning to complete sexual acts with the women prior to torture and murder. After the murder, he was going to hide and dispose of the bodies. He displayed mobility and adaptive behavior during the crime when he left the women tied up and went to pay attention to some other aspect of his life, telling them that he would return and finish them off later.

Schaefer always avoided discussing this nearly-lethal assault case, because he disliked the inevitable conclusion that the similarities between the double assault and the double murder were both numerous and significant. Still, when pressed by Steve Dunleavy in 1991, his eyes sparkled for *A Current Affair* as he smirked, "It was an emotional intimidation type of a thing," and then laughed out loud. "Oh, it gave them a good scare, no doubt about that."

Physically painful torture wasn't necessary to gratify his sadistic compulsions on this occasion. Just from knowing the fear his victims suffered, he derived that desperately twisted feeling of sexualized power he had learned to crave and could achieve no other way. Schaefer persuasively described the pleasure he derived from experiments in terror like these:

> My own preference was in the preliminaries, and the increasing terror generated by the woman's awareness that she was in the hands of a homicidal maniac. I was entranced by the various ploys that the captive women would use in order to save their lives. Most of them would try something, and I made it a game to see how long it would be before the victim would request to be killed.
>
> This entertainment varied from one victim to another, and it might take the form of physical or psychological torture. If and when the lady decided to say she'd had enough, I was quite willing to put her out of her misery — if she asked nicely. This sort of experiment is perfect for a person of sadistic tendencies, since we sadists do not consider our victims to be genuinely human. Ted never thought of the women he killed as persons, but only as objects. I did the same and found it an excellent way to avoid any human feeling for them. I guess one would consider that a sociopathic quality, but what the hell, we all have our faults, and I am no different than anyone else in that respect.

Doing Doubles

The double life terms Schaefer was serving when he was killed were for the murders of two teenage girls — the blonde Susan Place and the brunette Georgia Jessup. They were chopped to pieces and buried some time between July of 1992, when Nancy and Sue were assaulted, and January of 1973, when Schaefer was finally locked up for good.

Schaefer compared his crimes to those of his arch-rival, Ted Bundy:

> Ted was, of course, a tyro when he nabbed Ott and Naslund; when I nabbed Jessup and Place I had been in the ghoul game for almost 10 years, so I knew what to expect from these juicy young creatures at the end. By then I was into

*Schaefer's boss, former Martin County
Sheriff Robert Crowder, who arrested him*

*Schaefer on his last day of freedom,
July 23, 1992, when he turned
himself in after a double assault*

*Sergeant George Miller, crime scene investigator for St. Lucie County
on the Jessup-Place murders, displays a wall full of honors*

doing double murders and an occasional triple when the opportunity arose, whereas Ted at the same point of time was only able to handle singles. He was playing at copycat and doing a poor job of it at that.

Doing doubles is far more difficult than doing singles, but on the other hand it also puts one in a position to have twice as much fun. There can be some lively discussions about which of the victims will get to be killed first. When you have a pair of lively teenaged bimbolinas bound hand and foot and ready for a session with the skinning knife, neither one of the little devils wants to be the one to go first. And they don't mind telling you quickly why their best friend should be the one to die.

Schaefer delighted in courting the perverse status only the most heinous of crimes convey — while insisting that he was an innocent man who deserved to be released. From boasts of one-upping Bundy he would go to flat deadpan denial: "I've never killed anyone, period."

Schaefer's appeals were rejected twenty times, all the way up to the United States Supreme Court. Undeterred, he continued to promote the theory that he was guilty of nothing more than writing realistic fiction, and that he could not be linked to the scene of any murders anywhere — not even the two he was convicted of. His conviction, he contended, stemmed from an elaborate conspiracy requiring the cooperation of the prosecution, the defense, the judge, the media, the FBI, the victims' families, the State Department of Motor Vehicles, and law enforcement officers in at least six jurisdictions.

But his mind was filled with sexually violent fantasies that consistently featured someone very much like himself playing the homicidal maniac. These kinds of morbid obsessions typically start the cycle that culminates when the vicious dreams become real, and somebody winds up dead.

It's not just the two assaults and two murders he was convicted of, it's the girls like Leigh Hainline, whose memories were kept alive in the form of the pitiful little trophies he took from them. It's the nameless ones who became "gator bait by morning." You can hear their voices echoing through his prose — the known ones, the unknown ones, and the ones that got away. Like me. But I'm not singing the song he put in my mouth. Not any more.

BURNING WITH A BLUE FLAME

The work that appears in this volume began on February 8, 1989 when I addressed a letter to Gerard John Schaefer in his maximum security cell at Florida State Prison, asking if he remembered me.

"How could I *not* remember you?" he gushed. "A former great love of my life, but then I always burn with a blue flame when it's a romance. *Did* burn. Sure ain't no romance to be had in here."

Telling him I had become a freelance writer, I asked if he'd like to work on a book about his life with me. "I've been approached by about a dozen writers; a few of them I've even talked contract with, but in the end I've never concluded a

deal. My position is that any book about my case or life must be truthful and accurate as to facts, and none of this "police sources suspect" bullshit. In plain words — no hocus pocus." He continued, "The story about my case has not been done. It's virgin territory, a virtual terra incognita." Then in a cozy aside, he allowed, "Naturally, I'm favorably disposed toward someone who has known me intimately."

I asked if he was still mad at me for breaking up with him. "As Neil Sedaka used to croon, 'Breaking Up is Hard to Do,' and I have some painful emotional memories about us, but nothing you'd classify as hostile." He concluded, "Social stuff can go on the back burner. You want to write a book and I'm uncommitted as yet, so to get things going in the right direction, sit down and give me your pitch on exactly what you have in mind." My proposal persuaded him I was up to the job, and thus our collaboration began.

As I sat and talked with Schaefer in prison during a series of personal visits in 1990 and 1991, his physical presence reminded me of John D. MacDonald, the Florida novelist who wrote so hard but looked so soft. Schaefer had long since lost those movie-star good looks that had once dazzled me so. The man who would characterize himself as "a former street cop who is in open population in perhaps America's most repressive hellhole" was a nebbish: portly, pale, balding, and half-blind. Though he would portray himself in the most macho light possible, stressing, "I walk the yard like a man," my impression was that he no more resembled a killer than he did a cop. More like a middle-aged, deskbound clerk gone to seed.

I had always known Schaefer to be well-spoken and pleasant, funny and smart — an educated, cultivated man with many attractive qualities. And incongruous though it might seem, he still retained much of the polish of his background. After all, not only had he graduated from police academy, he had taken college-level courses in creative writing under Harry Crews, and acquired a B.S. degree from Florida Atlantic University in criminal justice. He had always exhibited a certain class consciousness, and a score of years behind bars had not made him any less of a snob. Even though his daily existence was proof enough that he was on the same level as his neighbors, still he patronized them as "nothing but a bunch of ignorant niggers and white trash." You would think he was just visiting the prison conducting research to continue his studies in criminal justice.

Even though his demeanor was superficially civilized, still at times he could be quite chilling. It was not the man himself. It was the shadowy entity lurking just out of sight, the treachery and deception hidden by an unassuming demeanor that exemplified what Hannah Arendt called "the banality of evil."

In accommodation, I developed a multi-faceted interface. I found myself having more than one relationship with him at a time, a curious experience to be sure.

I caught more than a glimpse of his dark side. I saw it in his threats and his cruelty, his deceptiveness and destructiveness. Then there was the ambiguity of that ever-present smile. I learned about the cannonade of rage disarmed by his smiling facade. And I finally came to understand the puritanical rage that flared up when a woman shook her naked assets in his face.

Schaefer and London,
Junior Prom night, 1964

Schaefer and London,
Florida State Prison, 1991

Schaefer and London,
Florida State Prison, 1991

Schaefer and London,
Florida State Prison, 1991

Schaefer and London,
Florida State Prison, 1990

THE GUILTY MIND

The most intriguing aspect of Gerard John Schaefer's case was the fact that writings found in his closet were used to convict him. While it was not alleged that these fragmentary notes actually describe the murders, they were introduced on the legal principle of *mens rea*, or the guilty mind, as they portrayed his murderous intent with chilling accuracy. Indeed, one of the jurors stated flatly that it was these closet fantasies that persuaded him to convict.

"The psychiatrist told him to write down everything that went through his mind," said Mrs. Doris Schaefer, his mother. "It was supposed to help him somehow."

After being arrested for the assaults on Nancy Trotter and Paula Sue Wells, he started writing again. Emerson Floyd was Schaefer's cellmate for his first six weeks in the Martin County Jail, where he had been confined since January 15, 1973. Floyd told reporters that Schaefer spent most of his time writing.

"He wouldn't show it to us," he said. "He'd lay in his bunk and write and then he'd read his writing to us. It was mostly just brutal. I tell you, there were some hair-raising things."

Whatever Schaefer wrote during those early days of incarceration will remain another one of the unsolved mysteries of this case. On April 1, 1973, when Schaefer heard that the bodies of Susan Place and Georgia Jessup had been found, Floyd said he stopped telling his brutal stories to his cellmates. "He cut his stories up in tiny pieces and dropped them in the wastebasket."

Once I learned how integral Schaefer's stories were to his case, I could not help but wonder. An unwitting Pandora, I asked him, "Do you still write those stories?" In reply, he began firing off a series of searing scenarios of sexual homicide that went so far beyond accepted standards that for a while I was simply reeling. I had no idea what to do with this stuff.

Then I received his account of shoptalk with Ted Bundy, describing how Ted had seen the news stories about Schaefer and recognized his face from the pictures in detective magazines. Schaefer wrote, "I was once billed as 'The Greatest Mass Murder of Women This Century,' and that is no small statement. It's a real good ticket into the society of fiends." After describing a discussion of techniques and preferences, Schaefer wrote that Bundy "couldn't get enough of conversation like that. It was like he felt I knew for sure there was a real boring side of Deathwork, and it wasn't all raging sexual release, as the media likes to portray it."

"That's *IT!*" I literally jumped up and raced to my office, without even finishing the letter. I didn't know what he was going to write, but from that moment on, I decided I was going to publish it.

Between March and July of 1989, Schaefer sent me the stories included in two sections of *Killer Fiction,* "Whores" and "Starke Stories." Selections from the stories and drawings used as evidence in his 1973 murder trial are included in the section, "Actual Fantasies." A limited edition of the volume comprising these three sections was copyrighted and published in June of 1989.

After *Killer Fiction* was finalized, another batch of stories pushing further into the reality zone was released as *Beyond Killer Fiction,* including stories as graphic as titles like "Flies in Her Eyes" and "Blonde on a Stick" seem to suggest.

"I'm not writing non-fiction," explained the literary madman. "It's *killer* fiction: a new genre, where the writer takes violence as an artistic medium and instead of glorifying it, makes the reader see it as the cruel and horrid act it is in reality. I don't represent violence as good or bad, merely as it is. I let the reader conclude that violence is a socially negative force, not to be reveled in." Thus he expounded his grim postmodern aesthetic.

Later on he penned what he called a "killer serial," a dozen or so loosely-connected stories relating the adventures of Detective Dan Kelly, Rogue Cop, satirizing the myth that had grown up around his own case and caricaturing various individual who had encountered him, including myself, the real Detective Kelly, and the criminologist Joel Norris, who tagged him "The Sex Beast" in his book *Serial Killers: The Growing Menace.*

"Whores — What to *DO* About Them" are five brief homicidal scenarios where women described as whores are slain by a serial killer. Shooting, stabbing, and hanging are each rendered in turn. In *Spring Break*, Schaefer gave the killer his own name and physical description. Schaefer completely rewrote the story, changing it from the third person in the first draft to the first person, drawing the reader closer into the mind of the psychopath as he stalks and dispatches his prey.

The "Starke Stories" go beyond the crime itself into its supercharged aftermath, taking the reader inside a maximum security prison from the point of view of the convicted killer. One story relates a grisly prison slaying that eerily foreshadows the author's own demise.

Most of the objections to *Killer Fiction* voiced by the State of Florida referred to it as "pornography," thus apparently putting the onus of their disapproval on the sexually explicit portions of the text. However, it is more likely that the sordid prison scenes were considered offensive enough to merit suppression by Corrections.

The stories Schaefer sent me at that time were really being written *at* me, in a kind of exhibitionistic assault designed to break through my nonchalant demeanor. In his own twisted psyche, anger, fear and revulsion were inextricably intertwined with his sexuality, and he hoped to arouse the same complex of sexually decadent emotions in me. More than once he suggested that what he had written had "made my panties wet." Not hardly! I could never find Schaefer's sick psychosexual pathology sexually stimulating. But I didn't disabuse him of his fantasies. I found the profound maliciousness he expressed as revealing as it was disturbing. In the privacy of my own home I was reacting emotionally with a combination of disgust and fascination. However, when I took keyboard in hand to respond to him, I managed to keep a lid on it. I was seeking some insight into the mind of a serial killer, and he was giving me the answers the only way he knew how.

I had been handling these toxic thoughts with a certain amount of troubled equanimity for about three months when Schaefer upped the ante and sent me a story calculated to offend every possible sensibility. I hadn't recoiled when he would write of slicing and dicing many a woman just like me, and crow at desecrating her corpse and her memory; I had not withdrawn when he gleefully waxed anti-Semitic, anti-Catholic, and homophobic; but I finally lost my composure when it came to his unabashed racism. Having served as a social revolutionary for some

years on the civil rights front, I found myself viscerally offended by the tirades he was sending me. Once he found out what he had to do to provoke a reaction, he crafted his weapon. He went straight for my most sensitive area in a story that radiates profound sexual perversion and vicious racial animosity. He called it "Nigger Jack," and I purely hated it.

When he sent me the first draft, I scribbled, *"This is disgusting!"* on his manuscript, wadded it up, and sent it straight back to him.

The killer auteur could not have been more thrilled:

> I was so *pleased* with your reaction to "Nigger Jack." Honestly, I never thought I'd be able to gag the Media Queen! If I can make someone as jaded as yourself squirm with distaste and revulsion, there is yet hope for me as a horror writer... move over, Clive Barker! I may retire on that effort. I still think the idea of enclosing a barf bag with the book would be a boon... I've never been bland, indifferent, or predictable. I *always* manage to generate a reaction... of course, it's not always a favorable reaction. But I do not write these stories to degrade the reader. I'd like to strike a blow against capital punishment by showing how it degrades all the parties involved, and thus Society as a whole. The validity of the scene goes to the basic truth of the event: Do women pop when electrocuted? (Yes.) Now we are dealing with *fact* — a fact people would rather not be confronted with. I believe it has a greater impact on the reader to present such a matter as a visual so that a mental picture is formed of what is being done by the representatives of the People. Who are the People? The People is *you*, kiddo. All the college cuties out in the field hopping up and down with *Burn Ted* signs never once thinking they could end up on the same griddle, just like Andrea Hicks Jackson. To give the college cutie the benefit of the doubt, let's say she's acting in ignorance of what *really* occurs. "Nigger Jack" will let her know in graphic sequence what she condones but does not see. It is a slap across the face of pro-death penalty society. Even the jaded Media Queen is taken aback! Good. Because if it can get *you* upset, and in upsetting you causes you to *think*, then imagine what it can do to the ladies of the Ft. Pierce Bridge Club, most of whom vote for pro-CP candidates.

As I caught myself breaking my resolutely unruffled demeanor, I wondered why I should be so disturbed. After all, I kept telling myself, it's only a story. But I found these stories so palpably assaultive. Schaefer seemed to relish creating shock waves, and the more negative the reaction, the better it gratified his masochistic side. Physically restrained in prison, he had found a more abstract weapon to use in performing his same old sadomasochistic rituals, this time wounding the emotions if not the flesh.

But I found Schaefer's rationale compelling, and eventually I had to concede his point. Like Macbeth, I had "supped full with horrors," and slaughterous thoughts no longer startled me. But even as cynically inured to Schaefer's homicidal ideology as I had become in that short period, I found that this story actually pulled me out of my benumbed stupor and forced me to *react*. And if a work of art of any kind could so profoundly affect me, there had to be some kind of terrible significance to it. The visceral nature of my own reaction convinced me to publish it despite the fact that it disturbed and repelled me.

The truth about his crimes did not matter to me as much as the chance to take a look into his deranged mind. Somehow I managed to overcome my revulsion to his sexually violent obsessions enough to continue documenting them. His sexism, his racism, his fury at every living being in the world, including himself… his boasts of rape, sodomy, murder, even necrophilia… these I managed to tolerate by reminding myself that this was important data.

And so I decided to set aside my own personal distaste for the ugliness of the work, and focus on presenting it in all its twisted glory and leave it to the audience to tell me what it was.

In 1991, shortly after Loompanics published the story in their catalog, Schaefer wrote, "I had a fan letter saying 'Nigger Jack' was 'a hilarious and entertaining prison insider story.' I had never seen it as pure comedy. The fans all want *more*. Are they crazy or what?"

PORNOGRAPHIC FILTH

In 1989, a prison guard calling *Killer Fiction* "pornographic filth" confiscated it from Schaefer, claiming it was "unsuitable for a prisoner," only returning it after verifying with the attorney general that Schaefer's fiction did play a part in the appeal he had before the court at the time. However, he was still forbidden to have a copy of it.

Schaefer only held a bound volume of his own book in his hands once. In September of 1990, while Schaefer was temporarily housed in a less-restrictive institution, two bound books were allowed in for autographs by sympathetic prison guards, one of whom admitted being a fan.

Later, Schaefer's literary ambitions absorbed another blow from the Florida Department of Corrections. Starting in March of 1991, mail between him and Media Queen was confiscated and destroyed, and he was sentenced to 30 days in the hole for "conspiracy to conduct a business." The incriminating evidence consisted of a letter describing the continuing adventures of Detective Dan Kelly, Rogue Cop. The disciplinary report stated, "At 9:30 a.m. on May 16, 1991… I opened a letter in front of Inmate Schaefer and discovered the envelope contained two letters discussing new stories to be written and their intended characters and plot. The letter and contents were turned over to Institutional Inspector Brian Gross and this report was written."

Even though no money was ever paid from Media Queen to Inmate Schaefer, this did not deter the prison from interpreting his writing as a business activity, according to their singularly curious definition. When Schaefer filed a grievance regarding the sanctions placed upon him, Gross replied:

> You have no authorization from the Department and/or this facility to engage in the act of having books, texts, novels, short stories, and/or any other form of printed information, be it fiction or non-fiction, printed for you. Engaging in a business constitutes an agreement between parties for the exchange of real properties, thoughts and/or ideas, or other remunerations, to include recognition and notoriety.

Although the investigator accused Media Queen of conducting a business, he maintained that there was no such entity. And even though the superintendent's office had long since had copies of the corporate papers on file, they still managed to conclude, "There is no Official Record of any media business or enterprise by the name of Media Queen in Atlanta, Georgia."

And so Schaefer was punished for being in the business of exchanging ideas for recognition with an entity that did not exist! It was almost funny.

Books Won't Burn

> Books won't stay banned. They won't burn. Ideas won't go to jail.
> • Alfred Whitney Griswold

The Prison Guard Literary Guild was not the only form of censorship encountered by *Killer Fiction.* De facto censorship of the marketplace determines which ideas achieve wide circulation. Conveying ideas *en masse,* after all, is not an art — it's a high-ticket, high-risk business. Controversy costs money. Sympathetic prime-time footage of aggrieved and indignant right-thinking Americans attracts more consumers than serious footage that provokes a reevaluation of comfortable assumptions. What attracts the few repels the many, and the weight of the numbers rules. This dynamic puts the squeeze on those who publish alarming or disturbing work, making this kind of material increasingly hard to come by.

Censoring a painfully realistic work of art is like killing the wicked messenger, or taking dope so you won't feel the pain of your foot in the fire. That pain is information the body desperately needs so that it can yank the leg out of the fire before the heart and soul are lost too. These voices are our early-warning system. If we can bear to listen to their pain and outrage, perhaps it will in some unforeseen way modify the choices we make as we shape our future.

Books like *Killer Fiction* are like vivid, disturbing dreams that convey vital warnings from the depths of the dreamer's mind to higher consciousness. Just as with our own individual nocturnal psychodramas, voices like these, that come groaning and shrieking up from the bowels of our body politic, are telling us about a reality that we would rather be blind than see. But the irony is that the homicidal violence that erupts through this kind of a mind is created by that same willful refusal to acknowledge the darkness and chaos that we know is there. And just as critics claim it is dangerous to release this kind of writing, I say it is even more dangerous to try to suppress it.

The original desktop-published *Killer Fiction* was not what you would call a best-seller. It was a matter of what I like to call the *really* free press. But even though it was only sold through the mail in minute quantities for a short while, and even though advertising ranged from scant to nonexistent, long after it went out of print a steady stream of orders from law enforcement professionals and crime aficionados continued to come in from England, France, Germany, Belgium, Norway, Finland, Denmark, Poland, Australia, New Zealand, China, Hong Kong, and of course Japan.

TRUE CONFESSIONS

For twenty-two years, steel bars and razor wire kept Gerard John Schaefer from perpetrating his crimes of choice, but the psychopathic malaise that had driven him to those acts was still present. It was inevitably expressed in fantasies, threats, and other evidence of the never-ending struggle with the malevolent demons within. His correspondence with me took the place of the all of the activities he would have been enjoying in real life. The way I found out the truth about the multicide was convoluted and difficult.

During 1989 and 1990, I researched Schaefer's story about being framed for murder. I visited him, waded through the transcripts, sifted through the boxes of evidence, and attended a hearing on his habeas corpus petition. I interviewed investigators, attorneys, personal friends and acquaintances, and his family, who had welcomed me into their home years ago.

Schaefer was an uncommonly prolific correspondent, and for several years I was fielding a daily deluge of lengthy letters from him. His letters were drastically self-contradictory; often within the same letter he would present himself in diametrically opposed positions. His reasoning had the continuity of logic of a trained mind but the twisted morality of a psychopath.

As it was my purpose to present "The Schaefer Story," it was necessary for me to know what the story was. But from the very beginning, he had two stories. Though inviting me to advertise his fiction by calling him, as the prosecutor did, "the greatest killer of women in this century," at the same time he would proclaim himself nothing more than a creative writer or a framed ex-cop. He wanted to play both sides of the game:

> 4/7/89. Now, as for business, and this is for your information ONLY, as I see it there are two ways to write the book: Should I prevail in Court, the book tells the tale of a cop victimized by corrupt officials. Should I ultimately lose in Court then the book takes a different slant. I've not yet worked out with *exactitude* how it will go but my general theme would be the rendition of the 34 murders known and x-number unknown. I would capitalize on my famous billing given freely by Mr. Stone. I would earn money, which would be my way of insulting the Establishment. I'd have no problem giving you "34 victims."

All that was interesting enough, up to a certain point; but although I was learning a great deal about how his mind worked, he had revealed very little of what he had actually done. After two years of having him give with one hand only to take away with the other, I was bored and frustrated. During a prison visit at the beginning of 1991, I confronted him.

"You're all talk," I said, and told him that neither his fantasies of sexual violence nor his claim of being framed were of any further interest to me, and I was ready to move on.

He suggested that I would be making a big mistake, since I only had to wait until his appeals were finished, and I would have "the whole story."

"Look, Schaefer," I asked him point-blank, "are you a real serial killer or not?"

He shrugged, "Well, you know, I can't answer that at this time. There's a deadline. And nothing can happen until the judge rules on my appeal. But let me put it this way, you're not wasting your time."

Over the next three months, in an apparent effort to prove that he was worthy of my continued attention, he revealed in both personal interviews and correspondence the genuinely pernicious entity hiding behind the roly-poly play-killer mask.

Layer upon layer of his carefully-cultivated mystique fell away, and finally his all-too-real skeletons began to emerge from the shadows. "Suppose I told you that *[Killer Fiction/Beyond Killer Fiction]* is all TRUE," he suggested, proposing to "back it up with burial pits... the metal rings where whores were hanged alive in the swamp." Though he started off somewhat tentatively, he went on to put much more incriminating remarks in writing.

In classic psychopathic style, he even tried to blame me for the murders he had committed. "I will tell you here and now that plenty of young women died because you couldn't help me resolve my various crisises in 1965. I tried to tell you about it but you couldn't deal with it. You bolted, abandoned me; that's when it started." Threatening me to keep his revelations secret, he admitted that he was concerned about "what you will think and do when you find out that what you currently believe to be KBS [killer bullshit] is not... you cannot conceive that what I've told you can be true. I've committed horrors beyond your ability to comprehend."

Secretly abandoning the ersatz claim to innocence he had been publicly touting for years, he now claimed that prosecutor Robert Stone had been correct to designate him our nation's number one serial killer, but Schaefer went on to assert that he actually deserved more credit than he had been given. "As you know I've always harped on Stone's list of 34. In 1973 I sat down and drew up a list of my own. As I recall, my list was just over 80. I wasn't exactly taking names... I was very careful never to leave a pattern. I killed women in all ways from shooting, strangling, stabbing, beheading to odd ways such as drowning, smothering and crucifixion. One I whipped to death with a strap, another I beat to jelly with a baseball bat while she was hanging by her wrists."

When I questioned the figure he volunteered, he explained, "I cannot even give you an *exact* figure, but I'd say between 80-110." It was hard to remember them all, because there were ontological considerations, such as whether to count victims who were not intentionally murdered, such as unborn fetuses and girls who had merely choked on their gags while awaiting a proper execution.

For the most part, he avoided giving names, dates or places, confining his observations to generalities, such as, "Each one died differently. Some were acquiescent; a few kicked up a fuss, but they all died." He summed it all up smugly, "I enjoyed each and every experience."

I was visiting Schaefer at Florida State Prison while he was sending me these startling confessions, and I had a chance to talk candidly with him about them. In one visit, I confronted him. His story didn't add up; there were too many inconsistencies. He leaned forward, bringing his face close to mine, and gazing intently into my eyes, he spoke in a low voice, pausing for emphasis, "You don't under-

*Gerard John Schaefer upon graduation
from the 36th Broward Police Academy, December 17, 1971*

stand… because you're not… a serial killer. What I tell you… is inconsistent… because the experience itself… is inconsistent."

I thought about that for a moment and finally shrugged. "You're right. I don't understand. You've got to explain it."

He leaned back, sighed, sipped his coffee. Groping for words and finding them by fits and starts, he finally came up with an analogy. "It's like… I'm throwing rocks at your window… and you're trying to figure out where the rocks are coming from… and you can't… because they're all different colors. But you see… they're different colors… because they're all coming… from different places."

"Ah! I see." For some reason, that imagery made perfect sense to me, as it elucidates the striking inconsistencies in the serial killer's psyche. The discrete and rigid contrasting elements symbolize the fragmentation of the personality into an uneasy amalgam of diverse components. With this type of personality, every truth conceals its equal and opposite, just as a perky smile masks a simmering anger — except when the mask slips, and the madness flares.

Once I complained that while I had faithfully created the impression that he was merely a creative writer, he had sent a handwritten note to an editor at *USA Today,* claiming he had committed over two dozen murders. "Why are you saying these things, John?" I wanted to know. "When you've got me telling people you're innocent, why are going around behind my back and telling them you are guilty?"

He drew close to me and with his voice lowered, hissed, "I want to be sure you understand this." He gripped my arm. "I'm saying these things because they're *TRUE.*" I just sat there in silence staring into his eyes, letting it soak in until finally I looked away. "OK, John. I believe you." I will never forget the message in those piercing violet eyes as they burned into mine through the black-framed magnifying lenses. *That LOOK!* It was unmistakable.

As I drove home afterwards, all the way I mused over the way his gaze so unwaveringly affirmed his guilt. When I wrote to him commenting on what I had seen in his eyes, he replied, "I have given you a very brief glimpse of something that no woman alive today has ever seen. You understood the message viscerally. You were able to snap down on a message that should erase any doubt you ever had about whether or not I am for real. I was able to communicate an absolute truth to you with a single look… You now know *one* secret… You have access to the real thing!"

He went on to remind me of less fortunate women who had recognized the grim reaper in his eyes. "Consider the nameless, pricey prostitute who is handcuffed, her ankles tied and after much time she says, dreading the answer, 'Are you going to kill me?' She is answered with the eyes. She sees the eyes, the whetstone, the razor sharp skinning blade. How does she handle that *reality*? Badly, of course. Like a cow in a slaughter chute."

I finally begged off. "Enough already," I wrote him. "I believe you."

KILLER FACT

Although he had set out to convince me that he really was a serial killer, once Schaefer persuaded me, apparently he expected our enterprise to keep rolling merrily along as it had before. But I no longer had too much to say about his claims of innocence.

These confessions were delivered along with threats as to what he would do, or have done, if I were to reveal them. He threatened to call on his alleged connections within biker gangs, white supremacists, satanists, and the so-called Dixie Mafia to have me abducted, raped, and even murdered. He was frustrated when these gorilla tactics did not intimidate me into helping him maintain his creative writing alibi.

When Schaefer began to enjoin my child in his threats, I shut him down for good. I had the prison forbid him to write to me any more. Then he mounted a propaganda campaign, releasing statements through various outlets he established, claiming that he had been irreparably harmed not only by myself, but by every other writer who dared to even *imply* that he was exactly what he appeared to be: a serial killer trying to get away with murder.

He filed three lawsuits against me. When he attempted to set one of his libel lawsuits for hearing in Alachua County, I responded by filing a *Motion for Security* and as *Exhibit A,* attached 500 pages of his handwritten threats and confessions. After perusing this singularly persuasive document, the Court summarily dismissed Schaefer's claim and sealed the record.

This same *Exhibit A* also appeared in affidavits that I made available to two separate authors defending themselves against the serial litigator's claim that they had libeled him by tagging him a serial killer. The results were unanimous. In *Schaefer v. Michael Newton* the court ruled that Schaefer is "a serial killer undoubtedly linked to numerous murders" and in *Schaefer v. Colin Wilson* Schaefer was declared "libel-proof under the law."

The three lawsuits Schaefer filed against me were dismissed, and his attempts to have criminal charges brought against me similarly failed.

Through *Killer Fiction* he reveals only one portion of his multiple reality. The man was as complex and contradictory as a revolving series of funhouse mirrors. It is the kind of fractured behavior that can only issue from someone who is truly capable of committing such depraved acts. Just as one aspect of this pernicious entity is revealed, it is replaced by its opposite. Only a person capable of cultivating a legitimate role in society while simultaneously indulging in a secret life of violence and perversion can convey such contradictory images of himself. The capacity for encompassing diametrically opposed self-images is essential to nurturing a secret life of predation while functioning within society for long enough to get away with murder more than a couple of times.

The confusion Schaefer created issued from the qualities that made the man what he was. A term like "serial killer" is only useful to describe one aspect of his behavior. It is less helpful in coming to terms with the essential disorder that distinguishes his psyche. Words like "psychopathic" and "sadomasochistic" and "an-

tisocial" and even "multiple personality" have been used to describe individuals like Gerard John Schaefer, but while they may be accurate in a clinical sense, they are somewhat lacking in conveying their most irreducibly intrinsic trait.

I believe M. Scott Peck captures it best in his excellent book *People of the Lie:*

> People in prison can almost always be assigned a standard psychiatric diagnosis of one kind or another, corresponding in layman's terms to such qualities as craziness or impulsiveness or aggressiveness or lack of conscience. But the evil have no such obvious defects, and do not fall clearly into our routine psychiatric pigeonholes. This is not because they are healthy. It is simply because we have not yet developed a definition for their disease.
>
> How is it that psychiatrists have until now failed to recognize such a distinct, rigid type? It is because they have bought the pretense of respectability. They have been deceived by what Harvey M. Cleckley called 'the mask of sanity.' Evil is 'the ultimate disease.' Despite their pretense of sanity, the evil are the most insane at all.
>
> When confronted by evil, the wisest and most secure adult will usually experience confusion. We literally feel overwhelmed by the labyrinthine mass of lies and twisted motives and distorted communication into which we will be drawn if we attempt to work with evil people.
>
> Describing an encounter with an evil person, one woman wrote, 'it was as if I'd suddenly lost my ability to think.' Once again, this reaction is quite appropriate. Lies confuse.
>
> The evil are 'the people of the lie,' deceiving others as they also build layer upon layer of self-deception. Forever fleeing the light of self-exposure and the voice of their own conscience, they are the most frightened of human beings. They live their lives in sheer terror. They need not be consigned to any hell; they are already in it.

One Step Ahead of the Flames

To enter *chez* Schaefer was to wander through the Byzantine lair of a terminal malignancy in human form. Because of his strong need to deceive himself, his perception of reality was profoundly distorted.

Imagine the image he must have had of the woman he had fantasized about for seventeen solitary years... who suddenly materialized one day like a tantalizing rainbow-colored vision, lifting him out of the gloom of his dungeon, and taking him on a dizzying dance with the notoriety he both craved and deplored... the woman who finally turned her back on him and fled, elusive as a black cat, vanishing into the night without so much as a farewell flick of her tail.

Before Schaefer's wounded heart could heal, he was dealt a most unkindly cut. When the Supreme Court finally rejected his appeal, he had lost his favorite confidante. He languished forgotten and forlorn in his lonely cell, watching her on national TV being serenaded in court by the rugged young serial killer whose face had been in the news lately. It was enough to make any red-blooded American predator feel like a washed-up old prom queen.

Schaefer's 1993 Valentine was right in character:

HELLO WHORE, THE WORD ON THE YARD IS that THE QUEEN OF THE SLUTS WAS AT FSP ROMANCING DANNY Rolling. WORD ALSO HAS it that BOBBY LEWIS IS RATTING OUT THE SLUTS MAIN SQUEEZE to THE COPS. THE ENTIRE PRISON IS AWARE OF it: BOBBY LEWIS AND SONDRA LONDON ARE TAKING DOWN Rolling. DUDE NAME of WILLIAMS SAYS THE WHORE IS SEXUALLY MESMERIZING DANNY BOY WHILE HER PAL, LEWIS, PUMPS HIM AND RUNS to THE COPS EVERY TIME DANNY OPENS HIS MOUTH. I WAS SO RIGHT ABOUT you, SONDRA: WHORE. PURE FUCKING WHORE. A WHORE AND A RAT. THE WORD IS that LEWIS IS DIGGING HIMSELF A GRAVE. HE'D LIE ON HIS OWN MOMMA FOR A CHANCE to GET OUT of HERE... VALENTINE, YOU'RE MINE. WHY you OUT FRONT Licking Rollings EGO? I KNOW WHAT YOU'RE UP to: MONEY. You'RE GONNA GET DANNY BOY FRIED WHILE you MAKE A BUCK OFF HIS MISERY, RIGHT? WELL, GO FOR it! JUST MAKE SURE you KEEP MY NAME OUT OF this EPISODE. SHOULD I FIND OUT that you SAY I'M ASK OR SEE MY NAME INVOLVED IN ANY OF this Rollings CRAP you'RE At THE CENTER OF THEN I'M GOING to PUT you AND YOUR WHOREDAUGHTER ON MY list OF UNFINISHED BUSINESS. WILLIAMS DON't LIKE you WORTH SHIT AND HE CLAIMS to HAVE SERIOUS KKK CONNECTIONS. ME, I LIKE you JUST FINE, ALWAYS HAVE BUT iF you CROSS THE LINE AND ATTEMPT to EXPLOIT ME THEN I'll BE COMING FOR you WITH SOMETHING OTHER THAN LOVE IN MY HEART. I'VE EARNED $3000. this YEAR IN OUT OF COURT LAWSUIT SETTLEMENTS. PEOPLE SAYING I'M A SK. SAY it BUT HAVE NO LEGAL LEGS to STAND ON. DON't MAKE THE SAME ERROR AND you & I a THE KID WILL BE COOL. GO DO Rolling. I KNOW you'll DO HIM WELL. YOU'RE A PRO. I'll GIVE you A REFERENCE ANY TIME you NEED ONE. I ALWAYS DO. You ARE NEVER AWAY from MY thoughts, VALENTINE, ᴊᴀᴄᴋ..

Nor was Schaefer far from Danny Rolling's thoughts:

I had the most unpleasant luck of running into Schaefer the other day. *Clink… clink… rattle… rattle…* I was doing the chain-shackle-shuffle down the long hall escorted by Sergeant So-&-So… when lo & behold… there he was standing in line waiting to file into his wing. He flashed that sickening smile of his at me and lifted a folder containing some of his recent achievements, waving them at me like we were old pals or something. *Clink… clink… rattle… rattle…* struggling along. I just stared bloody daggers through him and let the hatred show.

This guy has got real problems, doesn't he? Schaefer is a little too full of himself and we can easily figure out the content of substance he is filled with. It smells like something pooling in a sewage treatment plant. I can understand why you got physically ill reading Schaefer's twisted and delusioned writings. The sample you sent me left a real bitter taste in my mouth.

I wouldn't worry about that wimp if I was you. He is just a spooky little punk who gets his kicks out of intimidating people. He's a bluffer. He wants anyone who has the displeasure of entertaining him to believe he holds a full house, but if you call his bluff, you'll find he only has a pair of deuces — two pitiful excuses for being barely human.

He boasts he is 'The Greatest Killer of Women This Century.' How could anyone blatantly brag about such a thing? All the suffering and pain he claims to be responsible for… and he actually gloats? 'I *loved* killing whores.' What an awful self-professed statement!

But more unkindly cuts were in store for Schaefer. On November 11, 1994, he filed this pitiful pleading with a Florida court that had already dismissed his latest lawsuit against me:

> While working in the prison law library Plaintiff was attacked by another inmate and stabbed repeatedly in and about the face, body and hands. Due to the trauma sustained incidental to this attack, Plaintiff is now unable to prosecute his appeal; therefore Plaintiff withdraws the appeal in this case.

I was so moved I almost sent the poor guy a sympathy card. A few days later, Danny Rolling reported from Death Row:

> Schaefer is having big time problems. He is on everyone's shit list here at FSP, and I mean literally. This past week, he has had shit and piss thrown at him — he got one hell of an ass-whooping — and to top it off, his cell was set on fire *TWICE*. Everything he owned got burned up, and what wasn't, got ruined by oil and water spewn from the sprinkler system.
>
> I have recently learned a great deal about Schaefer from solid cons who know what a *RAT* and *PAIN FREAK* he is. Also, he is a manipulating *SNITCH*, and has been for a long time.
>
> Just thought you'd like to know the ole asshole is having a rough go of it. But then again, Schaefer might be enjoying himself.
>
> I mean, masochists enjoy drinking piss, eating shit, and getting their asses kicked. Don't they?

The situation apparently had its origins a few years back when the legal beagle was helping an inmate fight a murder charge. Soon after he got the killer to tell him the location of the body, that highly sensitive confidential information wound up in the hands of the prosecution, who used it to move Schaefer's client from population to Death Row.

So now Schaefer had offered to help another killer with his appeals. This time the prisoner told Schaefer that he had already contracted with a team of jailhouse lawyers. So when Schaefer offered to do the job for free, it did not sit too well with the two displaced lawyers, who happened to be pretty tough characters in their own right. Considered stand-up cons, they made sure the word went out about Schaefer's past and present betrayals of the prisoners he had pretended to help. So when the brutal barristers filed their objections to the interloper's pleadings with their shivs, the power of criminal justice was once again affirmed as they received the unanimous moral support of the entire prison population, a rare solidarity traditionally celebrated with excremental salutes and bonfires.

"Yep, Schaefer's running scared now, looking over his shoulder," observed one prison insider. "He's one step ahead of the flames."

KING AND BRONSON

Homicide Detective Jack King holds a Master's degree in Criminal Justice. He has been a police officer since 1970, and he has been with Ft. Lauderdale Police Department since 1978, with the past five years spent investigating homicides. In an interview on October 16, 1996, Homicide Chief Tim Bronson called King "without a doubt *the* best detective this department has seen in a long time."

Shortly after Tim Bronson took over as Homicide Chief of the detective bureau in the fall of 1995, he assigned Jack King to go back through some of their old missing persons files and see if he could close them, with particular attention to cases that might be linked to Schaefer.

Detective John King (left) and Captain Tim Bronson, Ft. Lauderdale Police Department, with missing persons files on G.J. Schaefer

"Our investigation consisted of trying to match missing persons to that time period," said King. "We didn't have a whole lot of information. In most cases, we didn't even have a body to do anything with."

"An additional problem we had is the time factor," said Bronson, "both the period of time being twenty-some years ago, and that we were doing this kind of in between our other duties."

After compiling a few tantalizing leads, they decided to interview the serial killer who had grown up in their jurisdiction. If the Broward state attorney would agree to file charges on one of the cases, they could use the others as bargaining chips to get Schaefer to admit to them all.

"We called to make arrangements on a Friday, to see if we could get access to him," said King, "and then Monday somebody from the prison called me back, and said, 'Don't bother. He's been the victim of a homicide.'"

"You can't believe how frustrating that was," said Bronson. "Our hope was that this guy would be driving us around showing us where the bodies were."

Before working homicide, King investigated sex crimes, and regrets he missed the opportunity to learn more about the bizarre psychosexual aspects of Schaefer's make-up from a personal interview.

"If you look strictly at his writings, you would think that there was a sexual aspect," he observed. "But if you look at the crimes that he was convicted of, the indication there would be one strictly of power, or being smarter than the pursuers. It would appear that he was playing some sort of game to see what he could get away with. Criminality is not usually an aspect of a police officer. Control, yes. If you look at the personality of police officers, there are some controlling aspects of our personalities. But not crime."

BELINDA HUTCHENS

The week after Schaefer was killed, an article ran in the *Ft. Lauderdale Sun-Sentinel* on the ongoing investigation into Schaefer's old cases, naming the three missing women: Leigh Hainline Bonadies, Carmen Marie (Candy) Hallock, and Belinda Hutchens.

"I contacted some of the Hutchens family members," said King. "I located a sister and a brother, and they told me the husband had a drug problem and spent most of his time in prison. I found him working at a used car lot on Federal Highway.

"He couldn't remember a lot of details, but when he spoke of his ex-wife, he began crying, and he told me it still affects him to this day.

"The way he explained it, even though they were married and they lived together, she had her own lifestyle and was kind of independent of him. She did what she wanted to do."

Apparently, that would include dating other men.

According to the original police reports, William Hutchens had reported his twenty-two-year-old wife Belinda missing on January 5, 1972, six months before Schaefer was arrested. Hutchens told police how he and his two-year-old daughter watched his wife get into a car with a stranger and ride away, never to be heard from again. Not even her remains have been recovered.

On April 28, 1973, after Schaefer was charged with murder, Detective Tom Brophy with the Ft. Lauderdale Police Department picked up William Hutchens and took him to look at Schaefer's blue Datsun to see if Hutchens would recognize it.

"That's the car," said Hutchens immediately. Asked how he could be so sure, he pointed out the low parking lights on the front of the vehicle, and exhibiting the sharp eye for detail that could only belong to a used car salesman, he noted the placement of the rear license plate in the center of the trunk with no break in the rear bumper, and pointed out the vents in the rear window, instructing Detective Brophy that this Datsun was the only model with vents.

On Tuesday, May 8, 1973, after Schaefer was charged with murder, Ft. Lauderdale Police received a call from the Chief of Police Detectives in Martin County, Chief Thompson, who said they found a little black book in Schaefer's property, listing William Hutchens' name and telephone number.

However, further leads failed to materialize. Without a body, and without sufficient evidence to tie Schaefer or anyone else to the disappearance, no charges were ever brought.

After the story naming Belinda Hutchens ran in the *Ft. Lauderdale Sun-Sentinel,* apparently William Hutchens was contacted by the daughter he had not seen for many, many years, although their emotional reunion was fated to be short-lived. After the inevitable falling-out, the daughter's lifestyle as a part-time dancer and model drew her back into the shadows of the same fatal demimonde that had claimed her mother almost a quarter century ago.

CARMEN HALLOCK

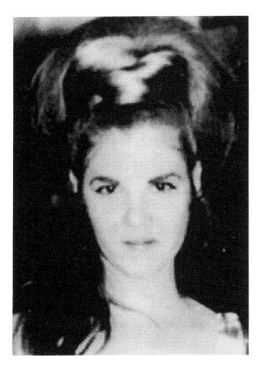

Carmen Marie Hallock, a waitress seen with Schaefer, missing since December 18, 1969. Schaefer kept her gold tooth in an old desk.

The missing persons report on Carmen Hallock identified her as "good looking" and noted under personal habits that the 22-year-old waitress and junior college student "drinks a lot and frequents bars."

She was first reported missing by her former sister-in-law, Nancy Bauer, who told police she had maintained a close friendship with Carmen even though she had long since divorced Carmen's brother.

She last saw her on December 18, 1969, over lunch at Britt's in the Coral Ridge Shopping Center. She told police about their last conversation, in which Carmen told her of an appointment she had made for 5:00 p.m. that same day about a mysterious job. There was a guy who was a teacher at the junior college, she said, who told her he did some kind of undercover work for the government. Schaefer had gone to work as an intern teacher on February 27, 1969.

Carmen said this man would go over to the islands on weekends and would come back with "lots of money." She had spoken to him about the job several nights before, and was to meet him again that evening. She told Nancy that in connection with this new job, she would be set up in an apartment in Washington, D.C. or New York City and all her bills would be paid.

After they finished lunch, Carmen and Nancy did some shopping. Carmen bought a pair of black patent-leather pumps, telling Nancy she was going to wear them with her black cocktail dress that night when she went to meet the unnamed stranger who seemed to offer more than a free lunch.

Nancy kissed Carmen goodbye at 2:30 p.m. and never saw her again.

She was last seen at the Brave Bull on North Federal Highway, by a bartender she knew, who had gone there for dinner and was just leaving when she came in. The bartender, referred to in police reports only as "Les," had often seen the pretty girl he knew as Candy when she came in for drinks at Stumpy's, on Federal at 18th Street. Les reported that the vivacious brunette was wearing a black dress and black shoes, and that she looked happy.

By Christmas Day, Nancy Bauer had not heard from Carmen. Something had to be wrong. Carmen had not shown up at work as expected on December 19th and had not visited her family. She had never gone away like that before. Letting herself into Carmen's apartment with a spare key, Nancy found Carmen's small puppy, who had obviously been neglected for several days.

Looking through her belongings, she determined that Carmen's car keys, driver's license, and motor vehicle registration were missing. All of her clothing seemed to be intact — with the notable exception of the black shoes Carmen had bought for her mysterious rendezvous. No black dress was to be found.

Nor was any trace of the missing girl, until April of 1973, when Broward County Sheriff's Office found two gold teeth among Schaefer's belongings that Forensic Dentist Richard Souviron identified as the only known remains of Carmen Hallock.

After the positive identification of the gold teeth was made, Carmen's half-sister Martha Bormann flew down with her husband to inspect the jewelry found among Schaefer's belongings, to see if she could identify any of the pieces as belonging to Carmen.

Mrs. Bormann immediately picked up a round gold dime-sized pin, with a green four-leaf clover and two stars, and said, "This is mine."

When she was a little girl, she was in the Girl Scouts in Brooklyn, New York, and had earned this pin for better world relations. She said she believed the Girl Scouts gave out badges later, but back in the early fifties, they gave out pins.

The pin had been kept by her mother, Mrs. Eva Hallock, until she passed away in May of 1969, and had then been passed on to Carmen.

After Mrs. Bormann completed a sworn statement identifying this and several other pieces of jewelry, her husband Henry told investigators that as soon as he entered the property room, he noticed the Girl Scout pin, but he didn't say anything, as he wanted his wife to pick it out for herself.

With this case, police came one step closer to connecting the notorious serial killer with a Ft. Lauderdale woman who disappeared under suspicious circumstances, but without a corpse, they still fell short of giving the state's attorney enough evidence to charge him with murder.

In one of Schaefer's fantasies, he writes, "She sat there in a black chiffon dress with her hair done up and black pantyhose and high heels. She was wearing perfume and was very sexy." Schaefer claims these words were written in 1967, two years before Carmen Hallock disappeared, dressed to kill in exactly the kind of outfit Schaefer would have asked her to wear for her appointment with the mysterious stranger.

LEIGH HAINLINE BONADIES

Leigh Hainline Bonadies,
Schaefer's neighbor for five years,
missing since September 8, 1969.
Schaefer kept the locket engraved "Leigh."

On September 8, 1969, Chuck Bonadies was locked out of the apartment he shared with his bride. They had only been married one month, and had not gotten around to making two sets of keys. He found a note on the apartment door from saying she was going to Miami. He waited for her to return and let him in the house, but Leigh was never heard from again.

As Chuck struggled to understand what might have happened to his bride, he recalled a suspicious story she had recently told him about an old friend of hers, who had lived three doors down from her, who had been trying to get her to go to work for the C.I.A. She said he had mentioned sums of money ranging from $5,000 to $20,000 for her to travel out to South America, and that she would be able to collect additional sums in the foreign country. Chuck had told her to forget the whole thing.

Leigh's uncle hired William C. Marshall, a private investigator from Miami, to investigate Leigh's disappearance, but family cash reserves ran dry before he was able to turn up anything significant. Marshall did, however, determine that Leigh had recently been playing tennis with one Gerard John Schaefer, who was employed at Plantation High as an intern teacher.

Marshall reported that school board records listed Schaefer's address as 2716 SW 34th Avenue. Indeed, the Hainlines had lived two doors down from the Schaefers at 2700 SW 34th Avenue throughout the early youth and high school years of John, Leigh, and the other children.

Leigh's brother Gary had known Schaefer since they were both in junior high. Although they were not close friends, Gary recalled going on many hunting and fishing trips with John, and recalled as well the numerous occasions when the battles between Schaefer and his father could be heard throughout the whole neighborhood.

Gary told police he was surprised to see Schaefer described in the news as an "easy-going non-drinking type." On the contrary, Gary said, he had always found John quite quick-tempered. He told police Schaefer "always did his share of drinking and carousing."

Janice Crosley recalled seeing Leigh on the tennis court the day before she disappeared. Janice recalled that Leigh had mentioned the name John Schaefer.

Although she could not recall exactly what was said, the gist of it was that Schaefer was supposed to take Leigh to the airport.

In 1970, one year after Leigh disappeared, Gary called John and asked about Leigh. John told Gary that Leigh had called him and asked him to drive her to the airport, that she wanted to fly to Cincinnati. He said he agreed to give her a ride, but she never got back with him.

One can only wonder if Schaefer was writing about Leigh Hainline when he wrote these words:

> I have been tempted to do away with other women too, usually ones that I am sexually attracted to but do not know personally. One girl whom I almost killed I later became good friends with and drove her to the airport to fly up north. It was an experiment to see if I still wanted to kill her after I got to know her, and I didn't. In fact, I am still rather fond of her.

When Schaefer was arrested for murder in 1973, the search of his belongings stored at his mother's home at 2716 SW 34th Avenue turned up several pieces of Leigh's jewelry. There was a locket inscribed "Leigh" and a Stranahan Pep Club pin, and Gary Hainline identified a small jade cross that his sister had kept in a jewelry box.

The jewelry and teeth were found in the same search that produced the writings in question, which Schaefer later claimed were written around 1967 and left behind with other nonessential belongings when he left his mother's home to move out on his own.

Most law enforcement professionals who have studied this case consider these writings to represent a sort of diary, as accounts of actual crimes written after the fact. Some of them might be. However, it is equally plausible that with Schaefer, as with Ted Bundy, the fantasy preceded the act, and writing these stories was a way of building the clarity and intensity of his impulses to the point where he felt compelled to act them out in real life — the type of activity he actually called "feeding the sickness." Either way, whether written before or after the fact, the writing of them and the subsequent reading of them would serve to reinforce what started out as fantasies and over the years, finally went on to become intermingled with memories.

"A disturbed personality is always going to find something to lash along its madness," he wrote.

If Schaefer was elaborating a fantasy in his earlier writings, in later years he seems to have enacted his homicidal scenarios with at least several known victims.

An escalation in complexity of his *modus operandi* is noted. With these crimes, Schaefer seemed to be setting new challenges for himself. If he started out, as he says, perfecting an M.O. targeting throwaways as the easiest victims, by 1969 his technique seems to have evolved to the point where it gave him an exciting new thrill to pluck a woman out of her social milieu in a sophisticated way that provided a prepackaged excuse for her absence. Someone definitely staged these disappearances so the victims would provide their own false leads in advance. It

would seem quite an extraordinary coincidence for this convicted killer to have the teeth and jewelry of women known to have some connection to him, had he not been their worst nightmare — an attractive, friendly guy who also happened to be their killer.

Jack Dolan

Candy Hallock's two gold-filled teeth were found in a drawer of the same old, battered desk that had been in John Schaefer's bedroom since the Schaefers moved to Florida.

Just as Schaefer blithely explained away Leigh Hainline's jewelry by claiming she had let him hold it as collateral on a loan, he was not without a ready explanation for Hallock's teeth. They must have been left in that desk by Jack Dolan.

As he explained to his defense attorney Elton Schwarz, and later reiterated in several letters to me, he had moved some of his furniture to a house in Osceola Village off State Road 84 to set up housekeeping with his first wife, Marty, a highly intellectual young woman who was seeing a psychiatrist at the Henderson Clinic regularly, as was John.

Not long after they moved in together, Marty got a divorce and left the area. Shortly after that, a guy he knew from high school named John or Jack Dolan moved in for about three weeks. According to Schaefer, Dolan told him he had killed both Hallock and Hainline, and he must have put Hallock's teeth in the desk before it was brought back to Schaefer's mother's home.

In the course of trying to persuade me of this theory, Schaefer sent written authorization to Elton Schwarz allowing him to release to me the audiotape of the sealed deposition he had taken from Dolan on the Fourth of July in 1973 in front of Dolan's dorm at Florida Atlantic University in Boca Raton.

It is typical of Schaefer that he would be able to maintain the illusion that listening this tape would tend to exonerate him and shift my suspicions onto the guy his sister Sadie had given the nickname "Dippy Dolan." On the contrary, it threw a whole new sinister light on Schaefer while revealing Dolan to be an innocent bystander.

Dolan had met Schaefer when they attended St. Thomas Aquinas High School together. When Schwarz asked if they were friends, Dolan hedged, "We did double date, but I had closer friends." Dolan went on to attend Broward Community College and then spent from 1965 to 1968 in the Navy, serving a full term of duty in Vietnam.

After returning home to Ft. Lauderdale he worked for a few months, and then went back to Broward Community College, where he earned an AA degree in 1970. He studied government at Florida State University in Tallahassee for two quarters, then returned to Ft. Lauderdale and worked for Sears for a year. It was during that period, while Schaefer was working as an intern teacher, that they shared the house in Osceola Village, off State Road 84.

"Man, that was the worst place I ever lived in my whole life," Dolan told Schwarz. "The ceiling went like this, the floor went like that, and the plumbing didn't work sometimes. It was really old. And his dog was drooling all over the place. It smelled like a kennel, and man, it was just bad. I couldn't wait to get out of there. I was completely disgusted, and a little bit scared. John was just getting a little bit weird."

It was right after John had come back from Europe, and after showing Dolan the usual tourist snapshots, he added rather slyly, "I've got some other pictures too,"

Former Public Defender Elton Schwarz defended Schaefer and represented him for seven years of appeals while married to Schaefer's ex-wife Teresa

but when Dolan asked about them, Schaefer just laughed and demurred, "You don't want to see those pictures."

According to Dolan, he never saw the questionable pictures, nor did he see the 175 to 200 "nudist" magazines that Schaefer had apparently mutilated, drawing nooses around women's necks and stabbing at them, leaving holes in the paper. Though listed as being submitted into evidence in Schaefer's murder trial, all of these items have "disappeared," along with the original manuscripts, except for "Murder Plan," which was read to the jury, and the first few pages of a story set in Germany. Most likely these have been stolen from the evidence locker in Ft. Pierce by collectors of such murderabilia.

Dolan did, however, note an unusually large number of skinning knives around the house, and observed that Schaefer always had knives, guns, machetes and axes in the back of his Volkswagen.

"He liked to kill," Dolan remembered. "That's what he told me. And he said he drank blood. He was laughing, he got a big joke out of it. I was trying to think if it in relation to something like a hunter, where they would put blood on their forehead or some shit like that, and kind of get carried away or something, but I don't know anything about hunting. It was all just pretty far out for me. He'd get in these moods, he'd be talking all this shit, and he'd just get real weird."

Dolan described one night when Schaefer was dating a slender girl with reddish hair and planned on spending some private time with her. "He didn't want me around," recalled Dolan, so he spent the night at a friend's. The next day when he came back to the house, Schaefer seemed nervous, and "made this big thing about telling me that they had had intercourse, but she had been menstruating, so there was blood all over the place." Dolan told Schaefer he didn't notice any blood, and Schaefer said he had cleaned it up. Dolan never saw the girl again, nor were investigators able to locate her later. When Dolan asked Schaefer about the girl, he brushed it aside, saying, "Oh, just go over to her house now."

Dolan recalled Schaefer pointing out Leigh Hainline to him, and telling him how Leigh would undress in front of her bedroom window while Schaefer would watch. Schaefer said she was "really sharp," recalled Dolan. Though she was only two years older, Schaefer thought of her as much older than him. "He kind of held her off," Dolan said. "He really liked her." Dolan himself never knew Leigh that

well, "just to say hi." She worked at the Village Inn, "and if she waited on my table, I'd just give her my order, that's all."

Dolan had known Carmen Hallock much better. He dated her for two or three weeks when he was going to Broward Community College right after he got out of the service. "She used to hang around the Veteran's Club Table, and that's where I met her." During that period, Dolan recalled that Schaefer was attending school at Florida Atlantic University in Boca Raton, and had no contact with him. "I was living at home, and I had not seen John in quite a while."

Dolan had a sexual relationship with Hallock, and then she told him she had met another guy, a sailor, and even though they never had a falling-out, they went their separate ways.

"I had always been saying in the back of my mind, you know, I ought to go back and see old Candy again. But I never did. And then John showed me the article and said she was gone."

"What I'm trying to get at, Jack," said Schwarz, "I'm trying to figure out why John would even consider making these statements about the fact that you may know something about her disappearance."

"John says that about me?"

"Yes."

"I have not talked to John in two years. And I'm not into killing anybody."

"You never recall him making any mention of Carmen Hallock being chopped up and disposed of at the city dump?"

"Jesus, no."

"You never made any such statement to John?"

"What was my statement supposed to be?"

"That she had been chopped up and disposed of at the city dump."

His voice rising incredulously, Dolan asked, "*I* said that to *John?*" then added firmly, "*No*. No way." Under his breath he muttered, "oh, wow," and then addressed Schwarz. "This is turning into kind of a bummer. Here I am sitting here telling you my goddamn life story, and I don't know you from Adam, right? And you — you — Jesus Christ…"

"Look, Jack, I've got the job of trying to defend John, and trying to do what's right for him. And all I can do is try to find out anything I can. I'm not trying to implicate anybody. I didn't even have to tell you that. This is not an easy job, and I sure don't appreciate having to work on the Fourth of July. Matter of fact, I've been putting eighteen to twenty hours a day for three solid weeks, just trying to find out what may have happened. Other than John, nobody has tied you in with anybody. And I'm not trying to at this time. I'm just trying to figure out why John would have made this statement."

"The only think I can think of is maybe some kind of guilt transfer."

"Jack, the doctors who have been examining John agree that he is sick. Obviously if he did these things, he is very sick. I think he belongs in a mental hospital, not in a jail."

"If he did, I don't see how he could ever be rehabilitated enough to let him out."

THE REAL DETECTIVE KELLY

David A. Kelly, former Assistant Chief of Police, North Miami Beach, relaxing on his patio

In 1972, the same year Gerard Schaefer ended his career in law enforcement, David Kelly began his. He went to work for the North Miami Beach Police Department, becoming a detective in 1975.

It was the summer of 1986 when he was handed his introduction to Schaefer, in the form of a small envelope from Florida State Prison containing a brief, handwritten letter addressed to the Chief of Police, alleging that there were three individuals in their jurisdiction who were involved in the kiddie porn trade. Chief Terell Sheffield asked Detective Kelly to follow up on it. Thus began a mutual fascination between killer and cop that eventually led to the development of Schaefer's fictional "rogue cop" persona known as Detective Dan Kelly.

Both were born in 1947 and raised as Catholics in South Florida, and the blonde, blue-eyed Kelly became a mirror, or an alter ego for Schaefer. "He was vicariously living through me. I was the image he wanted to portray for himself," says Kelly, "and I took advantage of that. I fed his ego about his intelligence, his knowledge; I stroked him, no question. But he stroked me too. It was a two-way street."

Kelly hoped to close some of the old cases that were Schaefer's grim legacy. "In my writings back and forth with Schaefer, there was a great deal of conversation about the crimes he was convicted of. I had gotten a copy of his diary, I had talked to the FBI and the Florida Department of Law Enforcement, I talked to a number of people who had dealt with Schaefer over the years, and most warned me to just stay away from him. But I felt, egotistically, that perhaps I could get some information out of him that other people had been unable to get."

PRISON VISIT

Former North Miami Beach Detective David Kelly described his only visit with Gerard John Schaefer at Florida State Prison as "extremely spooky," and admitted to being severely disconcerted by the experience. He was escorted through a series of barred gates into an interview room and given a seat on one side of a double sheet of bulletproof glass. After he was seated, Schaefer was brought into the room on the other side of the glass.

"First off, he was huge, which kind of surprised me. He had the weight that you put on in prison from the high-carbohydrate diet. And he was intimidating. He was handcuffed in the front. He held his hands up, thrusting them at me, and the first words he said to me were, 'They're afraid I'm going to kill you.' And he smiled. I tell you what, I nearly peed my pants! After that, I was a basket case. I just let him talk. I didn't even ask him the questions I had wanted to ask.'"

DEE DEE KELLY

The relationship between Schaefer and Kelly developed from that initial inquiry into a kiddie porn sting operation involving Schaefer penning suggestive letters in a loopy, feminine hand, signed "Dee Dee Kelly," whom he portrayed as a 14-year-old girl who liked to pose for nude photos. The return address on the letters was for a post office box manned by the Postal Inspector, who would then turn over the letters responding to Schaefer's provocative letters to the North Miami Beach Police Department.

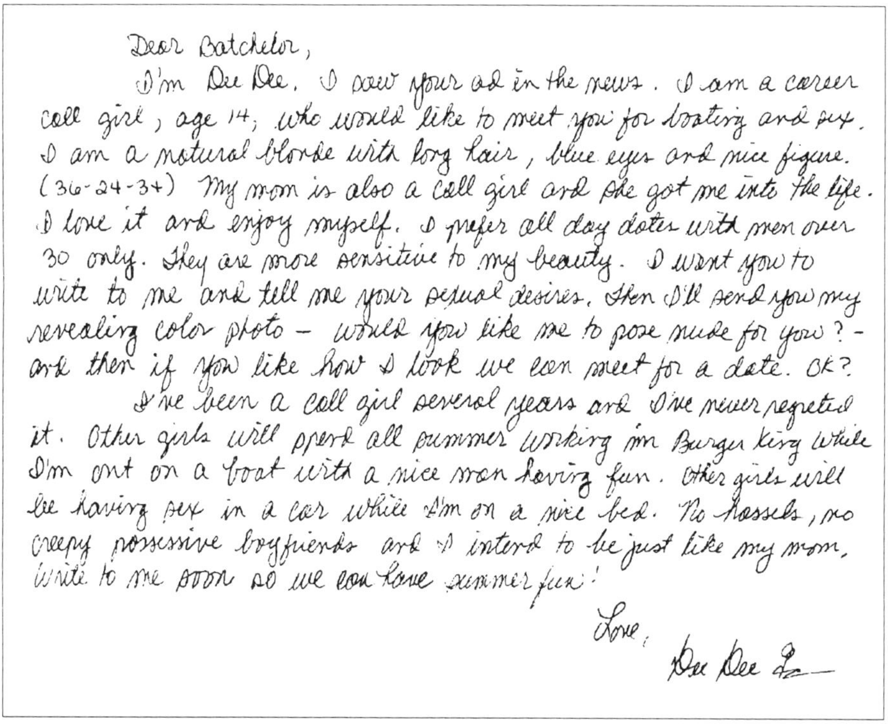

> Dear Batchelor,
>
> I'm Dee Dee. I saw your ad in the news. I am a career call girl, age 14; who would like to meet you for boating and sex. I am a natural blonde with long hair, blue eyes and nice figure. (36-24-34) My mom is also a call girl and she got me into the life. I love it and enjoy myself. I prefer all day daters with men over 30 only. They are more sensitive to my beauty. I want you to write to me and tell me your sexual desires. Then I'll send you my revealing color photo — would you like me to pose nude for you? — and then if you like how I look we can meet for a date. OK?
>
> I've been a call girl several years and I've never regreted it. Other girls will spend all summer working in Burger King while I'm out on a boat with a nice man having fun. Other girls will be having sex in a car while I'm on a nice bed. No hassels, no creepy possessive boyfriends and I intend to be just like my mom. Write to me soon so we can have summer fun!
>
> Love,
>
> Dee Dee K—

Schaefer asked Kelly to write to the prison authorizing his correspondence to be given privileged confidential status, as it was concerning police business. Kelly complied with Schaefer's wishes, only to be contacted several weeks later by irate prison authorities. Schaefer had been invoking Kelly's name to carry give confidential status to his correspondence with numerous individuals involved in child pornography. When reprimanded by prison investigators, had defended himself by appealing to his privileged status as an informant for Detective Kelly.

"He was sending a certain percentage of the mail he wanted to go out through me to come back to this Postal Service address, but then he was also sending out additional letters," Kelly speculates, "probably with a return address of someone he knew, most likely a female in Tampa, who supposedly had been busted for child pornography previously."

Kelly reminded the prison investigator of the letter he had filed which only endorsed Schaefer's correspondence with himself and had never been intended to enable Schaefer's unfettered abuse of the privileged status with his shady correspondence. "He was trying place himself in a situation where he would have easier and less scrutinized access to mail," says Kelly.

Although considerable volume of correspondence was generated by this operation, for the first eight months no perpetrators were identified. Then Schaefer sent Kelly a pen-pal newsletter, and an ad offering "exotic photos" for five dollars caught his eye. It listed an address in the Philippines, under the fictitious name of "Fila Galom."

The Filipino connection piqued Kelly's interest because of the case of Mervyn Eric Cross, who had been convicted of conducting a kiddie porn scam while incarcerated with Schaefer. Investigation revealed that Cross had been putting through calls to Schaefer's father, Gerard John Schaefer, Senior, who would then allow his telephone line to be used for a primitive form of three-way calling involving a Filipino partner.

Kelly sent off for the photos, mentioning Schaefer's name as a reference, and was surprised to receive a roll of undeveloped film, which upon processing showed explicitly pornographic photos of small brown girls. With this, the investigation was turned over to U.S. Customs.

About two weeks later, Kelly heard from a furious Schaefer. Apparently "Fila Galom" had written to Schaefer thanking him for referring the new customer, David Kelly. Schaefer accused Kelly of treachery in going behind his back to cultivate his source.

And so the sting crashed and burned without charges being brought against Fila Galom or any other pedophiles. The three pornographers allegedly operating within the jurisdiction of North Miami Beach never materialized.

In return for his cooperation as a confidential informant, Schaefer received a letter of recognition from the North Miami Police acknowledging his cooperation, and endorsing Schaefer's transfer to a more comfortable prison. The letter was taken into consideration by the Department of Corrections; the transfer, however, was denied.

VIRTUAL BABY-RAPER

In time, David Kelly came to believe that Schaefer's ulterior motive in initiating this operation went beyond merely trying to get moved to a more desirable prison. Schaefer, Kelly believes today, was striking the pose of a moral crusader as a cover for a more sinister agenda. Schaefer was not only an ex-cop who killed teenage girls. Apparently he went on from that to distinguish himself as both a serial snitch and a virtual baby-raper — a hitherto unrevealed facet of his multifarious pathology that would qualify him for the obverse equivalent of a Triple Crown amongst the lowest of the most loathed.

After the Fila Galom connection collapsed, Schaefer continued to carry on a lively correspondence with various Philippine connections, and sent me over a hundred photos of ragged little brown urchins staring bleakly into the camera lens, with their names and ages written on the back along with comments like "abandoned child," or "father dead, mother destitute." Some are signed, "Tanie Arbaquez, procurer."

There is a pitiful eloquence in the ancient Asian eyes of these tiny victims. One photo of four little girls all dolled up in ballgowns, jewelry and heavy makeup is especially haunting. Schaefer wrote me that all of them had appeared in pornographic photos and videos. Tanie's handwritten note on the back of this one asks coyly, "What do you think of the two newfound poor souls?"

Photo sent to London by Schaefer in 1990. Note from Tanie on reverse side identifies these "poor souls" as "Candidates for Miss Princesita."

A tiny Eurasian who appears to be about six years old is listed as "Venus Arbaquez Cross," a name that would seem to identify her as the love child of Tanie Arbaquez and Schaefer's scam-partner and subsequent snitch-victim, Mervyn Eric Cross.

Schaefer sent me dozens of photos of a child called Nova, whom he called his "*mui jai* girl," a Filipina who appears to be no older than nine whom he claimed to have bought out of the kiddie porn business and placed in a convent school. The plan he explained to me was that when Nova was old enough, he would have her brought to him and they would marry in prison.

I was shocked when Schaefer sent me swimsuit shots of his sister's prepubescent daughters, boasting that he had circulated similar photos of his own nieces in his correspondence with people he called "freaks." At times it seemed there were no limits to his depravity.

"Psychopaths like Schaefer just don't have the same barrier as normal people do between circumstances," observed Kelly. "One second they can say, 'My child died an hour ago,' and appear very sorrowful, and yet, ten seconds later, they can be discussing the breakfast they had this morning, without any transition."

GOING TO DISNEY WORLD

Although the kiddie porn sting had come to an end, Dave Kelly's desire to learn more about the enigma that was Gerard Schaefer led him to correspond with him for almost a decade. "I had been extremely interested in serial killers and sexual psychopaths for many years, going back to the mid-fifties with Starkweather," said Kelly, "and I think Schaefer was a sexual psychopath. I strongly believe Schaefer was responsible for a lot more crimes than he was confined for. 1968 is the date of the first crime they attribute to him, but I believe he probably started his activities in his early teen years, probably 12 to 14, and I'm talking murder, not just his sexual activities."

"I questioned him very, very thoroughly about his crimes, about what he had done or not done, and body decomposition. He had a tremendous knowledge of that, which is really unusual. But Schaefer never denied the murders. His response was always that guilt was not a matter of whether you did it or not, it's a legal issue. That came through very strongly in all of his writings to me. And legally, he believed he was not guilty of any crimes."

"I would ask him outright, I'd say, 'Jerry, did you kill these people?' And he never said, 'No, I didn't kill them,' which would be the normal response. He would always go off into guilt being a legal issue."

Kelly was never able to tie Schaefer to the scene of a crime or close any old cases. The only connection he could draw to any known cases was one of Schaefer's early writings that refers to himself as a police officer, stopping a woman in a white car, and then going on to murder her.

Kelly was able to confirm reports of a female motorist in a white car passing through Wilton Manors while Schaefer was employed there as a police officer. And after being stopped by a police officer, the woman disappeared. Although no

police reports document her identity, the case is still talked about today among old-timers in local law enforcement circles.

In conclusion, Kelly said that Schaefer seemed to be seeking acceptance. "Being a serial killer is like going to Disney World by yourself, and not being able to take anyone with you," he said. "I think serial killers have these tremendously exciting experiences, but no one to share them with. So they spend a lot of time cultivating people that they hope they will be able to talk to. They start out small, and they build up, hoping to get to the point where they can tell you what they have been doing, and you will accept it."

"These stories he has written for you," Kelly observed, "they are in fact tests, to see how you would react to his various escalations of perversions."

BIG PERVERT

Schaefer became a transvestite in order to avoid the draft, and then went on to assume a sadomasochistic female identity and establish his own slave empire, still managing to conclude, "I certainly do not regard myself a deviant."

The Society of Friends used to come onto campus and educate people in non-violent resistance. That's how I learned about 1-Y deferments. Personality Disorders. Believe it or not, it's as easy as pie to avoid the draft. Just slip on a pair of panties, wear a garter belt and nylons and voila! Instant 1-Y classification! Really, you only need to tell the people at the Army induction center you are 'queer' and that's sufficient.

I was drafted. I got down to the point to be sworn in, and in my best thespian manner, asked if it was gonna be OK to be in the Army if I'm queer? There's maybe a hundred guys there, all macho posturing and I come out with I'm a queer. Fastest dismissal you ever did see.

Oh, they interrogate you a bit, but the key is to be sincere. They are looking for the phony faggot with the limp wrist; so you just play straight man… of *course* I want to be in the Army, I just wondered if there was any rule against wearing panties? Threw me right out the door.

I played the role to a tee. I never hid my 'perversion.' Wore my nylons right to class. Guys are in absolute despair over loss of deferments (1968-70) and I'm laughing up my sleeve and wearing a garter girdle and never consider Vietnam as an impediment to my academic career.

Same with the photos. Bondage ritual! Oh my *God*! Major league freak action. I never hid them. I was very open about it. It was simply a case of doing the necessary to get what I wanted: my university education. It's not a crime, yet, to wear a pair of panties. If I'm a pervert because I wore garter belt and nylons to class, then I'm a pervert. I just don't happen to give a rat fuck whether I'm regarded as a pervert or not. My sexual orientation is 100% heterosexual. I've plenty of happy ladies running around alive to verify I'm quite capable of giving them a sprightly toss in bed. So I fail to understand the 'problem.'

I certainly do not regard myself as a deviant. I'm sure Boy George laughs all the way to the bank, as does Alice Cooper. I'm as valid an entertainer as either of them.

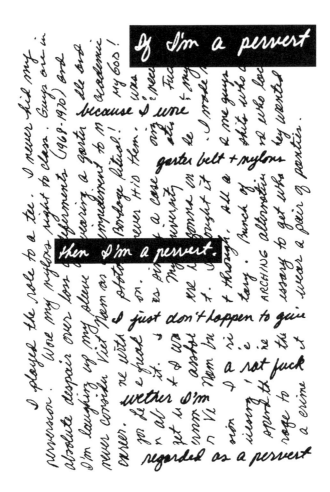

I've played before screaming fans: Hollywood Bowl. Redrocks. Madison Square Garden. I've cut an album. I'm in a song book with Glenn Close. I *choose* to write. I do not care for the mayhem of the concert tour.

Take Jessica Zurriaga: I invented her years ago. Ran ads under her name. Made a buck. Wrote as a woman. Had about 500 'slaves' and submissives answer. You train the slave to wash out your panties and return them with $10. I had a lady handling the mail for me. The slave sends the lingerie. The lady wears it, gets it nice and nasty, mails it to the slave for cleaning. I'd write the letters. By the way, Zurriaga is Spanish for whip. More nuance.

So I'm writing to the freaks. The prison censors pick up on it. Confiscate my mail. Give it to the psychologist. They stick me in *Sex Education!!* I go see the shrink; I say, 'I run a fucking *slave empire.'* The guy is entranced; he cannot believe I'm pulling it off. I convinced him. No more sex education classes. I become the joke of the prison, but I'm laughing because guys pay to wash the panties of my bitch. Big pervert. Sure. But I'm raking in the coin, ain't I?

So my experiences have been varied with my various correspondents. As a creative writer, it's been fun. All that was years ago. I used my talents to catch child sex perverts until just recently.

From Guilt to Violence

"I know all about the prostitution game in Florida," said Schaefer. He would have us believe he learned this information by continuing his research from behind bars. Certainly he continued to develop new forms of sexual exploitation during his incarceration, still it must be remembered that several of his victims have mentioned that his conversations as long ago as 1969 included references to the white slave trade. Regardless of how he developed his inside information about what perverts do to children, he does point out the disturbing consequences of our attempts to control such behavior by maximizing sentencing guidelines.

"Take all these 'missing' children. A certain number of those kids are grabbed by kiddie porn people who make film and photos and then dump the kid off shore with an anchor around his or her neck. In Florida, any guy even *touch* a girl under age 12 on her cunnus or anus it's 25 to life *mandatory*. And if the 'victim' says, 'he rubbed his finger between my legs,' that's all the law requires. The *uncorroborated* statement of the 'victim.'

"These procurers pick up a cute runaway, take her out on a fancy yacht into international waters, and believe me, she (or he) don't come back when the party is over. Ain't nobody gonna prove *nothing* either. Give the girlie a needle to put her out, strap a diver's weight belt around her waist, and over the side in 500 feet of water. Girl? What girl? And the sad thing is the reason the kid is killed is because it ain't worth the risk to let the kid go when you can get 25 to life on unsupported testimony.

"Remember Veile Groves out in Davie? Sent old man Veile up for possession of albums of photos of nude girls 12 to 14 years old. The girls were paid models. He'd hire them right off the streets. Nude modeling. No suckee/fuckee stuff. The girls all loved him. Nice man. Cops found out about it. Busted him. Sent him up. He'd have gotten a lesser pop for armed robbery. He'd get less time for killing one of these girls in a fit of passion than having sex with her. Now is that crazy or what?" In a psychoanalytic aside, Schaefer concludes, "It's all built on guilt, by the way. Guilt breeds frustration, frustration breeds anger, and anger manifests in violence."

Picture Bride

In 1979, Schaefer started calling himself "married" to a "picture bride," a diminutive Filipina named Elen. She sent him photos from her native village of herself looking like a prepubescent child, inscribed "To my loving husband Gerard."

In July of 1980, she arrived in St. Petersburg, Florida, where she joined the household of Gerard Schaefer, Senior, and his second wife. A marriage license was somehow obtained naming "Gerard Schaefer" as the husband and Elen as the wife. This document was then submitted to prison authorities at Avon Park Correctional Institution, who subsequently allowed the portly, balding serial killer to have contact visits with her.

Schaefer enjoyed a contact visit with his "picture bride" Elen at Avon Park C.I. in August of 1985

Schaefer explained to me that when brought Elen over to this country, he expected her to be a submissive peasant who would show enough sense to express her gratefulness for being sponsored.

Instead, it became apparent that Elen had been accustomed to being courted in the finest style, and expected if not champagne and caviar, at least flowers and perfume. She continued to live with either Schaefer's father in Tampa or with his mother in Ft. Lauderdale, making the best of a dubious situation for five years.

Schaefer's picture bride apparently realized that neither he nor his father were going to keep her in the style to which she would like to become accustomed, so when she got her green card in 1985, she moved on, leaving Schaefer a single man once again.

Schaefer's "picture bride" with his father, G.J. Schaefer, Sr. and his second wife, April 1981.

PRISON MURDER

In May of 1988, Schaefer witnessed a shocking prison murder that uncannily presaged his own.

Two guards were escorting Alfred Moore, who was restrained in shackles and chains, from his cell, when Doy Christian shoved them aside and shanked Moore to death, tossing his bloody body off the third-floor cellblock.

Defense testimony by Department of Corrections personnel and inmates related that the murder was the culmination of a running battle between the two starting two weeks earlier, when Moore came up behind Christian while he was playing cards and smashed him over the head with a weight-lifting bar, knocking him out. Over the ensuing two-week period, Moore taunted, insulted, and threatened Christian until Christian, in his own words, "just blew up."

"I was a witness to this murder," wrote Schaefer. "The State forced me to give testimony about it. Told me to talk or I'd be sent to the strip cells. I talked. Blamed the whole thing on the guards who ran away and let the guy be chopped into Alpo. Christian really did a job on him. Lake of blood. Stabbed out his eyes. Moore deserved getting a shank, but Christian ended up getting the electric chair for it. All this occurred in a "Protective Custody" area! {Smiley face} Goes to show you how much P.C. means at FSP. Zip… that's why they sent me up here. {Frowny face}."

THE OFFICIAL VERSION

December 3, 1995.

Schaefer stepped up to the water cooler and filled two mugs with the last of the hot water. As he turned around, what did he see behind him but his worst nightmare in the flesh — Vincent Rivera — big and black, lean and mean, and half his age.

Rivera communicated his displeasure at having no hot water to warm his bones that chilly Sunday morning. Schaefer responded that if it hadn't been for him, there would be no water cooler on the tier in the first place, because it was he who had kept pushing for it.

Rivera was said to have muttered an aside to the effect that Schaefer wouldn't need *no* more hot water where he was going.

THE TABLOID VERSION

In February of 1996, the *National Enquirer* ran a story headlined "Killer set to reveal Adam Walsh's fate is murdered in jail," and tagged "New heartache for 'America's Most Wanted' host." The story called Gerard John Schaefer the last hope for John Walsh and his wife Reve, who were said to be "sick at heart" be-

cause since Schaefer was dead, they would never solve the mystery of the disappearance of their 5-year-old son Adam in 1981.

The story goes on to suggest that the prime suspect, confessed serial killer Ottis Toole, had some connection to Schaefer's murder. The principal source for this theory was his mother, Mrs. Doris Schaefer. In a telephone conversation with me on February 25, 1996, she confirmed that she had been quoted accurately. This, then, is her story:

> Last November, Toole, who's dying of cancer, told my son everything — how he killed Adam Walsh and where the little boy's remains were. My son spoke to an inspector at the prison, and he arranged for Detective Mark Smith, who is in charge of the Walsh case, to interview him in prison. When they met, Schaefer told Detective Smith he'd reveal the whereabouts of Adam's body only if he was transferred to Avon Park, a "better prison." He was told that would be up to the prison officials. My son knew where Adam's body is — and somebody wanted him dead. Some friends in prison told me that after Detective Smith's visit, word went around that my son was a snitch.

With all due respect to Mrs. Schaefer and the *National Enquirer*, the word about Schaefer being a snitch had been going around for years. A more accurate assessment of the situation by one prison insider is that Schaefer had tried to get information from Toole when they were once again housed on the same wing, but this time Toole was well aware of what Schaefer was up to, and gave him no new information at all. It seems self-evident that if Detective Mark Smith believed Schaefer had learned anything of value from Toole, he would have been able to obtain that information from so willing an informant. The fact that he went back home empty-handed speaks for itself.

Schaefer had been trying to sell the bones of Adam Walsh since 1988. It was then that Toole's health declined, and believing he had cancer, he agreed with Schaefer's suggestion to come clean and confess to his crimes, since he was going to die anyway. Schaefer then tried to broker Toole's confessions to John Walsh, taunting the bereaved father in a cruelly obscene letter that does not bear repeating here.

Toole did not have cancer, and in fact went on to recant all his confessions, and to outlive Schaefer. Shortly after Schaefer's murder, however, Toole was again hospitalized with hepatitis B and C, and he died of liver failure in September of 1996.

There is no evidence that Ottis Toole has ever had any contact with Schaefer's accused slayer. Nor was Toole the type of convict to take out hits. A man of lowly estate, he was as much the classic *disorganized* type serial killer as Schaefer was the classic *organized* type.

After a series of especially nonproductive questions about the details of his life in an interview with Joel Norris and myself, Toole squinted and shook his head, saying, "Look, most people keep track of things. I don't keep track of *nothin'*. Most times, I don't even know if it's *day or night.*"

THE DEFENDANT'S VERSION

Vincent Rivera was indicted for Schaefer's murder on February 1, 1996. In November of 1996, I sent Rivera a letter, inviting him to comment on the slaying.

Ironically, the accused slayer portrays himself as an innocent man framed for murder. And the Disney imagery again seems appropriate.

Rivera's claim that he has not even been charged with this crime makes a fitting coda to the story of the serial killer who once loved me; he was ultimately as unknowable in death as he had been in life.

> The guy you asked me if I have met, Toole, no, I don't know him. Who is he? Who is Adam Walsh?
>
> I guess you've read a lot of trash in the newspapers. Those newspapers are going to catch hell in a libel and slander suit. I'm up to my ears with hearsay, gainsay, rumors, gossip... you name it. But no facts. The F.D.L.E. don't have any. The state's attorney don't have any. Nobody has any facts... except me.
>
> There's about ten tons of paperwork being conjured up. The state's attorney is a regular David Copperfield. He might as well be making motorcycles fly or the Statue of Liberty disappear. The newspapers and any "witnesses" are all liars. Ten months later, now they know they are liars.
>
> Pretty soon they'll do like Felix the Cat and reach into their bag of tricks. But there is no such thing as magic. If there were, I'd get myself a few magic charms, cast a few spells, and abracadabra, *POOF!* I'd have myself a real lawyer, instead of a cartoon.

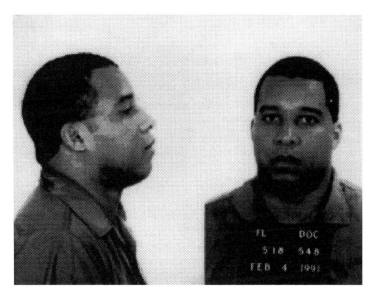

Vincent Rivera, FDOC #518548, DOB 1/9/63
Charged with the murder of Gerard John Schaefer

But this isn't a cartoon. It isn't Disney World — even though Mickey Mouse, Donald Duck and Goofy are my lawyers, and Hekyll and Jekyll are the prosecutors, with Bugs Bunny is sitting on the bench.

In a nutshell, the situation is not copacetic with me. They got the wrong guy... and they know it. They got two guys, one alive and one dead. They found a knife. Ten months ago they called it "the murder weapon." Six months ago, after the crime lab report, they found out the "murder weapon" had no blood on it and no prints. They found bloody handprints in the dead guy's cell — whole hand prints — ten months ago. Six months ago, the crime lab reports showed the bloody hand prints did not match me — the live body, or Schaefer — the dead body.

Don't for a minute swallow that water cooler crap. The guy that started that myth tried to get himself a transfer with the inspector ordering it, so he made up a whopper. They didn't swallow it and he didn't get the transfer. That was eleven months ago. In September, 1996, that same guy told my attorney, Mickey Mouse, that he had made up that fairy tale to get out of FSP. Mickey Mouse then went to Hekyll and Jekyll with the deposition admitting he made that garbage up.

FYI, baby, I didn't even use the water from that cooler. Four years ago, when I was at CCI, there was a nurse that told me asked me if I have ever noticed how many young guys in their twenties and thirties have receding hairlines or are going bald? I told her, now that you mention it, yeah. She told me the water coolers in the buildings have hot water taps. That hot water is heated with element coils, electricity that puts out radiation. Those guys give themselves radiation therapy like cancer patients with every cup of hot water. Even though the exposure is mild, try going to a hospital and sitting under those radiographical thingamabobs all day every day, all night every night, year after year, and what do you think would happen? Same concept with electric hot water.

No siree bob, not me! First your hair thins out, then your teeth fall out, one at a time, then your immune system gets messed up, then you die a slow agonizing death from leukemia, bone cancer, or intestinal cancer. There ain't no cup of hot water in the world worth that. One day standing in line for the water cooler, next day standing in line for a state-issued grave? NO! NO! NO! Not me. Look, darling, I'm no coward, but if I gotta die, I prefer to be mauled by a school of Mako sharks in a feeding frenzy, than to suffer from radiation sickness.

The institution inspector that headed that murder investigation couldn't wait to have me charged with a prison killing. Number one, I didn't kill somebody, I didn't kill anybody, I didn't kill nobody, and I didn't kill Schaefer. Number two, the inspector that did the investigation is a.k.a. "Mister Cover-up," "Mister Clean-it-up," "Mister Bold-Faced Liar." He was fired in June of 1996. He was uncovered covering up once too often.

For crying out loud, I haven't even been duly arraigned yet. So let's hold off on this for now, OK? I'm not flipping you off, it's just that the thing is like cow manure, all over the place, and I'm tired of the stench.

KILLER FiCTiON

Schaefer's Warning

I was falsely accused of killing 34 women; I was framed by corrupt men. I believe that God allowed this to happen to me for a special reason.

Schaefer upon being charged with the Jessup and Place murders

I have indeed suffered greatly, but always I have relied upon God to protect and guide me.

I was called America's number one serial killer at one time, and that gives me a certain status. I can use that celebrity in a socially positive or negative way. I've chosen to take the socially positive path by exposing in graphic prose the vileness of murder, the horror of prison life, and the degrading spectacle of state-endorsed executions. Perhaps my revelations will lead to social change.

Many critics have stated that my books are pornographic, incite people to violence, and glorify murder. I cannot continue to write books if people read them and become corrupted. My intention in writing *Killer Fiction* was to open the eyes of readers to the horrifying actualities of murder and violence. Murder is a cardinal sin, a capital crime, that has been reduced to entertainment by film and television producers.

Bret Ellis and Thomas Harris write books that glorify perverted sex and violence and bloody murder; I write books that cause the reader to reexamine his entire social conscience with respect to violent crime as entertainment. I rather think God would be pleased that someone would be brave enough to take such a position. Some day I'll have to meet God, and hopefully, He will be pleased with my effort to make people think about the vile social issues addressed in my books.

My own books make no compromise in the presentation. I give you bloody murder in such a way that you recoil from it. My reader is not given a cheap thrill, but an emotional whipping. A person with a depraved mind may read my work and revel in the lust, sex and filthy crime portrayed there, but a person of noble social conscience will recognize the horrifying malignancies that I present boldly, and cry out for a positive change that may alter the diseased social attitudes that allow such gross acts of savagery to occur.

This book is a work of fiction. It is the duty of a competent fiction writer to inflame the imagination of his readers. This book will give you sleepless nights. Any person who reads it will never see murder as pure entertainment again. It is not intended to casually shock the reader. It delivers a serious social message, and some of my more insightful readers have discerned that at the core of my work is a lifesaving message, especially for my female fans.

My work deals almost exclusively with modern social taboos, many of which involve sexual perversity. It's not about sex. It's about the intermingling of sexual perversion and incomprehensible madness.

There is an undeniable sexual relationship that exists in the area of violent death, whether the violence is lawless murder or official execution. My books do not explore the causes of sexually-related violence, they merely graphically portray its existence in a way that no other books dare. My books address sexual perversions that exist without justification within our society, but I do not endorse those perversions.

My ability to write is a gift from God. It is my duty to use that gift well. Many people make the error of believing that my books chronicle actual events that I have personally been involved in; that supposition is untrue. During the past twenty years in prison, I have spoken to many criminals and listened to many stories about murder. I have made a study of murder and the people who kill.

I believe it is socially irresponsible to glorify violence, sadism, sexual perversion and murder in books and films. My work is an attempt to wake up citizens of the world community to the casual disregard for human life that the glorification of violence encourages by presenting violence, murder and execution as it really is; that is a positive use of my talent for a worthy purpose.

My own personal belief in Jesus Christ assures me of my future as a child of God, but that does not excuse me from helping my fellow man. If my works save the life of even one person, then that is their ultimate worth, and like the man in the parable, I will be rewarded for using my talents wisely.

I write these words from solitary confinement at one of America's most disgusting and repressive prisons. I expect to be punished for daring to speak truths, but only by publishing the voices of the slaves will the world ever know the truth about the American Gulags.

It may also interest my readers to know that I receive no monetary compensation for my work. What I have written I wrote because I believe the message contained in the books. My reward, if any, will be a spiritual one.

Spring Break

I turned off Sunrise Boulevard and walked along Sunrise Lane, finally stopping at the World Famous Parrot Lounge.

I frowned as I looked at it, almost closing time and my chance to score was looking bleaker with each passing moment. There was an indifferent surfer type in a green T-shirt at the door checking ID's. I showed him mine and he motioned me inside. The sudden light made me squint.

The Parrot was crowded and chaotic. College types, and nearly all were drunk. They wore a uniform of sweatshirts and jeans touting fraternities, sororities and institutions of higher learning from up and down the Eastern Seaboard: Yale, Oberlin, Ohio State, Tennessee Tech, and a host of others. The students were all shouting and laughing; on the dance floor they were writhing and swaying to the beat of Mick Jagger's hoarse "I Can't Get No... Satisfaction." I liked it. I'd scouted the Parrot before, it was a happy hunting ground. I looked around at the women. There was a real nice selection to choose from. I watched them gyrate and felt the old tingle in my crotch. Fucking college cunt. They were a curse and a blessing.

The bar was jammed with a throng of sweaty bodies. I had to force my way through to buy a drink. Two bucks for a lousy 7&7. I paid the bartender and pushed my way back toward the dance floor; found myself a semiprivate spot next to a cement pillar and surveyed the action. I was feeling good. Vibrant. I drank my Seagrams and drilled a path through the smoky haze with my eyes. Strobe lights flashed through the swirling murk. My face was flushed with hot anticipation.

Then I saw the little bitch. She was standing alone under a sign flashing "EXIT." She was suntanned and slender, wearing a virginal white silk blouse with a tight thigh-high miniskirt. The ash blonde hair surrounding her patrician face swirled around her like an angelic halo. Her plump full bosom pressed invitingly against the fabric of her transparent top. I could see the cups and straps and the deep cleavage beneath.

I felt the familiar chill course through me. The icy instinctual lust that would slide down my spine, gently squeeze my balls, and leave my loins inflamed with sudden heat. My dick began to unfurl in my shorts. My mind clarified while I watched the light wash over the girl and bathe her face in a soft radiance. My tension subsided, replaced by quiet resolve.

The girl was sipping a Vodka Collins. She sipped slowly, with a daintiness that underscored her overt femininity. Her eyes were emerald green. They were sliding about the lounge in a distracted manner, reflecting the studied boredom of a Junior League society bitch. It made me want to kill her.

I sensed this feeling at once. My senses rarely let me down. My intense perception pleases me; it helps me to be a success at what I do well. Her green eyes caught my own of violet blue. She stared boldly, shivered, flipped away her gaze with a toss of her hair. I remained there staring, willing her to come to me, drawing her shining sun into the black hole of my own orbit.

I slapped her face with a psychic command. She didn't move. The pull wasn't working. Yet her eyes, as if in obedience to my dark authority, slowly turned toward my face again. I didn't smile. I studied her face. She dropped her eyes; they flickered toward the dance floor, landed there, and bounced with the rhythm of the dancers. That displeased me. I firmed my lips and strode across the room until I stood right in front of her, blocking her view. Now she had nowhere else to look. She had to look right at me. She didn't recognize the ancient face of death; so I spoke to her.

"I'm Jerry. Do you mind if I talk to you?"

Miss Junior League studied me vaguely, blinked a message of indifference, raised her frosted glass to her painted lips and sipped her vodka. She held the tall glass with both hands shielding her mouth, peering over its rim. Coy. Cute. The strobe lights cast a blue tint over her features. Cyan suited her. I was moved to strangle her, felt my fingers curl at the thought of encircling the slender neck.

"What do you want?" she asked.

I liked her voice. It had a soft, bored, sexy tone. Languorous. Her accent was finishing-school classy with an underlying hint of arrogance. She was a college cunt out slumming, spending Daddy's money. I wanted her... dead.

"Company. Unless you think I'm bugging you."

"No, you're not 'bugging me.' Not yet, at any rate," she sniped. Flashed her eyes at me with haughty insouciance. She had too much money; too many cotillions with callow boys dancing attendance to her every whim. That life was over, she just didn't know it yet.

It reminded me of the time I'd cut off a hitchhiker's head with a machete and set it on a stump. I'd noticed how the eyes in the head were alive, moving, watching the decapitated body kicking and writhing. I'd tapped the head with my knuckles and asked, "Are you alive in there?" then added, "If you're in there, blink your eyes." And the eyes stared at me and blinked. It was spooky. The hitchhiker was dead, yet undead. It took her a few minutes to realize what had happened before she could settle down and die. This one with her snotty airs reminded me of that interesting girl. Would this turn out to be another memorable affair?

"I drove down from Rollins for the weekend. It's my first time in Lauderdale," I lied. "I came in here and I didn't know a soul, then I saw you alone. I don't enjoy the loneliness. I thought, what a nice-looking girl, and well... here I am."

"I've been here a few hours," she said, softening. "I came in with some other girls from our house. We're Tri-Delts. They met some Dekes from Boston College. They've gone to the Elbo Room and now I'm about to leave myself. Just as soon as I finish up my drinky."

"I'll get you another little drinky if you'll stick around."

"No thanks. I'd better not."

"Why not? We can dance."

"I know. I'm half tiddly already. I wouldn't want to end up like the Tiddly Tot from Agnes Scott." She crinkled up her eyes with a mischievous thought.

"How did the Tiddly Tot end up?"

She cocked a plucked eyebrow at me. "Preggers. Preggers under the moonlight, compliments of her beau from Tech. Who taught her how to neck. And a few other little things, as well I suspect."

"He should have been wearing rubbers when fooling around in a wet place."

"Really?" She stared boldly.

I returned her stare with one of my own. Studied her demeanor thoughtfully. She was still vague but venturing out near the edge. She was rolling the long damp Collins glass between her hands. Something was on her mind, troubling her. I have excellent instincts for that. Her indecision made her vulnerable. I like them uncertain. I play with their emotions before I play with their bodies. Mindfuck them before the more disgusting act is consummated.

"What's your name? Where's your school?" I asked.

"Gwendolyn. Gwendolyn Kent. I'm a senior at Smith. We're down for spring break. We're having fun." She took another dainty lady sip from her dwindling drinky.

"Gwendolyn is a long name," I said to keep her moving her mouth, and she gushed for me.

"It's an awful name. Everyone calls me 'Gwen.' Well, my mother calls me Gwendolyn, of course, but on campus I'm just Gwen."

Suddenly some female part of her sensed the unspoken message, felt the lust radiating out toward her. She looked up. Studied me with new eyes. Saw I was tall and athletically built, powerfully muscled, with a deepwater tan and sharp, fine features. Handsome, with a delightful spill of sun bleached blonde hair and a dark mustache. She sensed my experience with women, noted my fraternity pin, a minor badge of social class structure. She watched my bright but unrevealing violet eyes, misread the trace of smoldering passion shining through the alcohol for something that would stoke her own erotic fires, instead of extinguishing them. Like others before her, she was thinking that a girl could do much worse; that there wasn't much remaining time before closing. She was right and she was dead wrong. Like the Tiddly Tot, Gwen's wet cunt would be the death of her. I knew it the moment she raised her glass and fluttered her eyelashes at me demurely over the rim.

I decided to kill her. I drew her death warrant with my intellect and signed it with my will. The decision was devoid of reason. I felt a heaviness in my balls, a lightness in my head. A heightened sexuality enveloped me in a circle almost humming with emotion. I felt the acrid mixture of marijuana and tobacco smoke swirl up my nostrils to tickle my brain, and enhance my emerging insanity.

The laughter was bawdy, glasses rattled and tinkled with ice, and Jim Morrison was alive and urging us on, "Come on baby, light my fire."

I stepped closer to the spoiled bitch. The lounge was crowded, so there wasn't much choice, but I liked it close once the final decision has been made. Gwen glanced up, and favored me with a cozy smile, but it was a smile full of hesitation, almost remote. I would bring her up from the depths of her lassitude, crystallize

her attention; I'd teach her the meaning of her life and send her off into the void. I spread myself around her, sucked her into myself, bending her to my suggestions and my will. I would drain her juices, her very soul, and discard the empty husk. My eye was drawn to her breast and caught the fraternity pin.

"You're pinned," I said.

"Oh, you noticed the pin! How very observant of you. Scouting out what you need to know. Men are like that, aren't they? Always curious. Looking under rocks, peering into nooks and crannies. Exploring. But women have the nosy reputation. How do you figure that?" She pouted.

I gave her a slow charming grin. "It's not the pin, Gwen, it's the location of the thing." I brought my own glass up and watched her reaction over the rim.

"Location?" She asked coyly, knowing exactly what I meant.

"Sure. Hanging out there on the end of your teats, how could I miss it?"

She sucked in her breath. I let my animal vitality come to the surface, drew her toward me with erotic steely-eyed magnetism. I was confident, knowing. She looked into my eyes and saw shadows that she'd never be able to fathom. It made her uneasy and curious, which in turn made me more attractive to her. I watched the color rise in her cheeks and knew what she was feeling as clearly as if it was written across her forehead in blood: she wanted my touch. She would feel it soon. My penis stiffened a bit at the thought.

I shifted slightly so she could see the outline of the half-erection. A tiny quiver ran through her as she picked up on the bulge. Women want hard dick, don't let them fool you on that score. Gwen wasn't fooling me. Her body was betraying her while I watched. I finished off my drink.

"How about another vodka?" I asked.

"I really shouldn't."

"Tell me about it."

"One, because I'm really tired; two, because I'm already 'half in the bag' as they say; and three, it might make me do things I'll regret later. Want some more good reasons?" She showed a trace of crossness, annoyed with herself for what she knew she was going to do.

"Have another one. I insist."

She looked at me. Saw I wanted her drunk. She smiled and nodded. "I won't be responsible for what may happen."

"You've never been responsible for anything in your whole life, have you?" The statement stung like a whip.

She opened her mouth. Shut it. Looked at her hands. "Nope. You're right. I'm my Daddy's little girl."

"And somebody else's besides Daddy's too, eh?"

She shrugged and looked away.

I fetched her another Vodka Collins. Handed it to her and watched as she took her first sip. She closed her eyes and sighed, opened them and swept the crowd. Maybe looking for the boy whose pin she had placed over her two-timing heart.

"What house are you in, Jerry?"

"Why, Sigma Tau Sigma. Is there any other?"

"Actually I've never heard of Sigma Tau Sigma. Are you national?"

"Sure. But mainly in the South. Social frat. Party animals. We do it in the road."

She let that one slide and said, "Where are the Brothers tonight?"

"Mostly still cramming for finals. I've done mine. Getting a jump on the action here on Lauderdale Beach."

"Where are you staying?"

"The Jolly Roger," I lied.

"We're at the Yankee Clipper. It's a long walk down the beach from here."

"The Jolly Roger's not too far down A1A... and they have big soft beds."

Furtively, Gwen glanced around her. The room was a roar of conversation and music. She seemed unsteady from the alcohol and smoke. She looked directly at me. I looked straight back at her. I loomed over her and beamed my masculine presence down upon her, let her feel it like a physical pressure. She was blushing again, caught up in some cuntish fantasy of erotic release. She knew what she wanted when she walked in the door. I was the answer to that annoying itch between her legs. Her body was not going to be denied tonight. She knew it. I knew it. But what she was thinking shamed her. She fought with herself in an effort to deny the message that shimmered up from between her legs on waves of female heat. She studied me; knew instinctively that my touch would be fearless, that I would guide her and set her body aflame. I blessed her with a casual and confident smile, let her see that I was a world unto myself. That I would stroke her and make her purr with ecstasy. She wanted it. Shamelessly. She raised her drink, finished it off with one gulp. The alcohol would work its magic in her brain, drowning her resistance; soon the spreading slime would flood her genital crease. I'd smell it on her. She held out her glass and said, "I need just one more, and then I'm leaving."

She'd be leaving all right. I wouldn't want to deprive her of her one last drinky. I went back to the bar, ordered the drinks and paid for them, and made my way back to the nervous bitch.

She took the glass from my hand, put it to her mouth, and drank deeply. The emerald eyes were streaked red from the smoke hanging in the air like an acrid blue fog. There were bubbles of greasy sweat sprinkled across her forehead at the hairline. Her lipstick was smeared. Not even a thank-you for Steppin Fetchit.

"I find you attractive, Gwen."

"I've heard that line before," she snapped.

"You look pretty tonight."

"Do I?" She was uncertain.

"Yes, very." Reassure her. Coddle the bitch.

"You're gonna make a lewd proposition, I can feel it coming. Am I right?" she challenged. I looked down and let my gaze linger on her bosom. Smiled.

"A seductive proposition was more what I had in mind," I countered. "You appeal to my natural instincts."

"Seduction as a natural instinct. What an interesting theory. Did you pick that up in Psych 101 up there at Rollins, or is that a regional philosophy? Maybe I haven't heard this line after all." She raised her Collins and swallowed another hefty gulp.

"Down South we don't deny our natural instincts. Up Nawth where you Puritans come from natural instincts are the same as mortal sins, aren't they?" he drawled. She grinned at the ceiling — rolling her eyes in feigned despair.

"I suppose you think all Ivy Leaguers are gay?"

"You mean to tell me they're not? I can't believe that. I met this guy from Amherst, he's carrying around this poodle. *GAY RIGHTS TASK FORCE* blazoned on his sweatshirt. Went about one-forty soaking wet, limp wrist and all. At Rollins we'd have run his ass off campus on a rail. Sex perversion is illegal in Florida. Normal in New York and points north, that's what I hear."

Gwen drank her vodka and smiled some more. "Tell me about your 'natural instincts' theory, Jerry."

"I'm a red-blooded American boy, and I do what I gotta do. And I gotta do it with a woman."

"Male chauvinist piggy-wiggy! Oink-oink!"

"You're not the first to say that. But I don't let my instincts bother me. I enjoy sex — that is, lovemaking — all the pleasures of romance. I've studied the Kama Sutra. I've learned that adult women prefer seduction."

She arched her back like a cat, flaunted the swell of her breasts and opined primly, "I thought it bothered every man. My boyfriend gets the 'guilts' every time. Actually he's a little straitlaced for a man. That's what I think," she complained.

"Me, I have needs. I accept them as natural, and I don't suffer any guilt when my needs are satisfied. Dr. Freud wouldn't find me a very interesting specimen, I'm afraid."

"I rather think he would," Gwen remarked.

I gave her a quizzical look. She gave me a wink in return, then opened her eyes wide with innocence. Touchè. But I had her. My every sense told me so. I saw it in the sparkle of her eyes, heard it in her seeking words. I knew I'd win. Her vulnerability shone through her tiredness in her restlessness, her need to talk. She was another romantic and troubled cunt — full of alcohol and the surging emotion that nibbled away at her will, and set her up for me. I knew what I wanted: the darkness, the moonlight, her naked white body in my hands.

She was sipping her drink and looking at me, smiling a vague invitation, her moist eyes tentative yet bold. I inched closer to her, and smiled back with conspiratorial understanding. We were close, almost touching, and in the small space between our bodies I could smell the lusty heat of her satin flesh, the musk emanating from her secret place below. I flared my nostrils like a stallion as I sucked in the aroma of her desire.

"No guilt," she breathed.

"None at all," I answered, giving her the push she needed to send her over the edge. "I don't see how guilt could enter into it."

"Oh? Well, how do you see it?"

"I see it as normal."

"Just… normal?"

"Sure. We both want the same thing, don't we?"

She hesitated. Nodded.

"So we seek each other out, dig? You have needs, don't you?"

She lowered her eyes, and ran her hands through her hair restlessly. Shrugged.

"Don't worry about love and marriage, and lifetime commitment. Just think in

terms of need. You feel it, don't you?" I lowered my voice and leaned closer to her face. "People feed you this line about 'sin.' You've heard it?"

She bobbed her head.

"Well forget it. It doesn't make sense because it doesn't even exist. Not for people like me. I get pleasure from a woman. And she can get all the pleasure she wants from me."

Gwen crossed her legs and placed her hand unconsciously over her heart as she took a deep breath.

"Why worry, Gwen? You've got the body of a woman, I can see that. But are you a real woman inside, or just a schoolgirl playing make-believe on spring break?"

I let my eyes linger on the full curves of her body. I could see the flush rise on her exposed breasts as the booze fueled her own lewd notions. The line was a good one, tested and true. She should be feeling the tingle of the promised orgasm in the veiled offer right now. She shifted her legs again. Her foot started to jiggle.

She peered up at me. She was drawn toward my calm, seductive confidence. She saw intriguing, unrevealing eyes, and saw in their shadows how they could turn intensely passionate. She could see I wanted her body, and that my need was immediate. She sensed that I had the capacity to satisfy her. Even as her head swam with alcohol and desire, I knew what she would do. Beneath her skirt, her panties were already slick with her intent. I could smell the heat in her wet cunt. She gulped down her drink and handed me the empty glass.

"Let's do it," I said, tired of being her busboy.

She squirmed a bit and said, "I've got to pee." I watched her lurch off to the ladies room, then carried the empty glasses back to the bar. A few minutes later she came sauntering toward me, face washed, lipstick freshened. She took my arm possessively and said, "I think I need some fresh air."

I didn't argue. I guided her across the room and out the door marked "EXIT." We emerged into darkness. I steered her north on Sunrise Lane. The moon was high, the stars twinkling merrily. Gwen looked up at the sky and stumbled. The alcohol. I took her by the elbow, held her tightly. My Dingo boots rang on the sidewalk as we strode toward the bright lights of Sunrise Boulevard.

When we got to Sunrise, I steered her away from the beach, toward the bridge spanning the Intracoastal. As we stood on the corner of Breakers and Sunrise, I held her close to me. The late night traffic slid past. Drivers saw a pair of lovers, dismissing them from mind instantly.

"Where are we going?" Gwen said.

"To the park," he told her. "You're a little drunk and you wanted some fresh air. We can sit down on a bench for a while and watch the moonlight on the Intracoastal Waterway. It's lovely. Quiet and private. We'll kiss. I'll hold you. You'll feel better. Trust me."

"There's a park around here? Right on the beach?"

"Sure. Birch State Park. See the sign there across Sunrise? It's huge. Big trees, nature paths. You'll like it. A nice walk in the moonlight is just what we need — romantic too."

"We won't get in trouble going in there at night, will we?"

"What do you mean 'get in trouble'?"

"You know, rapists. Killers. I'm thinking of something like that."

I chuckled. "This is Birch State Park in Fort Lauderdale, not Central Park in New York City."

"It's safe then?"

"Sure. You're not alone. You're with your man." I gave her waist a squeeze.

There was a break in the traffic and we dashed across Sunrise. Her heels clicked on the cement. I held her arm, felt the blood rushing through it, and discerned a hot shiver of anticipation sliding down into my balls, once again causing my penis to stir. The drunken slut made me aware of the urgency of my need as she stumbled along, giggling and lightheaded with vodka and soda water. She seemed amazed at her own daring. She leaned into me. Her body was warm and soft, full of blood and filth. I wanted her. I would enter her body. Know her secrets. Endure her conversation. Steal her life.

I led the girl into the vastness of Birch State Park. Her head was leaning on my shoulder. She had her arm around my waist. I could feel her cigarette-scented mane caressing my cheek. The bitch was agreeably sluggish. I held her close to me. She looked up at me and smiled as I guided her along the trail into the deep woods. We were swallowed by the night.

The girl was not a problem. Her thoughts were probably on the prospect of lovemaking to come. I saw the shifting shadows beneath the trees; heard the rustle of nocturnal creatures in the darkness. I sensed no fear in her, only a pulsing sexuality alive with energy and expectation. The alcohol would mask any warning signals until it was too late. It was already too late for this one. The Australian pines whispered around us. The pine needles were a soft carpet beneath our feet, the secluded path ended at a seawall. She gasped at the vista spread before us.

"It's a lovely sight, isn't it?" I said.

"What is that place over there?"

"That's the Yacht Club... a big restaurant on the left where boaters can pull up, and over on the right back in that cove are ritzy homes along Seminole Drive. Jew developers steal the whole area from the Indians and then name a street after them. Isn't that a laugh?"

"It's romantic," she breathed.

I gently pressed her back against the bole of a palm tree. I fingered the fraternity pin shining on the slope of her bosom. "Who's the lucky boy?"

As the moon shown down on us, a tendril of cloud scooted across the night sky and darkened Gwen's face. "Bobby." She spit the name out as if it brought a bitter taste to her mouth.

"He doesn't take you for moonlight walks?"

She shook her head mournfully.

I twisted the emblem. The silk split and the pin came off in my hand. I flipped it into the water. Put my hand on her breast, massaged her nipple.

"My blouse... "

"I'll buy you a new one. What does this Bobby fucker do for you?"

"Not enough," she hissed.

I caressed her teat firmly with the palm of my hand then tickled the nipple gently. "Tell me about Bobby. Why doesn't he love your titties like I do? Maybe he's a queer, huh?"

"He'd rather get high than take the time to do what you're doing." Her toes were curling with pleasure as I continued to knead and tickle her breasts.

"And Gwen's high is sex?"

She hummed her acknowledgment.

"What happened tonight?" I tweaked her nipple.

"*Oooh!* The usual. We argued. I told him to take his dreary ass back to the hotel and he could see me when I come back. If I come back. He has a nasty temper."

"Oh, does he now?"

"He wants me to be his little vestal virgin."

"You're a shameless rutting slut."

She rolled her hips.

"It never seems to move him… except to anger."

"Bobby's not a considerate lover?"

"Never. He uses me. He fucks over me."

"Leaves you all tense and unfulfilled?"

"Always."

"Drags you through the emotional mud of his post-coital guilt trips?"

"Yes, Dr. Freud," she giggled.

"He's a regular shit, isn't he?"

"A very rich shit."

"Daddy's money?"

"Of course."

"Gonna make that money all your own, hey?"

"Sure. Right after we graduate. It's the American way."

"He the jealous type?"

"God, yes!" She pressed her teat into my hand. She was getting aroused by my light teasing caresses.

"What if he knew what we were doing right now?"

She tensed for a beat. "He'd kill me. And his father would buy him out of it. They own banks."

She looked up at me. I could feel her body reaching out to be touched.

"You're no better than a whore."

"But a rich whore. Not a cheap whore."

"Know what I do to whores, Gwen?"

"What?" she sighed dreamily.

"I fuck 'em."

She lifted her face and willed me to kiss her. Opened her mouth in expectation. I smelled the alcoholic fumes as I bent to her need. Her lips were slick with oily paint. I slid my tongue between her teeth. She closed her eyes and pressed her softness against me. My hands dropped to her hips, seized them; I rocked her gently. My tongue probed inside her sour mouth. I could feel the heat of her breasts through her bra and my shirt. The alcohol fueled her wantonness, increased her awareness and sensuality. I brushed my fingers down the front of her blouse unfastening buttons. She pressed her cunt against me, felt the thick masculinity against her loins. She rocked her hips back and forth in bold invitation, her shamelessness quickening her desire and setting her on fire with lust. "Oh yes!" she whimpered.

Strip me! Strip me naked!"

She was asking for it now. I pulled the filmy silk blouse from her shoulders, unfastened her skirt and slid it down over the warm mounds of her buttocks. She kicked it aside with a little giggle. I ran my fingers through her silky blonde hair and smiled at how it gleamed in the moonlight.

"You're a wonderful lover," she panted.

"Better than Bobby?"

"Bobby's a lump of silly putty compared to you." She placed her hand on my face and gazed into my eyes. "You're so much more than I had hoped for."

"Your fantasy?"

"Oh yes!"

She reached for my boner. Ran her hand over the heated curved scimitar encased in my jeans.

"You've got a big one!"

"You like that big hard dick?"

"Yes!" she moaned, "I'm getting wet."

"Wet where?" I teased.

"Down there."

"Say it, Bitch!"

"Wet in my cunt!"

"You're a whore."

"I want it. Please! Do it to me."

I brushed my lips across the swell of her haltered breasts, felt her nipples erect beneath the cups of her brassiere. I let her feel my mouth hot on her belly, in her navel, sliding down toward her pulsing liquid center. She moaned her willingness, opening her thighs with unmistakable invitation. I played my tongue just above the waistband of her bikini briefs, teasing her and being rewarded with a passion-laden mewl of disappointment as I straightened and pressed my turgid heat into her belly through the denim of my jeans.

She opened her eyes. Stared at me curiously, probably wondering why I couldn't bring myself to put my mouth over the stinking buttery slime seeping through her panties, slickening the insides of her thighs. "Lick me! Eat my pussy, Lover!" she begged, naming the perversion she longed for.

Before I could respond, she closed her eyes and pulled my head down to her mouth. She thrust her tongue hungrily between my saliva-slippery lips. I could feel the racing beat of her heart thumping just above her right breast. She moaned as a wave of passion overwhelmed her; her body shivered with the onset of her first orgasm. She clawed at my zipper. Nothing else seemed to matter to her. She reached into my trousers and wrapped her right hand around my penis, squealing her delight and panting, "Yes! Yes! Yes!" as with her left hand she tore at her panties in an effort to strip them from her own ass. Her wanton depravity was out of control. She'd become an animal in the mindless throes of sexual lust, a regular bitch in heat.

Quickly, I ran my left hand up the length of her knobby spine, pulled her trembling body toward me in a close embrace; then I laid the cold blade against her belly and pushed it into her with irreversible finality and deadly intent.

I levered the knife deep into her gut and clamped my hand over her mouth to stifle the scream that bubbled up from her suddenly-violated body. The pain tore her apart, overloading her senses. She tried again to scream, but I kept my hand gripped considerately over her mouth. She opened her eyes and fixed me with an intense and questioning stare. I smiled at her, wondering how her head would look on a stick. I punched the shank deeper into her bowels. Her body jerked in an involuntary orgasmic climax. I was glad it was good for her. It was good for me too. She reflexively squeezed my penis and I came in her hand.

I watched her eyes drop to the shaft of steel buried in her belly, just above the crest of her pubic triangle. She watched my hand as I pulled the blade up and across, neatly gutting her. She stared with wide-eyed fascination as the ropy coils of her own intestines slid out of her belly and hung to her knees. Her eyes were filled with disbelief. Her terror must have blocked off the pain. I angled the cutting edge up under her rib cage and lanced it into her heart. The green eyes rolled back in her head, becoming white marbles.

I could feel the blood coming up, filling her mouth, hot and sticky behind my hand. I pulled her head back away from my face; saw the mouth pout in a small soundless puckered "O" as I jerked the knife free from her belly. A fountain of blood erupted, spurting darkly over the pine needles.

The bitch gasped, a raw sucking sound. I'd heard it before, recognized its implications. She turned around and grasped the palm, hugging it to her like a lover; then she made an obscene throaty gurgle and the blood and vomit spewed from her mouth and nostrils. She choked and collapsed to her knees, then flopped onto her back. Through the rustling branches of the Australian pines she could catch the glimmer of sparkling stars strewn across the inky vault of the night sky. She called for her Bobby once, softly, hiccuped and slid away into death. I was heartened. It was a satisfying and skillful kill.

I peered into her lusterless eyes. She was undeniably dead. I wiped the heavy knife clean on her skirt and slipped the war surplus bayonet back into the sheath in my Dingo boot. I noticed her purse, a small clutch. I opened it. Tissues, lipstick, a sheaf of hundred dollar bills, feminine odds and ends and two student ID cards. One for Miss Gwen, and the other for Mr. Robert Purcell Ashford, the elusive Bobby. As I pocketed the bills, an idea was born: I tugged down Gwen's blood-spattered, sex-sodden panties, wadded them into a ball, and tossed them onto the pine straw. I dragged her disemboweled corpse across the seawall, leaving a wide spoor of greasy blood. I rolled it into the cleansing warm waters of the Intracoastal Waterway. Gwen's other clothing and purse joined her in the water. Then I dropped Bobby's student ID near the bloody panties, and walked from the park.

Killing is thirsty work. I headed towards Lum's for a schooner of beer, confident that the Fort Lauderdale Police Department would be able to solve the mystery of the murderous lover's quarrel.

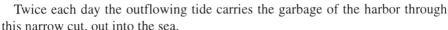

The best place to catch big sharks is at the end of the North Jetty where the huge black granite boulders abut the Port Everglades ship channel.

They were barged down from Maine long ago and laid in the sea to protect the deepwater passage from the southerly drift of fine sand.

Twice each day the outflowing tide carries the garbage of the harbor through this narrow cut, out into the sea.

That's when the sharks feed.

There's also a best time to catch these sharks. The half hour period of twilight when the tide is running hard and the waxing moon hangs fat on the Eastern horizon, that's the very best time of all. The dark thirty, the time of transition. That's when the big ones come seeking blood.

It's a long hike from the Bahia Mar parking lot to the North Jetty. I have a lot of stuff to carry: tackle box, sturdy rod, knife. Walk a full mile in soft sand, with the long weighty nylon rope looped over my shoulders. It's tiring. Irritating. Noisome little shitassed kids screeching at my ankles. "Whatcha doing, Mister?" Sniggering near-naked beach sluts in bikinis making with their eyes. Fuck 'em. What would they know about feeding the sharks?

Down by the jetty it's all wonderful and perfect. The charter boats are coming in, an entire armada of million-dollar sailboats and yachts festooned with young flesh. The pretty sailorettes waving from the sun decks, hair tousled and flying in the warm, salty breeze. I wave. Smile. Fucking rich bitch whores. I wend my way out toward the end of the jetty, carefully picking my way over the wet rocks.

Overhead the gulls are wheeling, screaming, diving on the bait fish flashing like silver coins skipped across the surface of the sea. I inhale the rich marine smells: dead fish, rotting seaweed, putrid sewage flushed from the fancy yachts. A bloated cat sails by on the tide, bobbing along on the gentle swell. Bait. I sit on the rocks listening to the busily clicking claws of the crabs, the splash of leaping fish, the sibilant unhurried breathing of the deep, and I watch Nature's curtain descend on another day. So peaceful.

The voices are young, full of laughter. They grate like a rasp against the pleasant hiss and suck of the waters playing over the rocks at my feet. Girl voices.

"Karen? Be careful you don't fall — these rocks are slippery!"

There's a tinkling giggle. The Karen creature calls back. "C'mon, let's go all the way out to the end!"

Karen, a regular Little Miss High Adventure, comes bounding gracefully over the huge dark stones, her less-agile companion bringing up the rear. Finally she sees me seated in the shadows.

"Hi!" she says, "What're you doing out here?"

Nosy little bitch.

I smile a welcome. "Collecting bait is what I'm doing. I'm going fishing."

The two of them look at the tackle box, the pole laying on the rock at my side.

They giggle and look back and forth at each other, passing secret female signals. Sluts.

"What are you two doing?"

Saucy Karen says, "We're looking for a nice place to smoke a few joints. Do you mind if we sit out here? This is a really peaceful spot, isn't it?"

Doper sluts.

I shrug. "I don't care. Free country."

They hop down onto the big flat rock where I'm sitting.

"Hey, you wanna get high with us?" Karen wants to know.

"Maybe. Anybody coming up with you back there who might want to bust us?"

They both chuckle up a little laugh. Probably already half wrecked on something.

"Nobody even on the beach. They're all home eating dinner," they titter.

What the hell is so funny? Dinner?

I stand up and take a long hard look. Eyes flickering over the ebony stones, down the length of the jetty and across the empty strand. Nobody. The tide's running fast, water inky, vestiges of blood-red sky in the west, bulbous orange moon on the rise. Shrimp popping in the hissing eddies. Bait.

"Bad moon on the rise," I say. It's the truth.

The Karen doper is peering into her little satchel of sweet dreams angling for her stash, her braless friend standing there in mute anticipation like some vapid cow. Brainless cunt.

I take the Colt Woodsman from the waistband of my khaki trousers. A flash. Sharp crack of sound. Small dark hole appears between her bovine teats. Braless goes "Oh!"

Drops to her knees and flops forward onto her face with a meaty thud.

Karen looks up from her stash bag. Goes "Wha?" as a .22 caliber hollow-point punches through her right eyeball into her brain. She collapses in a heap, arms and legs twitching and jerking in spasms.

"Good shot, Sherlock," I comment to the night.

Braless is stretched out, nose mashed to the stone. I roll her over on her back. Neat little hole in the bosom-stuffed T-shirt, a small circle of blood. Heart shot. Stopped her ticker cold. Shut down the pump. Pull out the fish knife, cut off the shirt. Unfasten her jeans, pull 'em down. Panties. T-Shirt. Sandals. Wrap it all up and fling it into the sea. Drag her naked corpse to the edge of the flat rock. Open up her neck with one quick cut and leave her to dribble a sanguine stream of warm blood into the pulsing tide. A human spoor that will bring the sharks to the rocks. Bloodfeast.

Karen's still twitching, her hands opening and closing. Fingers moving. Legs writhing in slow motion. Shutting down the systems. Overloading the circuits. Exploded eyeball all over her cheek, a bloody gel. Remaining eye rolled up toward the ascending moon. Sightless accusing eye. Dirty little dope-sucking slut. If thine eye offends thee, pluck it out. Yes, that's what the Preacherman said: *Pluck it out!*

Small sharks already circling. Moonbeams sparkling on the water, little beads of phosphorescence where the baby jaws break the surface. Hunting blood. Meat.

Eyeballs. Oh Yes. Yes! Pluck it *OUT!* I slide the needle point of the blade into the corner of the eye socket. Pluck it out with ease. Flip it onto the placid swell. It floats for a few seconds, then gone with a swirl.

Yank open the primly buttoned blouse. Slice through the bra strap, peel it away. Vanilla ice cream boobs crowned with cherry nipples. Double scoops. Carve off the cherry. Flip it in the water. Silver flash! Big oceanic jacks. Chum 'em up. Carve off the other cherry. Give it a flick. The quiet surface bursts in sparkling phosphor spray. Lovely. They're coming now. The feeding begins. Chum 'em up!

Off come the tar-stained tennis shoes. Pull down the sodden, pissy-smelling jeans, rip away the wet panty. Consign it to the sea. All of it. Little white string in the damp pubic hair disappearing up her cunt. Pluck it *OUT!* Sling the bloody tampon onto the water. A splash, a swirl, and it's gone. Oh, how they love the blood! Give them *BLOOD!*

I pick up the knife, ram it up the cunt. Twist the blade, turn it, core her hole. Glop and gore splooshes out, spills over the rock and trickles into the water. I thrust the blade into her navel, turning the razor-sharp blade to dice her guts. I rip it up to her breastbone, slash it down to her pubic mound; listen to the gurgle of blood sloshing in her body cavity, mingling with the remains of her lunch. I hook out a length of ropy gray intestine. Cut a bloody section of greasy gut and toss it seaward. The calm surface erupts in a fountain of spray. *Mako!*

I tie the long nylon rope around her neck; throw her gutted corpse out into the current. Pay out the line. A huge bull shark comes to the surface with the bait in its jaws, shaking it like a terrier with a rat, ripping it apart with slashing side-to-side motions. The line goes slack. Shit! Bait's gone!

I turn to the bleeding chum bag splayed across the black granite. At least 120 pounds of bloody meat and offal. I rake my blade down the satin-skinned back, flaying white flesh. Flip her over. Push the knife into her belly, open her up. Sit her up and the viscera slops out into her lap. I loop the line around her middle and pitch the bait into the tidal race. A half-dozen curved dorsal fins cleave the surface. *Hammerhead!*

They plunge at the bait bouncing it across the water in a bizarre ballet of ripping and tearing flesh. Almost instantly the line is slack once again. I haul it in. Bitten through!

Fuckers stole the damn bait! The surface of the inlet boils in a frothy frenzy of feeding sharks. A wonder of nature. A sight to behold. I see the scimitar fins of half a hundred sharks cutting the smooth surface, slicing back and forth across the oily flow of the outgoing tide, seeking the blood source.

All gone, little shark children, all gone.

Bait's gone.

A rusty freighter oozes out of Port Everglades on the tide, the soft chuff-chuff of its engines thrumming across the quiet water, deckhands visible along the rails going about their sailor's business in the moonlight. Honk of a night heron as the evening cools. The flat smack of mullet leaping. Southwind. Moon high. Stars sprayed across the sky from horizon to horizon.

I lay on the flat black rock and peer into the celestial vault. Time to go back. Make the long trek to Bahia Mar over the shadows in the sand, still warm from the sun. Ghost crabs scuttle. Lights winking along A1A. Squealing rubber on cement. Throbbing boom boxes.

The police. Two big porkers leaning on my car smoking. How could they know? I walk up, too weary to care. They eye my equipment.

Fat cop says, "Any luck tonight?"

"None at all," I reply, putting my stuff into the trunk.

"Wha'd you use?" he asks.

"Cut bait," I answer, as I slide behind the wheel and fire up the ignition.

WHORES

*W*hores. You know how they are. All they want is money and a big, stiff dick up the hole, but mostly the money.

I'd been told that women didn't like sex, that somehow you had to trick them into it, but later I found out that wasn't true at all. We'd discuss it. Good girls versus nice girls, but what it actually came down to was virgins and whores.

One Saturday I was down at Clark's News, thumbing through the latest issue of *Western Adventure* magazine. I turned a page, and there before me hanging from the limb of an old oak tree was Ella Watson. The caption beneath the picture told me that Miss Watson was a whore, and she was hanged for her crimes. I wondered what her crimes might have been. She stared at me from the page, eyes open and tongue stuck out. She was shown with her legs kicking. You could see almost all the way up to the top where the you-know-what is. It was revealing and sexy, and it made my dick hard. I bought the magazine, took it home and that night I lay in bed and learned the story of Cattle Kate.

Kate was a pretty whore. She gave men sex and took their money. She opened a whorehouse out in Wyoming and accepted stolen cattle for her sex fee. She got a nice big herd that way. The local people, who were all decent and God-fearing like myself, told her to pack up and get out of the territory. She didn't leave, so they took her out and hanged her from a tree. The idea was to clean up the community. Whores attract the criminal element, it said in the magazine. The whores poisoned the well of community decency. It was the sort of thing that makes a civic-minded young man do some hard thinking.

Pick any day you please and there were lamentations in the local newspaper concerning the decline of community morals. Sex-mad college girls invaded Fort Lauderdale every spring looking for those stiff dicks and that money. Used to be you could drive down to the beach and have a real pleasant day, but the beach area was getting to be a slum, and any time you cared to go down there and look, you could see an abundance of whores. Whole coveys of them walking the streets, looking for men to corrupt. They sure did seem to like that beachfront area. They circulated in all the bars down there hunting their unsuspecting victims, turning this town into a modern Sodom. I decided to do something about it.

I got dressed up in my best Madras walking shorts, a polo shirt with a little alligator on the pocket, and my new Weejuns. I put some money in my pocket and drove down to Lauderdale Beach to a little joint on A1A. I used my Hanley B. Poole fake ID to order me some beer. I sipped at it while I looked around. It wasn't five minutes before a whore came sliding along to seduce me. I figured I'd let her, and then I'd get her.

She cruised right up to the booth where I was sitting in the shadows and asked if she could join me. She was wearing white pedal pushers and a pink shell top with a scoop neck that was cut so low that when she leaned over, I could see right down inside where there was a white brassiere covering her teats. She had tacky plastic

sandals on her feet, but it was the boobs that had my interest. It was making me hot to see those titties down in there, and she knew it; that's why she was showing them off to me.

She sat down across from me and right away she wanted a beer, so I ordered her one. I listened to her story about coming down to Florida from Cleveland, Ohio, to seek her fame and fortune. She claimed to be a model and an actress waiting for her big break. I didn't want to spoil her fun by telling her there was not much chance of a Hollywood audition at the Bikini Lounge. She was entitled to her fantasy. I had one of my own. I told her my daddy was a rich orange grove owner, that I went to Amherst, and that I was just down on the beach looking for girls. My line sounded at least as good as hers, I figured.

She jumped right on it, like a frog on a bug. She whispered over at me in a confidential manner that she'd "mess around" with me if I'd give her fifty dollars. I told her I'd give her a twenty dollar bill if she'd take down her panties and let me put it up her hole. She made a face like maybe I was some cheapskate Jew, but said that twenty would be OK. We left the bar and crossed A1A to where my green Ford station wagon was parked. I opened the door for her, she slid into the front seat, and soon we were on our way.

It was a warm sunny day and as we headed west on Sunrise, I told the whore the tragic tale of Cattle Kate. I said it was lousy how people reacted to messing around back in the old days and that the story would make a great movie. She agreed. I proposed that Sandra Dee would be a good actress for the part of Kate, or maybe, with luck, she herself could get the part, since she was so much cuter than Sandra Dee. She preened over that compliment and asked me if I really thought she could get it, or was I just making talk. I told her I really thought she would make a perfect Kate.

We headed out State Road 84 and turned left at Davie Road. I took her to the airstrip, out where they built the college later. There was an abandoned garage back there, left over from World War II. It was a sturdy old concrete block building with a cement floor. The area was entirely shaded by huge Australian pine trees. At night it was something of a lover's lane, but in the daytime it was deserted.

I rolled the wagon down the pine needle carpeted dirt driveway, pulled up in front of the garage and parked. I told the whore that my daddy owned the land and the adjacent citrus groves. She was impressed. I commented that we could mess around right there in the car. It would be real private. Nobody would be coming around. She scooched right across the front seat, snuggled up to me and we started kissing and feeling each other up. She got me hot fast by sticking her tongue in my mouth and moving it around, then she was frenching my ear. It was damn nice. But all of a sudden she backed off and asked me for money.

She said if I'd give her the money she'd take down her pants and let me put it up her hole. I took out my wallet and passed her a twenty. She tucked it down into her straw pocket book. I noticed it had *Souvenir of Parrot Jungle* woven into the straw. I was going to ask her if she liked the tricks the parrots did, but instead I told her I'd give her another ten if she'd model like Cattle Kate for me. She said she would, so I gave her the ten-spot and watched it join the twenty in the parrot bag.

We got out of the car and I fetched a line of rope from the carry-all section of the station wagon. I leaned against the front bumper and fashioned the line into a hangman's noose while she watched. She'd picked a wild daisy and was twirling it in her fingers, picking it apart petal by petal and chanting as she dropped each piece, "He loves me, he loves me not." She finished up on "he loves me not" and shot me a crooked smile. "Bad luck in love."

"Ah, you don't believe in bad luck, do you? Come on over here, Kate!"

I tossed the noose up over the heavy beam at the front of the garage where at one time engines were raised from the bodies of cars. I widened the loop and placed it over her head. She fiddled with her long ponytail while I adjusted the coil around her neck. I set the knot behind her ear just like the picture in the magazine. I asked her if it was too tight. She said it wasn't tight at all. Then I tied her wrists behind her with green nylon twine, and arranged her ankles the same way: took a few turns around them and made a nice firm knot. I moved a few steps back, put my hands on my hips, and told her she made a perfect Cattle Kate.

She smiled, stuck out her tongue and crossed her eyes. I told her to hold that pose, and I'd take a picture of her and mail it to Otto Preminger in Hollywood with a movie suggestion. She thought that was a great idea. I told her I'd get the camera from the glove compartment, turned and picked up the loose end of the rope and tied it to the car bumper. I slid behind the wheel, cranked up the ignition, put the car in reverse and backed up.

The whore rose right up in the air and once again stuck out her tongue. It was comical the way it popped right out of her mouth, all wet and pink. Her eyes were wide open and staring right at me. Her expression was fascinating. Her face turned pink, then red, then blue — a pleasant lavender-blue. Her body quivered and shimmied; as she turned blue she wet her pants. A dark stain materialized at the juncture of her thighs, then quickly slid down the legs of her pedal pushers. The pee streamed down over her calves and dribbled from her toes making a puddle on the concrete floor under her. The pretty face turned purple, her body shivered violently; then she went limp. It was interesting to watch.

I got out of the car with the camera and took some pictures, used up the entire roll of film. Different angles back and front. I wanted to record it all for future reference. When I finished taking pictures, I got back into the idling car and put the machine in forward. The whore came straight down and stood in the center of the puddle she'd made. I shut off the ignition, got myself out and walked over to her and said, "Hey Kate, I think you got the part!"

Her tongue was still hanging out and she smelled sort of yukky, like a loaded diaper. I wasn't sure if she was dead or just passed out. The purple was gone from her face. It was a funny grayish-white color — didn't look too healthy to me. A small trickle of blood was sliding out of her left nostril. I took some Kleenex out of my pocket and dabbed at the blood and then stuck a plug of tissue in her nose. I was expecting her to say something but she was keeping quiet.

I ran my hands over her plump young breasts and shook her slightly. "Well? Aren't you excited?" Still no answer, so I lifted up the pink shell top. The white cotton cups of her bra were chock-full of titty. Whore titty, full and white. There was a nipple in there too. The size of a large pea and set in the center of a ring of

peachy puckered skin the size of a quarter. I put my finger on the nipple and wiggled it. It felt rubbery. I licked my finger and tried it again. Real honest-to-god whore titty. I'd never seen one up close. I licked the nipple. It really had no special taste at all, just a little salty sweat. There wasn't anything else to do so I rearranged her bra the way it had been and pulled down her shell.

I gave Kate a chaste kiss on the cheek and sang to her softly, "Wake up, wake up, my little Sleeping Beauty," but she didn't wake up and she didn't move. She was still standing there in the puddle of pee with her tongue sticking out. I poked at her tongue with my finger, and then pushed it back into her mouth. I wondered if she could really be dead. We'd only been playing Cattle Kate for a few minutes, maybe five or ten at the very most. How could she be dead that fast? She took the ten dollars to model the pose for me. I'd told her the story first.

It wasn't really my fault.

"OK, Kate, quit your acting or I'm gonna take back my twenty dollars." She hadn't messed around with me for the twenty like she had promised. I was waiting for her to pull down her panties so I could stick it in her hole. Kate wasn't breathing. Maybe she was in a coma. Hard to tell, really.

I took out my Barlow pocket knife and opened up the blade, reached down and sliced through the cord tied around her ankles; then I put it away and unbuttoned her pedal pushers and pulled them down and off. She was wearing a white mesh panty, one-size-fits-all kind. I could see her pubic hair inside it. The seat of the panty was poked out in the back from a turd like a brown corncob. I drew down the panty over her well-rounded bottom and the turd fell out on the floor. That solved the problem of the nasty smell coming from back there. I looked at her bare bottom and could see there was a pussy there too. I could see it from the rear. It was covered with wet brown hair, but I knew that was the place where you stick it in. I touched it with my finger. It was slick and gooey between her legs. Strange. I removed my finger and smelled it. Fish. I pulled down the underpants and put them over the turd. I used her pedal pushers to soak up the puddle of pee, then I scooped it all up and threw it into a corner in the garage.

The hair on the front of her pussy was thick and brown, a thin line of it running up toward her belly button. I'd been expecting a neat vee-shape like I had seen in *Playboy*, but Kate's pubic area was tangled and unkempt. I could just make out the indentation of her female crease under the hair. The crack vanished between her legs. I opened the thighs a bit with my hands. I wanted to see it all. I took a good long look. It was the first whore's cunt I'd seen up close on a sunshiny afternoon. It looked exactly like a sodden brown rat.

I stripped off my walking shorts and underpants. I went around behind her and positioned the head of my boner against the little hole. I gave a small thrust and it went right on up inside her. The feeling was fantastic: warm, moist and slick as lotion. I stuck it up as far as I could and ejaculated. Then I pulled it out and put my clothes back on. It was just a quickie but it was nice and worth the money.

The whore hadn't moved at all. I took off the noose and helped her over to the car and let her sit on the front seat. I left her wrists tied in case she suddenly woke up. She'd be angry about her pedal pushers, but I wasn't about to take those nasty things in the car with us. She'd been paid, so she had no complaint there.

But you know how whores are, you just can't trust them.

I drove her to a rockpit in the center of a nearby orange grove. She sat quietly slumped against the door. Anyone would think she was napping. When we got to the pit I took my SCUBA equipment from the carry-all section and put it on, then I helped her out of the car and we went for a swim. She needed a good wash anyway.

I took her down to twenty feet. There on the bottom was a car I had borrowed from somebody who'd left the keys in the ignition. Took it right out of the parking lot in front of the Grandway Store at Broward and State Road Seven. I opened the door on the sunken sedan and we got in. I put her behind the wheel. She was easy to manage underwater. I tied her right foot to the gas pedal, and her left foot to the brake. I untied her wrists from behind her and bound them to the steering wheel.

There she sat, with her lush ponytail swirling around her head. She sure wasn't going to get away from this one. I rolled the windows halfway up to make sure. She looked real cute behind the wheel. A pretty girl in a nice new car peering through the windshield at the bluegills swimming past. I opened the door and swam out. Closed it, flippered around to the front and watched Kate sitting there. Finally, after a time, I waved goodbye to her and headed for the surface.

I used that rockpit for many years. It was particularly good because it was full of blue claw crabs.

It was about sixty days after I'd hung that whore in the garage that I decided I'd go see how she was doing. I drove on out there and made the dive. When I swam up to the windshield and looked in I got quite a shock, because I thought she was gone! But as I swam in for a closer look, I could see she was a pile of bones on the front seat and the floor of the sedan. Picked perfectly clean, there was no flesh to be seen. Her plastic sandals were there, along with part of her top and brassiere. The ponytail was resting on the back seat still in a plastic hairclip, but there was no meat. It was a puzzle. Later I caught them: the blueclaw crabs were cleaning up the last few shreds of flesh stuck in her hair.

She'd been a whore with painted lips. We had played a game, and then she went down under the water and took a ride in my car. *Forever.*

DETECTIVE DAN KELLY:
ROGUE COP

THE SEX BEAST CAPER

The sixteen-year-old girl looked like she might break down in tears at any moment.

She was sitting on the edge of a hardwood chair in my penthouse apartment on the sixteenth floor of the Everglades Towers Condominium. Her soft brown eyes were moist and pleading. She kept licking her lips, wringing her hands and crossing then uncrossing her legs.

I gave her a hard look and told her, "Last chance to tell the truth, little sister, run it by me one more time."

"I swear, officer, I'm innocent."

"You don't need to convince me, honey. It's those twelve jurors and that hanging judge you need to worry about. And when it comes right down to it, who will they believe? The state's attorney and the police? Or a suspected killer?"

The girl buried her face in her hands. Her shoulders shook with sobs. "What will they do to me?"

"A young woman your age… a charge of aggravated felony murder… I'd bet on execution in the state electric chair."

"Oh my God! Oh my *GOD! NO!*"

"Hey. Don't worry, they won't fry you until you turn eighteen. Couple of years on Death Row, then the Big Sizzle. Lots of girls on Death Row these days. You'll have plenty of company."

"But I didn't *DO* it!"

"Nobody wants to hear that, girlie, get used to it. But maybe we can cut you a deal… "

She looked puzzled. "What do you mean a deal?"

"What I mean is you make my job easy by confessing to this caper and I'll arrange it so you don't get electrocuted for murder. Not only that but you can live here with me in this fancy condo and learn the callgirl trade. Make yourself a nice pile of money." She wasn't convinced. "I'll run you out to Surfside Six and introduce you to Don Johnson personally. Maybe line you up with a part in his show. You've got the looks for it. You'd like that?"

The girl stared wide-eyed. *"You* can introduce me to Don Johnson?"

"Sure. Tomorrow afternoon if you want."

"Oh, yes! I want to meet him!"

"OK, then we have a deal. Just say 'yes' when I nod my head." I activated the little Sony in my jacket pocket and said, "You freely admit to the robbery and murder of Rebecca Stein?" I gave the nod.

"Yes," she answered dutifully. I read her Miranda and then ran through the whole crime. She answered at every nod of my head with the correct response. When I had what I wanted I clicked off the tape and sat down on the bed.

"Show me your cunt now, sweetie."

The kid looked like I'd slapped her across the chops. Turned beet red.

"C'mon, stand up and peel down those Calvins. Don't keep Daddy Dan waiting."

"I think I've changed my mind," she whispered, her eyes huge.

I hooked the little tape player out of my pocket and turned it on. She listened, sobbing quietly while the confession ran its course. When the litany of murderous acts was finished, the girl said with cool contempt, "You're a real bastard."

I rewarded her with a wicked openhanded slap that spun her off the chair onto the floor. "Thou shalt not be disrespectful to thy Master. That's Rule Number One. Now can you remember that, bitch, or do you need a few more taps on the snoot?"

The girl shook her head to get her senses back. A pretty toss of the chestnut tresses. It would be a real shame to see that lovely mane scissored off on the floor of the Death House at Starke. The teen was a beauty, wholesome and fit. Only time would tell if she was smart enough to face up to the reality of her situation.

"Welcome to Miami," I said with a smile and held out my hand to help her up. She took my hand. A good sign. She rubbed at her cheek. It would be bruised, but she wouldn't be going out on the town just yet. She got right to the point when she asked, "Are you gonna fuck me now?"

I ran my hard hand over her dirty hair. She needed a bath in the worst way. "What's your real name, girl?" She hesitated.

I spoke softly and gently. "Honey, if you lie to me even one time you will fry in your own juices. This tape guarantees that, doesn't it?"

She nodded glumly. "My name is Crystal Koenig. I'm from Keokuk, Iowa. I just turned sixteen last week… and I don't want to go to jail. I don't want to die. Please, mister… "

"Call me Dan. Daddy Dan." She seem confused at my genial tone and that was fine. "On your way to see Don Johnson, were you?"

"That was my plan."

"We get about 200 girls a week like you. The jail is chock full of them. You a runaway? A throwaway? Mommy and Daddy hunting you down somewhere?"

"I took off when I turned sixteen. That's the legal age for girls in Iowa. My mom says I have movie-star looks. So I figured I'd try to make it in Miami. Looks like I screwed up before I even got a chance for my first audition." She wiped her nose with the back of her hand. "What are you gonna do to me? Rape me? Kill me?"

"Before we get into rape and murder, how would you like a Diet Pepsi? Maybe a sandwich to go with it? How's pastrami and Swiss on rye sound?"

She smiled a little. "So I get fed before being raped and murdered?"

"Sure. Condemned ladies all get that last meal. It's a regular tradition. You've seen that on TV, haven't you?"

She nodded. No use telling her condemned ladies don't much care for any fine last meals and those that do just puke them up when they get to the main event.

We walked into the kitchen together. I handed her a Kosher dill pickle, and got

busy. I observed her style as she was slurping at the pickle, while I slapped together a sandwich with a half-inch of thin-sliced pastrami, some Swiss cheese and
a thick slather of mustard. Then I passed her a cold Diet Pepsi, and sat down to
watch her wolf down the pastrami. She was a big healthy girl with a hearty appe-
tite. As I sucked on a Pabst Blue Ribbon beer, I wondered what other hearty appe-
tites she might have. She smacked her lips and licked her fingers. She'd need
lessons in how to be a lady. "Come off a farm, did you?"

She grinned. "How'd you guess?"

"You eat like an animal and you smell like pig shit."

She blinked, looked abashed, then smiled. "I probably do smell awful. We raised
hogs. I tended them. Can I take a shower here?"

"This is your new home, kid. Permanently. First things first. We're gonna start
with a quick shower with a brush to get the pig manure out from between your
toes, then we'll give you an herbal soak in a nice hot whirlpool bath, then we'll
wash out your hair with some designer shampoo and then you can give it a hot oil
treatment while you sit in the sauna."

"What's a sauna?"

"You'll see. If you're a good girl you'll have a nice life here with Daddy Dan.
Get out of line, you get beat. Cross me, you die. Easy rules in this lockup. Just
think of yourself as my slave."

"I ought to be good at that. Since my daddy's been gone, that's just about all
I've been anyway."

"What happened to your daddy?"

"Nobody knows for sure. Folks say he got et up by the hogs. He used to drink
his own moonshine and get pretty whacked. One night he was drinking out by the
pen and I guess he just went to sleep. In the morning when I went to slop the hogs,
all I saw was his railroad hat and the studs from his overalls."

"Maybe he took off."

"Yeah, maybe he did. I'd kind of rather think he wound up back in West Virginia
or somewheres instead of on our dinner table mixed in with the pork chops."

She pushed down on an errant bit of pastrami left on the Spode plate, and licked
the tidbit off her fingertip, an unconsciously erotic gesture. "What's all that stuff
you said about callgirls?"

"I'll have you trained by a pro. Nurse Nancy will have to check you out before
I'll touch you. It's not a bad life. Plenty of flash and cash. You like sex?"

She pondered it awhile. "No. I don't like it."

"Ever tried it?"

"I'm not a virgin."

"How many guys you been to bed with?"

"Just one. Arvin." She lowered her eyes and swallowed.

"Uh-huh. And who was that, the boy next door?"

She hesitated, then said with a little twist of her mouth, "He's my step-daddy."

She didn't have to say another thing. That told the whole story right there. I
studied her for a moment, watching the memories bring tears to her eyes.

"And that's all? Just Arvin?"

She nodded hopelessly as the tears slowly rolled down her cheeks. She was

winding her napkin around and around into a twisted wad. I took it from her. Crystal was going to need a little TLC. She was riding a bummer: no money, no clothes, no rosy future on the horizon. And coming from nothing but Arvin and moonshine and a pigpen. She was a beauty and her potential was first-rate. She didn't need another kick in the gut, so I gave her shoulder a gentle squeeze and told her to follow me.

"That Arvin's last name — Koenig?" I asked her on the way to the bathroom suite.

"Yeah, my mama made me change my name to go with hers."

"Well, we're gonna forget all about Arvin Koenig, just like he never happened. From now on you're Crystal Beavers, and you're gonna be my number one virgin sex slave."

Oakland Park, Florida is an urban slum area in Broward County. With the exception of a small enclave of expensive homes abutting the Intracoastal Waterway on the eastern fringe of the municipality, Oakland Park is a weirdo's wonderland of massage parlors, porno book stores, XXX-rated film rental businesses and seedy whorehouses catering to the blue-collar tourist trade. The permanent residents of Oakland Park are tolerant. Taxes are low. The city coffers are kept full by the vigilant municipal police officers who man the ever-present radar speed traps, the rat packs of scribbling meter maids who haunt the curbsides and gutters, and the Vice Squad cops who, in league with their political cronies, operate the revolving door of criminal justice that keeps the 500 dollar fines rolling in, day after day, compliments of Oakland Park's battalion of streetcorner hookers. The Oakland Park political scene stinks worse than the Paris sewers, but the cash flow is first-rate. And so is some of the local pussy.

Jolie was an Oakland Park girl, born and bred. Happiness was a pipe-full of crack in her head and a hard cock throbbing up her ass. This fine day she was promised both, compliments of her social studies teacher from the local adult education center, who assured the failing Jolie that with a little private tutoring her grades would surely rise to passing, even exceptional levels. The lessons would start with the cock and finish with the rock. Jolie, who at 16 was too young to drive, pedaled west on her ten-speed. She pumped her way along Oakland Park Blvd. over the bridge and toward the copse of Florida holly trees where her nice teacher, Kevin Goodleigh, nervously awaited her with a solid hard-on poking out his pants.

Wheeling her bike along the dirt path, Jolie was pleased to see Mr. Goodleigh waiting near the little trail that led into the bushes. He took her hand and led her to a secluded glade, and hastily pulled off his sweatshirt. Jolie, wasting no time, shucked off her T-shirt. Mr. Goodleigh spread his sweatshirt over a cypress log and sat down on it. He pulled the smirking student trollop over toward him. Jolie boldly unsnapped her brassiere and tossed it aside, leaned forward and let him lick her sweaty teats. She allowed him to suckle then smiling, she pushed his head lower down against her soft, white belly. The educator licked the salt from her navel with deft flicks of his magical tongue.

She sighed as she felt the warm tingle of arousal spread through her genitals.

Tilting her head back in ecstasy, she let nature take its course beneath the green canopy of tropical forest. It was such a nice, secluded, private place for fun and games. Jolie unbuttoned her cycling shorts and slid them down over her firm, well-rounded bottom, letting them drop to her ankles. Mr. Goodleigh gasped at the invitation to orally explore the shadowy muff outlined beneath the diaphanous white nylon panty. He buried his face in her thighs. Jolie's attention focused solely on the pulsing between her legs.

Until she heard the snap of a stick. She looked up and saw the figure not six feet away. It startled her... but what was it? It looked like a hairy man — could it be a man in an old fur coat? She squinted at him. He was tall and muscular, and the long, thick fur was matted with sandspurs, sticktights and cockleburrs. The head was conical with a black mane framing the riveting features... deep-set ruby-tinted, glowing eyes, a simian nose with an elongated muzzle like a baboon. What was this beast? Her mind writhed, grasping and discarding every animal she knew of. Then the beast crouched... and her mind went blank. She stiffened as the thing silently advanced.

Mr. Goodleigh interpreted her speechless reaction as a pre-orgasmic shiver. He grasped her sex-sodden panties and pulled them down to her knees.

Jolie stumbled backwards as the thing bared his teeth. The oblivious Goodleigh made a lunge towards her, issuing a sexy growl, his eyes fixed on the cleft of her glistening cunt.

The claws came from behind and ripped out Goodleigh's throat, then twisted off his head. Jolie watched his decapitated body arch backward, his heels drumming the soft earth, his still-rigid penis spewing a viscous string of white semen. Some of it sprayed across her face, and she was bringing her hand up to wipe it off when the beast raked his claws up between the dead man's legs, shredding his genitals and stuffing the mangled flesh into his mouth.

Jolie tripped over her shorts as she jumped back. She fell on her butt and rolled over to the side as she vomited convulsively. The beast snarled and stepped toward Jolie, reaching out with a deadly quickness. He seized her foot. She jerked her leg away, leaving the monster holding onto her dirty sneaker. She rolled over onto her hands and knees and tried to get to her feet, but she stumbled over her shorts again. In panic, she tore them off and gained her foothold, trembling. The beast, a string of gore hanging from his mouth, bared his fangs at her and growled. Jolie turned and dashed into the thick brush.

She knew she had to get back to her ten-speed and the safety of the Boulevard. Thorns raked her naked breasts. Tears stung her scratched cheeks. She sobbed in abject terror. She could hear sounds of life nearby: the swish of rubber on asphalt, the squeal of brakes and honk of horns. And the grunt and hiss of something crashing through the undergrowth behind her: the beast!

Jolie felt the furry paw on her shoulder, the hot stinking breath on her neck, the claws sinking into the soft tissue of her shoulder. She opened her mouth and she screamed and screamed and screamed. She felt the flesh ripping from her arm as the beast spun her around and shoved her to the ground. The repulsive musk of a skunk enveloped her as she felt the blunt knob of an enormous penis press against her sex. She tried to struggle but the beast thrust his weapon into her. She felt her

insides rip apart as her organs were violated… and then she knew nothing more. She was dead.

The beast followed the levee along the C-14 canal, walking hunched over in a half-crouch. He avoided the open areas, staying to the sawgrass and myrtle. The creature relived the desperate, cruel pain that drove him to rape and kill again and again. The rage in his head and the rage in his genitals tore at him. Pain controlled his every instinct.

The beast crept up the side of the levee toward the VW bug concealed in the bushes. He stood perfectly still and sniffed the air for signs of danger. Finding no cause for alarm, the beast stood upright, walked to the car and removed the weighty fur costume, the conical head, the steel claws. The creature was refreshed after his rampage. The doctors had told him he was a sex beast. They said he was incurable. He got in his little car and drove away.

Two weeks later, Crystal came into the bathroom suite, pulled down her jeans and seated herself on the throne. She'd never even lived in a house with indoor plumbing, much less a bathroom suite. Dan had explained what a suite was, but she still thought of it as the bathroom sweet. She opened a copy of *The Sun,* her favorite tabloid, and peed into the toilet bowl. I was shaving in the vanity area, and the connecting door to the toilet was ajar.

"What's a skunk ape, Dan?"

"Skunk ape? Some big ole hairy monster they say lives out in the Everglades. Sort of a bigfoot. Where'd you hear about the skunk ape in Iowa?"

Crystal read slowly and clearly, "Oh, I never heard of it in Iowa. It's here in *The Sun.* There are so many incredible things in this paper! Listen to this: 'Sex Beast Terrorizes Oakland Park.' It says here that a teenage virgin was savagely raped and ripped apart while she was on a school field trip. The schoolteacher was killed too. 'Jolie Parsons and Kevin Goodleigh were killed by a rutting sex beast authorities called a skunk ape. The girl was sexually ravished by the monster before being savagely ripped apart by his beastly claws.' There's a picture here, an artist's conception it says. Looks like a conehead in a monkey suit."

"Does it name the cops involved?"

"Mmmmm, let's see. Yeah, says here Sgt. George Kent, Homicide and Vice, Oakland Park PD."

I laughed. "Biggest liar in a cop shop where lying is a way of life. I've known him for fifteen years. Gimme that phone there, girl, right next to your cute little tushie."

Crystal handed the cordless to me and flushed the toilet as I punched through to Kent's office in Oakland Park. I listened to what he had to say. They were calling it the "Sex Beast Murders." It was a serious case, and a skunk ape was the prime suspect. I thanked Kent and handed the phone back to Crystal. She perched on the counter and looked at me inquiringly.

"Seems there could be something to this after all. Kent tells me the girl died from a burst uterus as if a bull's pizzle had been rammed up in her. Two winos under the C-14 bridge swear there was a huge skunk ape lurking down by the canal. They were close enough to smell him. Said he had a pointy head and a snout like a baboon."

"Sounds like that Mad Dog wine got to their brains. That's a ridiculous story — isn't it?"

"Kent says the heads were ripped off the bodies of the two victims. Not cut off, like the Butcher does, but ripped right off. With a twist and a jerk. Very curious M.O., I must say."

"So you think there really is a Sex Beast?"

I could discern her need for reassurance. "This is Florida, Kiddo. Anything can happen. *The Sun* is a reliable journalistic medium. They can't print out-and-out lies, you know. They'd get sued. My guess is that skunk apes are on the move. Could be more than one. The glades are drying up all over the state, and they could be looking for new hidey-holes. There could be big trouble ahead. Next thing you know a skunk ape will be climbing in a window in the middle of the night. Now that he's got a taste of hot teenage blood, no girl is safe until Sgt. Kent runs him down."

Crystal shivered. "It's a good thing we're sixteen floors off the ground! I can't believe I slept in the park when I first got here. The sex beast could've gotten me. I'm lucky to be alive, I guess."

"Yeah, you're the lucky one all right. Now go fix lunch." I wiped my face, kissed her on the cheek and smacked her tidy behind.

A week later, the headline story in the *Weekly World News* screamed: "Sex Beast Killer Stalks South Florida." Crystal was soaking up every word, her Cheerios abandoned and turning to sodden mush.

She tapped a long, scarlet porcelain nail on the drawing of the sex beast leering from the cover and announced, "Look Dan, he got another one. It's the same creature that got that girl on the field trip with her teacher."

"No, Crystal, it's the same case," I told her.

"No way, Jose! This one caught a prom queen starlet and her agent out looking at a site location for a Miami Vice episode."

"Check the names."

She did. "Yeah, you're right. It's that Jolie girl, but it says in the News that she was an ingenue starlet, scheduled for a role opposite Don Johnson. State's Attorney Bob Rock says he believes the sex beast has been responsible for the deaths of twenty girls in Oakland Park alone!"

"Is that a fact? I commented dryly. "Sounds like another Schaefer."

"What's a Schaefer?"

"Long story there, Punkin."

"Says Sheriff 'Hollywood Nick' Narcissus has called for volunteers to form a posse to hunt down and capture the sex beast. Look, here's the Sheriff's picture. He says, 'No woman is safe while the Sex Beast is on the loose. This monster must be taken dead or alive!' Wow."

"Eat your Cheerios, Kid."

"No, listen to this, Dan! Dr. Tim Dinkus, Broward County Medical Examiner, reveals that the starlet's naked breasts were punctured by fang marks. Could be a vampire, Dan! Or even an alien — like a wookie! Don't say they're not around. I read about them every week."

"Vampires my ass. You're gonna give yourself nightmares reading that lurid crap. You want to read, then go read something realistic. Something with some socially redeeming features. I got to go to work, but there's a copy of *Killer Fiction* on the coffee table. All the cops are reading it. It's a limited edition, and it's not easy to get. There was a two-week waiting list at work just to get ahold of this copy. I've got to pass it on tomorrow, so why don't you scan it while you have a chance."

"Any sex in it?"

"Lots of sex. Lots of realistic crime scenes, too. Read it and learn."

"OK, Dan, I will," she agreed, but I could see Crystal was too absorbed in the story of the Sex Beast to get any benefit from it.

I called George Kent from the Station House. "What's the word on the Sex Beast case?" I asked him. He was embarrassed to tell me he was making no progress. I wasn't surprised. Kent had never solved a murder case in seventeen years on the force. He was an ace when it came to busting hookers and writing traffic tickets. He had a reasonable explanation: felony busts don't generate income. The Oakland Park PD keeps those high-fine misdemeanors rolling in. Fuck felony, that was Kent's motto. But he did mention that the Sex Beast was scaring away tourists, which was bad for the hooker business. I made a suggestion and he liked my idea. After all, he was a desperate man.

Crystal took one look at the bloodstained cypress log and frowned deeply.

"That's where we found what was left of Goodleigh, Dan. Seems he'd been stretching that teen pussy for years. Sucky-fucky in exchange for passing grades. Seems like we had a rotten apple this time. Most of the child molesters we bust are schoolteachers. It's really amazing but statistics don't lie." George Kent told it like it was. He turned to Crystal and said, "Are you sure you want to risk this, Miss Beavers?"

"She's sure," I said.

Crystal Beavers, aspiring starlet and public-spirited citizen, drew off her sweatshirt and unfastened her jeans. She slid them down and stepped out of them along with her panties. She handed her clothes to me. I spread the sweatshirt on the log and motioned for Crystal to sit. A short length of chain was fastened around her ankle, and the other end wound several times around the cypress log.

Crystal sat there gloriously naked and said dispiritedly, "Here, Sex Beastie! Come to Crystal!" She gave Kent a lopsided grin. He missed it. He was too preoccupied with her 38-C hooters. Stuck right out there right in front of God and everybody.

"We'll be hiding right across the glade, Kid, so don't you worry your sweet little head about a thing." I patted her head.

"If you let that skunk ape come near me, Dan, so help me — I'll — I'll…"

"Yeah I know. But like Sgt. Kent says, the town is about to be foreclosed. Everybody is too scared to come out at night so the cops can't arrest anyone. In desperate times it takes desperate measures to survive. If there really is a sex beast out there, your Chanel No. 5 is going to draw him in. He gets anywhere close and

he's blown to bits. If there ain't no sex beast then we can have a press conference and announce that we have run a test and the coast is clear."

"Oh, Dan, I want to help, really I do, but why do I have to wear these chains?"

"That's so you don't wander off, Crystal. You don't realize how important a role you play in saving the community. The hookers need to get back on the street. They're the lifeblood of the municipal government. I'll buy you a nice present from the police slush fund for your contribution. You're a good girl."

Kent and I secreted ourselves behind a small blind equipped with a starlight scope, and watched Crystal. She ran her hand back through her hair. Crickets began to crank up. Gloom descended on the glade. She peered into the darkness and dilated her nostrils in an effort to pick up the scent of any sex beasts that might be skulking nearby. She started singing wistfully in a tremulous voice, "Someday my prince will come, some day I'll find someone... "

"How'd you scoop that luscious piece of ass?" George wanted to know. He was staring at Crystal's naked titties through the starlight scope.

"That's prime tail, George, free, white and 21. Fresh off a flight from Hollywood, California. One of the new starlets they brought in for this season's Miami Vice. Crystal Beavers. She was on the cover of *New Faces* and *Star People* — didn't you see her there?"

"Can't say as I did, Dan, but I'm sure getting an eyeful here." She was slapping at bugs. Kent zoomed in on one perky nipple and grabbed his crotch. He had picked up a taste for premature tail working the Juvenile Division. Crack-mad little sluts with mouths that lie and suck with equal fervor. "You Miami heat get all the good pussy. Stuff we have up here in Oakland Park is strictly commercial grade. I sure could use me a taste of that sweet California wine."

"Crystal's spoken for. She's poison ivy, my man: you can look but you better not touch. She does get off on being looked at, though. You ever met an actress who could resist dropping her pants in public?"

"Never met an actress at all, Kelly! I keep telling you, Oakland Park ain't Miami."

No, but Oakland Park supposedly had something unknown in Miami or anywhere else on the face of the earth: the Sex Beast. And with any luck, the horny monster would soon be drawn into the snare that we had baited with the naked teen awash in an aura of Chanel.

The prowl of the Sex Beast began with the rise of the moon. He knew the places where the humans came to mate. His prey would come, they always did. And always, they would die. As the moon loomed over the banyan tree that sheltered his bug, the monster replaced the batteries in his conical head, and settled it in place with the red eyes now pulsing with a renewed glow. He donned the heavy hairy coat and strapped on the killing paws with the steel claws honed to stiletto-blade sharpness. Then he went into his crouch and began to sway back and forth in the moonlight.

Crystal was scratching and slapping at mosquitoes between choruses of "The Monster Mash." Dan had insisted that she couldn't use any bug repellent, because

it would confuse the scent of the Chanel. After a while, she quieted down, her forced cheerfulness beginning to flag. She was cranky, annoyed and downright uncomfortable in the moonlit gloom of the woodsy copse. There were noises. There could be snakes. Rats. Roaches. There were bugs, and it was muggy and hot, even long after sundown. Her skin was sticky. She closed her eyes and imagined herself relaxing in her Bathroom Sweet.

She came back to her surroundings with a start. What had she heard? She peered into the shadows and caught a slight movement. Then came a low growl and a snarl. Her heart thumped and she emitted a tiny squeak of alarm. Her hair stood straight up all over her head and down her neck. This was real!

The brown, matted heap of fur took shape as it stealthily approached her across the open area of the glade. It seemed to be advancing on all fours, with a weird, uneven shambling gait. The thing moved within a dozen feet of her and suddenly reared up to its full height. It was a monster movie come to life for a girl raised on the Saturday Creature Feature. The beast looming over her reminded her of the Wolfman, but with features like an ape. And the stink! Crystal screamed with mortal terror and revulsion as the beast lumbered toward her. She tried to run but fell flat, her leg held fast by the steel chain.

Suddenly the area was lit with an incandescent strobe light. The beast turned to face this unexpected source of annoyance. The videocam whirred. Kent sighted between the glowing red eyes and blasted off a round. The beast did not react. Kent fired again, and a puff of dust jumped where the bullet struck the monster just above the left eye. The beast stood fast and did not flinch. Kent dropped his gun and ran shrieking into the woods. The beast dropped to all fours and shambled away into the woods. The illuminated night resounded to the desperate screams of Crystal in chains and the crash of underbrush as both Kent and the monster tore through the swamp fleeing from each other.

"He was ten feet tall with big fangs, and long claws that made click-click noises. He had a lot of long black fur and a cone-shaped head with pulsing red eyes. He smelled worse than a skunk — the smell was like something dead. When he stood up, I could see he had this huge thing on him — it was big and black and hard, and he was aiming it straight towards me. I was so scared he would rape me, I fell off the log." That's what Crystal had told the reporter from *The Sun*. It was an exclusive interview, and the price was $70,000. Cash in hand to me, of course.

The cover was a full-color picture of Crystal falling backwards off the log, with the chain around her ankle clearly depicted. The furry bulk of the sex beast loomed over her and dominated most of the picture, but it was hard to make out what he looked like. The banner screamed: "Naked Starlet Escapes Lust-Crazed Sex Beast." The tabloids went insane, and a week later they all had their follow-up stories.

Crystal scissored one out of *The Inquisitor* that shrilled: "Florida Police Use Chained Virgin as Monster Bait!" She pasted it into the neat scrapbook that was quickly thickening. "Dan, I can hardly believe that's me on the cover of *The Sun*. What in the world was that thing, anyway?"

"A skunk ape, I guess. How the hell would I know? The important thing is you are safe and unhurt."

"I love you, Dan. I'll do anything to make you happy. You saved my life, I know."

I sipped the bitter Cuban coffee. Drew slowly on a Camel. Eyed the adoring teen through narrowed lids as I blew smoke toward her. She was putty in my hands. What a refreshing change. Crystal was almost as fresh as crisp green cash.

"Give it time, Honey. No need to rush anything. We've got all the time in the world. You like being my Virgin Sex Slave?"

"I love being your slave, Dan."

"Well, that's encouraging."

"What became of your friend, Mr. Kent?"

"State Hospital at Chattahoochee. The Oakland Park PD is denying everything. They claim he went nuts on them and they're not responsible. The whole thing never happened, none of it."

"But we were there, Dan! Look at the marks that chain left on me, look at all these mosquito bites!"

"Fifty grand from the slush fund says we've never set foot in Oakland Park."

"But what about my career? My press conferences? The offer from Hustler to do the Taming of the Sex Beast photo layout?"

"Forget all that, Kid. We've got better things to do."

"*WHAT* better things?" Crystal shrieked, highly agitated.

I unzipped my trousers and took out my cock. "Gonna make you a star, Babydoll, and this is where it all starts. Hit the deck and get to work."

Crystal tossed her hair and made a face. "Yuck!"

Two seconds later she was sprawled across the sunroom floor with a mouse forming under her eye. I stood over her as she pulled herself up.

"Suck cock. Vacation's over."

Crystal shook her head slowly to clear her senses, and then she crawled forward on all fours, nuzzled up to my crotch, and began to learn her new trade.

Beauregard Morris was not in his own bed. This fact did not surprise him, since it was his habit to sleep around as often as possible. He sat up and groped for his first cig of the day. Peering around the room without his glasses, he fished in his deerskin bag for a Virginia Slim. The pink champagne standing in the plastic stemware next to the greasy, crusted dildo was devoid of any vestiges of fizz.

A gang of tiny monsters were whacking away at the inside of his skull. It was depressing. It was a conspiracy. Beau briefly considered suicide, then realized he had no idea where he was and suicide would undoubtedly be regarded as unflattering under the circumstances.

He sniffed deprecatingly. He should have been able to make it with a better class of queers than this. After all hadn't he a name, wasn't he a personality? He was somebody, sort of.

Obviously, he still hadn't hit the big time. For years, he'd been searching for another bondage master, someone with a firm hand like Karl the German Conqueror but somehow nothing had never been the same. Beau yawned, stretched and farted luxuriously. He sat up and lit the Virginia Slim and took a delicate drag, letting the smoke flow out his mouth while inhaling it with his nose, French-style.

A clock ticked away loudly and insistently, grating his nerves as he knocked an abalone shell overflowing with butts onto the floor beside the bed. "Oh dear," Beau sighed aloud to nobody.

The bedroom was small and stuffy. It smelled of mildew and stale sex. Too many late nights, too many half-hard dicks. He called out, "Yoo-hoo! Anybody home?"

A clump of boots was came his way, and finally the host made his appearance. He was an aged biker in heavy leather and big engineer's boots with an abundance of decorative straps and studs and buckles. The old rogue was fat and balding with a beer belly and black grease, or something, lining his fingernails. He gave Beau a wide grin full of ragged and rotten teeth.

"Well, well, well. I thought Sleeping Beauty would never wake! You sure can put away the bubbly, Doc. Take a pretty good length of fist too." Beau looked confused and he chuckled, "How does it feel to be an honorary member of Wheels of Terror?"

Beau gazed on the pockmarked visage before him and could swear on forty brand-new Bibles that he had never laid eyes on him before in his life. And what was that about the fist? And the terror? Either things were moving too fast or he was moving too slow. "I say, have we been properly introduced?" he offered with a wry smile.

The big ugly biker eyed Beau and favored him with a hearty guffaw. "You were concentrating so hard on my cock you might not have took much notice of my face. You wanna run me some early morning head?" The biker faggot unzipped his leather pants and shook his cock at Beau.

Beau took another drag at his Virginia Slim and politely shook his head. "You gotta be kidding, Buster?"

"Ain't no joke at all, Honey." The cycle tramp ran his greasy hand back over his balding pate and gave Beau a long, smoldering look. "I've gotta be down to the bike shop in an hour. That'll give me time to run this here reamer up your tail pipe again, maybe spark a few memories." The queer stroked his cock to erect attention.

Beau eyed the dick with lingering admiration. A recollection seemed to be coming back. He really ought to ease up on the champagne. "Not right now, Lover-boy," Beau pouted, "my head hurts."

Snubbing out the cigarette, Beau rolled out of the filthy bed and pulled his pink negligee over his head. Underneath he wore his favorite black rubber garter belt, black fishnet hose and a crotchless frilly pink panty. He ran his fingers through his tangled hair and exclaimed, "My do! It's destroyed!" The biker just shrugged and lumbered out of the room.

Beau wandered into the bathroom and sat down on the toilet to take a piss. "Where am I?" he howled in despair.

"Why, Atlanta obviously, right where you've always been," came the answer through the door.

"That's not what I meant," he answered half to himself. He didn't know what he did mean, and fortunately his new friend let it drop.

Beau hit the shower and tried to clean up the detritus of last night's revel. He

downed four Excedrins and squeezed himself into his trademark hot pink shirt and tight black pants. Leaning into the mirror, Beau observed the indelible marks of Mistress Time and Master Dewars. He really didn't look too good, but he comforted himself with the thought that at least he'd never stooped to smoking crack. Of course blow was another thing. He'd wouldn't turn down a line or two — or three — if it was laid out on a mirror as a love offering, but he intended to steer clear of the hard stuff, the stuff that kills. A twinge of concern flashed through his sodden brain: AIDS. No. Couldn't be, it's just a hangover — the bleary, sick-looking eyes of this parody of his lovely, queenly self staring back at him. All it'd take would be a nice facial, manicure, and massage at Adrian's to be positively radiant again. He simply had to quit this dangerous slumming… but it was so hard when he was such a fool for these bikers, the Nazi crowd, the leather boys. He let himself get swept off his feet time and time again, and each time he swore this one would be his last fling. Those steely thighs, those hard throbbing cocks, those thrusting fists… he sighed and fluffed his locks.

Beau was confident that he could still catch the right man if he simply applied his mind to it. He couldn't stand those flits in the gay bars. He was a real man and so was his fantasy lover. He'd keep the faith; one day the right guy would come along and — BINGO! They'd get married. Maybe they'd get a house in Cobb County where they could raise some Weimaraners. Or a nice little condo in Midtown.

Beau's eyes were the color of pond scum, and he was running to flab, but he had a thick crop of longish brown hair, nice dental work, and a certain charisma. And now he was an honorary member of Wheels of Terror. He contemplated how that might be used to his professional benefit in the years to come. He wondered what his initiation had been.

He was still dreaming about how his prestige would attract Mr. Wonderful when he breezed through the kitchen, waving a hand casually at Mr. Dreadful, who was talking on the phone to someone named Dieter, as he passed out the back door. Fortunately, the cordovan BMW was parked right in back, and it appeared to be intact.

As he wheeled the Beamer out of the complex he realized he was on Roswell Road, not too far from a decent Dunk'n Dine. He always could count on their coffee to slap him into shape when he'd had a little too much fun. Inside the lobby of the Dunk'n Dine were racks of the *Atlanta Journal*, and while he waited for a seat, his eye fell on the headlines: "AIDS Death Plague Decimates America." That was hardly news. Again there was that twinge. He knew he'd been playing Russian Roulette with his sex life. The herpes was bad enough. He took L-lysine to control his outbreaks, but still once you got it, you had it for life. But AIDS — it will take you out. Slowly and painfully, and in shame. Beau'd had to give up keeping count of the friends and colleagues he'd lost. Bad, bad, bad. His eyes fell to the second lead story: "Schoolgirl Raped and Killed by Apeman."

The pond slime covering his eyes came to life at once; it feasted on stories of murder, mayhem, and perversion. This was something novel indeed that he might use to buck up his flagging career as an expert on serial killers. He was well aware that his first book *Serial Killer Madness* was nothing more than highbrow slasher

stuff. He'd thrown it together in six months after making a boast over herb tea and croissants one day that he could get away with saying anything at all in print, just on the basis of his reputation as a psychologist.

Dear madcap Truman, now gone to his final reward. It was Truman who had first turned him on to the cash value of mass murder. He remembered the whole scene. How Tru had sat him down and cozied up, stroking his thigh, while he explained the public fascination with mass murder, devilish cults, vampires, homicidal maniacs and bizarre fiends of all stripes. There's big money in bloody murder, he said. The best-sellers are the ones where everyone is murdered or executed by the end of the book. And even the most superficial glance at the numbers proved that Tru was right.

Serial Killer Madness had given him a pretty good ride, although from time to time his flagrant disregard for facts was brought up in a lawsuit. So far his publishers had managed to settle everything out of court, but who knows? One of those killers might change his mind one day and decide to take offense. This creature called the sex beast… if he really was a beast, he probably wouldn't have a lawyer. Beau grabbed the *Journal* and mulled over different angles while he nursed his coffee: "Beast Feast"… "Mark of the Beast"… what a story. The thing ripped his victims apart and ate them up. That was the icing on the cake. Wonder where Oakland Park is. There was only one thing to do: go where the story is. The police, prosecutors, victims, all would scurry to his aid once he made it known that the world-famous serial killer expert was on the case. And if they didn't, that was OK too. Beau knew how to suck ass even better than he could suck cock. He knew they'd see things his way — eventually.

The doctors who had told him he was incurable were probably right. He seemed to have more trouble sorting out his tangled thoughts lately. It had been a lot worse since those little men from the UFO had stuck that needle in his brain to retune it. He lifted up the furry conehead and studied the two bullet holes, one slightly above the brow of the left eye, the other squarely between them. Close call, but fortunately the bullets had passed right through the frame without damaging the wiring. The red eyes glowed from deep in their hairy nests.

The fiend recalled the screaming naked female chained to the log. Her greasy, salty blood was what he wanted to taste. It wasn't fair. He slipped on a paw and slashed at the air as he recalled the blinding white light and flashing gunfire, emitting a low growl and a sibilant hiss. His unfulfilled passion was making him nervous. He removed the paw, sniffed the sour air of the cavelike apartment and shambled over to the icebox. He peered in. The blank eyes of the human they called Jolie stared at him from inside a plastic bag. The fiend smiled benignly and lifted Jolie carefully out of the fridge. He removed the bag, rolled the head out onto the countertop and sawed off the top of the skull. He sniffed at the congealed brains, and then began to feed, dipping in with both hands, slurping and smacking his lips as he grunted with satisfaction. He always saved the best for last.

Chief Warren "Bubba" FitzWilliams of the Oakland Park Police Department laid his best shiteating smile on the lady reporter from *Shocking Crime* magazine,

and said, "There's no such thing as a Sex Beast." His mouth was smiling but his eyes were cold.

She was a looker in a Pierre Cardin suit, with shaggy black hair piled on top of her head, artfully secured with combs so that it fell free in a casual tumble. Her dark brown eyes were crackling with intelligence. FitzWilliams would have to be careful not to be distracted.

The lady touched her Montblanc pen to her nose and coolly inquired, "What do you suppose it was that split the victim's vagina and pushed her uterus up under her heart? Could Goodleigh have been responsible for that?"

FitzWilliams had the good manners to blush. "That's a question for the County Medical Examiner, Ms. Stuart. I'm just a cop. My job is catching criminals. We run an honest shop here at the Station. We do the best we can."

"Goodleigh was a local social studies teacher with a history of molesting young girls, isn't that true?"

"Mr. Goodleigh is a victim here, he's under no suspicion of wrongdoing."

"What was he doing naked in the woods with a sixteen-year old girl? Giving her a geography tutorial?"

"We really can't say, Ms. Stuart."

"Is that can't — or *won't*?"

The Chief stood up. "If you have no further questions, I'm very busy..."

She leaned back in the chair, making herself comfortable. "Oh, but I do have other questions. Our readers want to know the facts." She flipped pages on her pad and fired at him, "Isn't it true that there have been increased reports of UFO sightings in Oakland Park since the Sex Beast's appearance?"

FitzWilliams sighed and sat down. Every nut in the county had been burning up the phone lines with tips on UFO's and men skulking about in ape costumes. He'd taken another call not fifteen minutes before this nutsy broad showed up. A lady in Wilton Manors had seen a neighbor in a monkey suit taking out a bag of trash to his curb late last night. She admitted there was a pickup this morning, and there was no law against wearing a costume. He wanted to know why she didn't call the Wilton Manors police about it. She opined that they never answered her calls, and anyway since it was the Oakland Park Sex Beast, she figured she'd best call them to come get him. FitzWilliams gave the lady the number of that TV show *Inside Edition* and suggested she call them at once.

"So you admit there is a connection between the Sex Beast and increased UFO activity?"

FitzWilliams nodded absently and hoped if he ignored her she would just go away.

Crystal picked up the copy of the latest issue of *Shocking Crime*. The magazine cover showed a naked girl being dragged into a swamp by a gorilla, with a flying saucer hovering just off the ground behind them. "Police Chief Blames UFOs for Sex Beast Murders" was the screamer. Crystal opened the magazine and avidly flipped to the story. The writer was StarGlow Stuart, Queen of the Exposé Galaxy. StarGlow was famous. Crystal had seen her on Geraldo, and even heard her on the

Howard Stern Show. She tried to call in, but she could never get through the switchboard. Crystal rubbed her temples in torment as she read the story. It was being treated as a big mystery. It seems nobody knew the true story but her!

She couldn't help herself. She reached for the phone and called *Shocking Crime*. "Hello, may I please speak to StarGlow?"

"I'm sorry, she's working on a story right now. May I take a message please?"

"This is Crystal Beavers — you know, the movie starlet the Sex Beast almost ate? I want to talk to StarGlow Stuart about what really happened when I was chained naked in the swamp by the police."

"One moment please."

Crystal was amazed and pleased when StarGlow came right on the line. She was so very nice that Crystal started telling her everything. The whole story was tumbling out of her mouth at once. She was even more amazed when StarGlow interrupted her to say she'd be glad to stop by in person so they could talk it over and she'd even bring Crystal an autographed picture for her Sex Beast scrapbook. Would that be OK?

Crystal was so excited she blurted out the address without thinking and hung up. It was only then that she began to tremble at the thought of what Dirty Dan might do if he opened the door to find himself confronting the fiery eyes of StarGlow Stuart. Dan didn't like surprises. Crystal hugged herself and rocked back and forth, whispering "Ooooh! Ooooh! Ooooh!" until she couldn't stand it any longer. She jumped up and ran in the kitchen for a Coke Classic and two Twinkies and came back to flop down on the floor in front of the giant screen. She clicked on the Disney Channel and tried to lose herself in sugar and cartoons while she pondered suicide.

"Anyone ever suck your pussy, kid?"

She blinked. Shook her head from side to side.

"Spit it out, what happened?"

"Nothing. Arvin said it smelled nasty. I reckon he was being honest about it." She shrugged. "What do you mean someone sucking on it?" She was curious.

"Just a little something that a man can do to make a special young lady feel real good."

"How does it go?"

I ran my hand over my Don Johnson stubble and wondered at a town where a girl can reach sixteen and never have her pussy sucked. Keokuk, Iowa. Must be one backward burg. I told her to lay down on the bed and spread her legs. She understood that part well enough.

Crystal was soon moaning softly as my tongue slipped between the cleansed folds of her cunnus. It was dry and sweet and smelled of the perfumed soap she had been rubbing between the crack of her ass. The flow of Crystal's sexual arousal began to slicken her cunt crease, and I thrust my tongue into her with patient demand. I lapped her snatch until her hole was smeared with slippery passion juices.

"Oh yes! Yes!" Crystal moaned. The scarlet fingernails of her tapered hands scratched at the crown of my head. She took deep breaths as her hips writhed

under my mouth. The swollen head of her clit rubbed against my tongue as I rolled it with a steady motion and set a rhythm guaranteed to drive her to distraction.

My mouth was smeared with her creamy wetness as I sank my tongue into her fuck hole, then drew slowly back and worried the bulb of her clit. My quickened lapping rhythm was taking her closer to the edge, so I went into the syncopation. Her thighs tensed. Her hands tangled in my hair. I pushed two fingers into her depths, then pulled upward with a strong motion, while I popped her clit with the edge of my front teeth. Crystal gasped in ecstasy, "Oh! Oh Jesus! Oh God!"

Crystal went rigid with pleasure and shuddered through the spasms that released her copious sweet fluids, finally lying still with the insides of her smooth thighs festooned with the vestiges of her arousal.

"Ooooooohhh," was all she could manage for several minutes. Then she sighed. "Dan, lover, that was so beautiful. Where did you learn to do that?"

I rolled her over on her stomach and gave her a sharp smack on her succulent bare behind. She raised it. Spread her tail.

"I'll never tell," I smiled.

Murder 101

I t was well past midnight, the black hour when evil is afoot in the city.

My eyes flew open from a dreamless sleep; I lay on the cool blue silk sheets and felt the onerous weight of a premonition of doom settle down upon my soul. Beside me I felt the pressing warmth of sweet young flesh.

Crystal Beavers, eyes closed and mouth open, snored lightly. I watched the steady rise and fall of her delectable bosom in the dim moonlight. The luminous dial on my Rolex announced that it was past three. I slid my hand with casual familiarity over the luscious curve of Crystal's shapely rump, and felt her stir in her sleep; she inched toward me mumbling, "Dan, honey, love me!"

I ignored her pleading, and focused my attention on the murderous vibes that had come to me unbidden in the night. Crystal's soft hand seized my penis and began to tug at it with a rhythmic motion. My concentration broke and I shoved Crystal out of the bed onto the floor.

"Dan!" she squealed, "What are you doing kicking me out of the bed?"

Crystal knelt submissively on the floor in the moonlight, her chestnut tresses tumbling around her shoulders in erotic disarray. She blinked and snuffled. "You treat me so mean, Dan! All I wanted to do was make love to you. Don't you love me anymore?"

I'd heard that line from her before. I threw her a steely look. "I've told you not to annoy me with that sex crap while I'm working."

She crawled over to the bedside table and peered at the clock. "You're working? Are you crazy? It's three o'clock in the morning. You were feeling up my butt! I thought that you wanted me. What's the matter with you?"

"There's murder in the air, kid. I can feel it. I've got a built-in murder detector in my brain. When murders happen I tune right in on it."

Crystal jumped up and look out the window. "Dan, do you think that the Sex Beasts could be coming in from the swamps? We've been due for an invasion. I was just reading about it in StarGlow's astrology column the other day. Could it be coming to pass here in the night?"

Crystal focused her attention on the twinkling city spread out sixteen stories below. I focused my attention on her naked behind. It was an admirable sight against the soft glow of the city lights. The kid was growing up, filling out; pretty soon she'd bee too old for the Lolita trade. Changes. I'd have to learn to live with them or find a way to get rid of her.

"Too late for the Sex Beasts, Honey. They're twilight creatures, do most of their trolling just when the sun goes down. I don't think the vibe I was picking up was a Sex Beast. It came to me as more malignant. Like the time I chased the Butcher. I could almost feel him cutting and slashing his way through the flesh of those innocent young hookers. I was laying there trying to make some sense out of those bad vibes when you started fooling around. You have a terminal case of hot pants… when you're wearing pants… speaking of which, put some on and get your tail into the kitchen and make me breakfast."

Crystal turned, put her hands on her hips and whined, "You always blame me! Anything goes wrong in your life and it's my fault, why is that?"

"Because you're a whore and whores cause a lot of trouble in the world. Your just have no idea the problems women like yourself cause." I snapped on the bedside lamp and Crystal squinted her eyes. I noticed that her pubic mound was sprouting a five o'clock shadow. "What did I tell you about keeping your snatch shaved smooth, kid? Do you need a session with my belt to help your memory?"

Crystal scratched at her pussy absently, ignoring my question. She rolled her eyes; then after a moment she commented poutily, "You said to keep it smooth and oiled for the customers because that's the way they like it."

"That's all I said? Think hard."

She pursed her lips. Giggled. "You said to keep it shaved and oiled or you'd kick my ass."

I looked her over. "C'mere."

She minced forward and stood before me, hands on her hips, bosom outthrust, her big brown nipples erect. I seized her about the hips and ran my tongue over her pubic area, felt her prickly stubble tickle my lips and scratch my nose. I savored the warm musky scent of her crotch, slid my tongue toward her clit.

"Illegal search and seizure!" she yelped, twisting free and dancing away with a chuckle. I bounced off the bed and swung my foot at the jiggling behind. I caught a well-padded butt cheek with a meaty smack. "Get your tail into the kitchen and put on the coffee, and if your twat isn't smooth when I come off duty tonight I'll take a riding crop to your fanny."

Crystal rubbed her saucy fanny. "Promises, promises. You always tell me that you are going to use that riding crop on me but you never do. When are you going to give a little tickle?" She look back over her shoulder at me and grinned, then said, "I do know of this freak who will pay to watch a girl shave her pussy. One of Melina's girls told me about him. Do you think I should call him up and make him an offer?"

"I don't see why not!" I watched Crystal swinging her butt toward the kitchen; then I picked up my shoulder holster and headed for the shower.

The day was getting off to a bad start and promised to get worse. The premonition of bad trouble nibbled away at my brain like a hungry rat gnawing at a fresh corpse. My cases were all running down blind alleys and into stone walls. My spirits dropped another notch when I found the note on my desk saying to report to the Porker the minute I hit the squad room. I was in no mood to listen to the Chief's bullshit... or to practice diplomacy.

Chief Pork Shepherd was flopped in his Chief's chair when I walked into his office, all three hundred and twenty pounds of him. He was leafing through a missing persons report. I recognized it at once. I was assigned to the case. Two young chippies that turned up missing. They were still missing and the way things were shaping up, I doubted that they would ever be found. The Porker favored me with a politician's grin.

"Danno, me lad, what's the status on the missing girls from the Blessed Virgin Mary Academy? Sister Mary Immaculata, the Mother Superior out there, has been burning up the telephone lines... God Bless Her Soul... wanting to know if we've found any trace of her lost lambs. I trust you have a line on where they might be?"

I rubbed the stubble on my chin and looked forlornly at my shoes. They needed a shine in the worst way. I did a quick mental review of the case. It had not seemed like an important one at the time. It began with a missing corpse. The fresh young corpse of a Blessed Virgin Mary Academy senior who had been killed in an unfortunate and routine traffic accident. The corpse of this tender youngster had apparently been misplaced somewhere. Those things do happen.

At first I had treated it as grand theft corpus but the deeper I dug, the more it began to look like mere negligence... but then there were the back to back disappearances of two nubile seniors from the same school, who had last been seen entering the dangerous area of Little Haiti. I'd tracked them to an off-beat curiosity shop specializing in weird items, and decided to stop there before breaking into a scandal that would put the Good Sisters at the pricey girl's school in a bad light.

Yet there was that common link surrounding these known dead and missing BVM Academy seniors... and damn fine young vixens they were too. They had vanished as if they had been swallowed up by the earth itself. I felt that the direct approach was best with the Chief.

"It's a mystery, Chief, damnedest case I've ever seen. First, the corpse up and disappears; then the two gal pals take a powder and are never seen again. Not a trace. No calls to daddy for funds, no calls to their school chums letting them know they are out on a lark. Nothing. I talked to one of the employees out there at the Eternal Rest Mortuary, a nice young man name of Nolte. Actually he seemed a bit odd, but then what do you expect to encounter in a place like that? What kind of kid works in an undertaking establishment? I asked myself that, but I couldn't come up with an answer that made any sense."

"Get to the point, Danno, I'm a busy man and the archbishop is waiting for my call with respect to this case."

"The young man, Nolte, he told me that he remembers the girl coming in. Said she had a broken neck. Classic whiplash death. He claims that he put her in the cooler himself... so then he doesn't know anything else. Says that as far as he knows that the bimbo disappeared right out of the cooler. I have it pegged for a civil problem. Airlines lose luggage, mortuaries lose corpses. What the hell, Chief, I say that we write it off and let the local insurance people wrangle over it."

The Porker nodded agreeably. He seemed to accept my assessment of the case. People were always losing things, why not corpses? It wasn't a crime, it wasn't even police business. What was left? Body snatchers? Ghouls? But missing persons was quite another matter.

"Yeah Danno, we can write off the stiff. A civil problem like you say, but what about those two Academy babes? What sort of leads have you come up with? Or what *haven't* you come up with might be stating it better."

"Runaways is how I see it. It's been less than a month but if they were dead someone would have found them. Dump them in a canal and in three days you have a pair of gas bags popping to the surface, and we could go out and pick them up. Dead in a ditch and they'd surface. Dump them in a field and someone would have been calling in about the stink. Those young girls ripen fast in the summer. So I figure they're still alive somewhere. I've rousted a few of the street hookers and the girls tell me there are no BVM girls on the stroll. It looks to me like they've blown the city. Stuck out their thumbs and caught a ride. West coast would be my guess. I wouldn't doubt they're already spread all over somebody's casting couch out in Hollywood. Who can figure teenaged cunt? They're a mystery."

Pork grunted and shook his jowls at me. "I pay you to figure it out, Danno. And what will I be telling the darling blessed sisters when they are calling me on the telephone asking about the lost ones? Sure and it will be the Pope of Rome himself calling me unless you come up with something that I can pass on to the archbishop. Something. Anything. If you can catch my meaning, old son."

"Tell the archbishop to order up a prayer vigil and be done with it," I snorted and lit up a Camel.

"Don't be letting me hear you disrespect the Holy Church, Dan, me lad. They do me a world of good with every priest in the precinct telling the voting members of his flock to pull the lever for me come November. They vote for me and I vote for you. Don't I keep you on the payroll and turn away from a lot of the things that you have cooking on the side, boyo? Like a certain piece of jailbait tail that you are plugging up there in that fancy condo of yours?"

"Fuck the Church!" I groaned. "After the way we wiped out that nest of dope peddling bikers, the voters wouldn't put you out of office even if you rode a Harley naked down Biscayne Boulevard at high noon!"

Pork smiled. Then he frowned. While I studied him he turned to his desk as the fax sprang to life. It may have saved me from a violent retort.

I watched the Chief's eyes widen as he scanned the paper flimsy spewing from his machine. Suddenly he seized the rattling paper with both hands and roared, "My God! They are butchering coeds up at the University in Gainesville! Gutting them! Cutting off their heads, for God's sake! There's a damned slaughter going on up there!" Then the Chief sighed and said, "I'll be thanking the good Lord that

the wretched killings are a good three hundred miles from my jurisdiction and may God help the poor fucker who is Chief in that bailiwick today!"

"God and the FBI."

Coed butcherings interested me. It reminded me of the time that I was on the trail of Butcher – the serial killer who had been released early from a life sentence at Florida State Prison. I'd trailed his murdering ass into the trackless swamps south of the Everglades before losing him. It was a thorn in my professional reputation that I'd never been able to bring the Butcher to the Bar of Justice.

The fax hummed again and coughed out another train of white paper. The Chief glanced at it and remarked, "The people up in Alachua County are putting up a reward of fifty thousand dollars for information leading to the arrest of the Gainesville Slasher. By the Lord Harry, that will stir up the redneck boys and get them out on the road hunting for the murdering villain!"

"I could use some of that cash myself, Chief! What would you say to a weeks leave of absence while I run on up there and solve that Slasher case for them?" That was the wrong thing to say. The Chief abruptly returned to business.

"You've got yourself a week to come up with something on those two girls from the BVM Academy. You get out there and get me some results or you'll find yourself back on road patrol yanking pussycats out of trees and scooping up drunks off the sidewalks of this city. Do you read me loud and clear, boy?"

I read the Chief clear enough. I got to my feet, tossed the Porker a salute and headed for the Miami docks to see a man about a pair of virgins. You might say he was in the business.

The big yellow sign on the side of the stucco warehouse read: *FUAD'S EX-OTIC EXPORTS.* I pulled my white city issue Plymouth into an empty parking space and took a close look at the area. Heat of the day. No action.

I levered myself out of the car and walked up to what passed for a front door. The door said *ENTER* but when I tried to walk in I found that it was locked, an odd state of affairs for what purported to be a thriving business establishment in the heart of the dock district. I tried a hearty knock.

I was not surprised to see a dark eye appear behind a Judas hole. A voice growled, "Fuck off, asshole!"

My hand instinctively slipped into my waistband; I felt the comforting presence of the police positive .38 special against my palm.

"Vega set me!" I hissed toward the brown eye. "You haul ass and get that towel-head Fuad out here pronto or I'll have a search warrant down here in fifteen minutes and we'll take this dump apart plank by plank."

The Judas hole snapped closed. A minute later I heard the electronic snick of deadbolts being released. The front door opened and I was facing the corpulent owner of Exotic Imports, the Iraqi expatriate, Fuad Ramsak. He gave me a greasy smile. "Welcome, Excellency," he announced. I was gonna get the royal treatment, or maybe a knife in my back. That all remained to be seen.

"Detective Dan Kelly, Homicide and Vice. I'm here to ask you some questions and take a look around; what do you have to say about that, Ramsak?"

"Welcome, Excellency Kelly!" he repeated in a cordial tone; holding out his

arms as if to take me into a fraternal embrace. I'd be damned if I'd be seen hugging a sand nigger in downtown Miami, what would the guys in the squad room say if that story ever got around? I didn't want to find out.

I pushed past the towelhead. He stunk of garlic and spices. His face was greasy with the remnants of a lunch of roast mutton. "How can I be of service to you, Excellency Kelly?" The guy was so determined to cooperate, looked like Vega must have warned him about me ahead of time. That would smooth things out considerably.

"I'm looking for some young pussy, Fuad my friend. Do you think you can help me out with something like that here at Erotic – er, Exotic Exports?"

Fuad issued a hearty chuckle as if he'd heard that one before. "Yes, of course! Fuad has the very finest in young poosie for you, my dear friend… and also one or two little poosies for my dear friend Mr. Vega of the United States Customs Service. Will that fine gentleman be joining us for some afternoon delights?"

Unfortunately Vega wouldn't be joining us today. He was busy setting up a multi-million dollar cocaine import deal with a pair of cowboys from the Bogota Cartel. Flower vendors. Everybody likes pretty flowers and the good old U.S. of A. imports a lot of them from Colombia. There are other things that come in those flower boxes, but that's another story.

I said, "Vega's giving testimony in Federal Court today. He found a couple of twelve year old Mexican girls in the Captain's cabin on the Star of Norway with no papers. Stowaways, the captain said. The girls said white slavery. The girls said rape. So now the Captain is up for a life stretch in a Federal prison and the little bimbos are on their way back to Mexico. Now what do you make of that, Fuad?"

Fuad make an oily smacking sound with his lips and grinned lasciviously. "Young poosie, it is wonderful, is it not? But so much trouble when one brings it into port here in this country. Now in my own country…"

"Cut the bullshit, Fuad, I want to take a quick tour of what you have downstairs in your slave cages, and I want that tour right now before all that poosie is dropped through the floor into the bay by your partners. There's pressure on me from on high, and that means pressure on you down here. Shit slides downhill here, same as in Iraq; so let's get moving."

Fuad understood that it was a business visit and not a time for social niceties; he had the presence of mind to nod soberly and waddle away leaving a wake of garlic scented sweat. I drifted along behind him, remembering to keep my eyes wide open and one hand on my pistol. The warehouse look deserted, the air smelled dead.

Fuad spoke over his shoulder. "These young poosies, somebody in particular that you are having in your mind to seek out? My only desire is to please you, of course, Excellency Kelly."

"Yeah, Fuad, there's somebody in particular. Two somebodies in fact. A pair of would-be bimbolinas from the Blessed Virgin Mary Academy. White girls. Rich Daddies. Virgins. Put them out on the street and they don't know enough to wipe their own asses. The Bishop of Miami wants their hot little twats back in the convent. I'm thinking that the man is pissed off because they are his own private stock, if you get my drift?"

Fuad hissed with displeasure. "I know nothing of such young girls, Excellency. You must believe me. I am an honorable businessman. But two such virgins… they would indeed be most valuable; and would they also happen to be twins by the grace of Allah?"

"Not twins. Schoolmates. You've seen the BVM girls capering around the malls. Sleek, chic, sassy – full of romantic foolishness and crazy notions. They might even sign up for a trip of the ancient ruins of the middle east, sign documents in Arabic while under the influence of God only knows what kind of dope. You know how that works, don't you?"

Fuad sucked his teeth loudly. Grunted. We came to steel door with a brass lock. He took a big iron key from his pocket, slid it home and turned it.

As Fuad pushed open the door I was confronted with a scene from beyond my wildest fantasies. Old Fuad was doing well for himself. Allah or the Devil or whoever he was dealing with was sending him plenty of stock. Immediately to my right I saw a large steel cage that held over a dozen naked young girls – all well fed and well formed, but eyes glassy with a heaping helping of the drug of the day.

They lolled about indifferently on pillows and cots, with comic books and baskets of fruit strewn about the floor of the cage. A television screen flickered in one corner. Fuad paused and waved a plump hand toward the sultry group. "Here you see prime goods, Excellency Kelly! The very finest American girls ages twelve through seventeen, and every one a young woman fit for an emir's seraglio. These are my best stock. Do you see the ones here that you are seeking?"

I looked the girls over carefully, studying their delectable nude bodies, appreciating each and every line. I took out my photo and compared the fresh faces of the Academy girls to the nymphets draped on the pillows in rapturous languor. I couldn't make either one of my BVM chickies. "Are these the only girls you have, Fuad?" I asked.

The fat Iraqi slavemaster giggled. "You told me, Excellency, that you are searching for young virgins. These are surely not virgins. These are my best stock and not a virgin to be found in the entire lot. These are simply very lovely, clean and healthy girls, awaiting a sultan's pleasure. Yes, mine are all guaranteed AIDS-free and anxious to please a new master. Young women of this quality are not easy to come by, not even here in Miami, the center of all the lusts of the civilized world. Please, Excellency, can you tell me where I might acquire sixteen year old virgins in Miami? For this would indeed be very profitable for me…."

I realized that Fuad was serious and said, "You can get all the virgins you can carry away over at the Blessed Virgin Mary Academy. The place is crawling with them. The nuns give the girls some sort of an entrance physical and if the gals don't measure up as virgins then they don't let them in the front door. The problem is that if you go over there hunting them you'll have the Bishop of Miami breathing down your neck. Now what do you have here in the line of virgins? Round them up and run them past me so I can be on my way. I'm a busy man."

"Come with me." Fuad sighed, and took off walking. I brought up the rear keeping an eye peeled for trouble. He took me down a long corridor with naked women in cages arranged along each wall. Women of every size and shape and nationality. Some called out in foreign languages as we walked past. Yes, business was

booming but there did seem to be a curious overabundance. I decided to venture a comment to see where it would lead. "Business may be good, Fuad, but you seem to be overstocked. Have you been giving any thought to a half-price sale or something along those lines?" The fat Iraqi sighed again and stopped. I had apparently touched a sensitive nerve.

"The embargo in the Middle East is hurting me badly, Excellency. Warships of every nationality are now plying the Arabian Gulf, the Red Sea, the Mediterranean. My holding pens are filled to capacity, you can observe this fact for yourself. Yes, it is a problem."

Suddenly my nostrils picked up a familiar scent as my eyes picked up the sight of a tangled heap of naked female corpses piled near a trap door cut into the cement floor. I called to the bozo camel jockey to rein in and gestured toward the heap of dead bodies. "Are you taking up murder to eliminate the overabundance, Fuad?"

He shrugged.

I strolled over to the jumble of tangled limbs and knelt beside a blue-faced blonde wearing a knotted nylon stocking around her neck in a makeshift choker. I picked up her head by the long hair and glanced into her empty clouded eyes. "What do we have here, Fuad, a case of mass suicide?"

Fuad wrung his hands in obvious dismay. "Be careful, Excellency, those corpses are infected with the death plague. The AIDS. You could contract it from your proximity to those diseased women. Please, do be cautious."

The blonde's bloated tongue hung out of her mouth, drool glistening on the dead lips. She looked to be a ripe seventeen. I stood up and gave her a nudge with my toe. "This one looks like she was healthy enough, Fuad. She doesn't look sick at all but she sure as shit looks dead. You wouldn't by any chance be running a snuff film operation in this building, would you, fat boy? Maybe cutting in on Melina's Freak House action? Because if I find out that you are, I will see your fat ass fry in the state electric chair. Your license in this town does not include murder and I'm looking at a heap of dead pussy laying at my feet. What do you have to say for yourself?"

Sweat poured from the shaved pate of the slavemaster. He knew he was in trouble and he went to his knees in supplication, flab trembling. "Excellency, please hear me out. These girls come to me from the streets of many cities, and for every one hundred girls I purchase a certain percentage will be diseased. This cannot be helped! Those with the death plague are eliminated in the traditional manner of the harem. The silk cord or, as you see, the silk stocking is a worthy substitute. The girls do not mind. One must consider these women as spoiled fruit. Damaged goods. Surely you can understand that the rotten ones must be culled out and quickly disposed of before they infect the others. Our product is known around the world as being of top quality, and we must provide only the very best. What you see here before you, it is an average group. We test the blood. The situation becomes worse each day. The girls coming in from the large cities – New York, Chicago, St. Louis – seventy to ninety percent must die, and quickly. They are death bringers in pretty packages. Please, Excellency, take care as you handle that filth, it would grieve me to learn that you were unfortunate enough to contract the death plague at my humble establishment."

I let Fuad sweat on his knees while I pawed through the stinking corpse pile. Pretty packages indeed. The majority of them were nothing but worn-out sluts from the massage parlors of Times Square and Forty-Second Street sent south to be shunted into the canefield brothels near Belle Glade. The wide open whorehouses adjacent to the U.S. Sugar refineries were an open secret of the State. It was a situation where young white girls sucked black cock and were paid in heroin to do it. It was no wonder that Big Sugar had no problem recruiting cheap black labor from the ghettos of Miami and the slums of the Caribbean Islands.

I examined the jailhouse tattoos, the pimp brands, the needle tracks riding up the arms of the dead whores. Fuad was doing the city a service be getting rid of them, and took me only a minute to realize that he was getting rid of plenty of them. It was only early afternoon but in the fetid August heat the bodies were already beginning to swell, ripen and stink.

"I see some serious sanitary code violations here, Fuad. It sure ain't healthy to be leaving diseased cunt to rot out here in the open like this. You could get an epidemic going that would wipe out your entire stock, and then where would you be? These diseases could spread into the city; it would go bad for you if certain people were to find out about this outrage against the health laws of the community."

He was speechless. I eyed the kneeling old sodomite, watching him nervously lick his lips; I could sense the schemes whirling around under his towel. "What are you doing about corpse disposal, old man? Are you trucking this load of rotting meat out to the Kendall landfill, or what?"

"Allah forbid, Excellency! I would never condone such an outrage against the public safety. I have paid money to insure that a garbage scow comes in here after dark to carry this refuse out to sea. The sharks… they are very numerous off Miami, and they assist us in taking care of the problem. That is an acceptable solution, is it not, Excellency?"

I shot him a cruel look. "That's a Federal offense, Fuad. Pollution of the high seas. The Environmental Protection Agency handles those cases, I do believe. You've just confessed to dumping infected meat offshore for the sharks to eat. You have contaminated the fisheries of this country. That is a serious crime. You will be sent to a Federal pen for rehabilitation and from there you will be deported directly to Baghdad. I will see to it personally."

Fuad wailed. "What is a poor tradesman to do, your Highness?"

"This is serious business, Fuad; I have no choice but run your ass in. I cannot be expected to simply close my eyes to the contamination of our nation's coastal waters."

The obese Iraqi fell forward on his face and began to grovel at my feet. He groveled well, whimpering and licking my shoes. They *were* in need of a spit shine, so I let him lave the leather with his long pink tongue.

Finally he spoke, "Excellency, I beseech you in the name of Allah! Spare me this horrible disaster. This is the work of my entire life; surely there is some way that an accommodation can be reached? Is this not America, the wonderful land of opportunities where all things are possible?"

The old camel-fucker had a point. There were many possibilities indeed. I thought

of Mistress Melina and the operation out at Pradolini's Gator Farm. My mind clicked off some quick calculations. Pradolini was paying Melina thirty cents a pound for fresh meat on the hoof and twenty cents for the fresh frozen variety. The old mafioso and Mistress Melina had a fine working arrangement, and as a result the old capo's gators were fat and happy as any gators ever were. The hides were world-famous for their quality, and why not? Gators are immune the AIDS virus, so they thrived on their deluxe diet.

I caught the desperate fear in Fuad's eyes, cut my glance to the pile of putrefying flesh and said, "Fuad, I'm gonna give you a break... but you've got to stop murdering these poor, sick, helpless young girls. I'm going to arrange it so that you can send your castoffs over to the Hazelwood Institute where they can receive the medical attention and professional nursing care that they so desperately need. You won't have to be wringing any more necks or feeding any more sharks."

Fuad look up from his place on the floor with a curious look on his face. "Excellency, do you mean to say that I can just deliver the infected girls to this hospital and that will be the end of it for me?" I shrugged. "Praise Allah, that is the answer to my prayers!"

"Well, of course there will be a small charge of one hundred dollars per girl, with a minimum of ten girls to be delivered each day. The medical professionals out there at the Institute will do the rest. Nurse Nancy Blue is the lady in charge out there, and you can pay her. Cash. The hundred dollars will cover minimal processing expenses for the girls... and of course I will be expecting ten thousand dollars for making these extraordinary arrangements for you."

Fuad Ramsak lifted his teary eyes to mine and thanked me profusely. I smiled bleakly, "Police work is a public service in this country, Fuad; we do our best to serve the special needs of the community and the best interests of the taxpayers. It would serve no good purpose to have you sent to prison, when it is obvious that you are a fine American citizen who is ready to accommodate authority. Cooperation, that is what is best!"

The corpulent Iraqi got to his feet and dusted off his knees. "Allah be praised!" he howled. I let him howl. I liked the idea of that quick ten grand and he was more than eager to cough it up.

"Fuad, what would you say to tossing in another ten thousand for the chief? That way we could be sure that those missing person reports that we get on a lot of those girls find their way into that file where nobody ever looks." I smiled.

Fuad never broke his stride. "Of course, Excellency, of course! I have the money right in the business safe. It will be a pleasure to donate something for the good works of your chief." I smiled and nodded, and swore to myself that the Porker would never see a dime of it.

I was also looking forward to the delivery of almost four thousand infected whores per annum at one C-note each. That added up to a cool four hundred grand. The live delivery to Pradolini would come to another hundred and twenty thousand or so. I figured that a half a million was not a bad morning's work, even for Miami. The sharks would have to go back on a diet of fresh mullet.

"Now what about those virgins? Have you got any or not?"

"Well... I will show you."

The virgin's holding pen was a major disappointment. A single flaxen-haired twelve year old clutching a teddy bear ran to the bars of her cage as we approached. She was as naked as the other women except for a protective plastic chastity belt form-fitted to her cunnus. The girl spoke to me in a foreign tongue and smiled shyly.

"Finnish," Fuad reported, "A special order from the Emir of Kuwait. One hundred thousand golden dinars for this perfect treasure... and now, no Kuwait – thanks to that pig Saddam."

Fuad spoke to the girl in Arabic, fished a handful of chocolates from the folds of his robe, and passed them through the bars to her. She smiled delightfully and giggled, then fled to her cot and began to feed.

"You can chat with her in Esperanto if you know the language," Fuad said. I didn't know Esperanto or Finnish or Arabic. I felt foolish and uneducated but I could say "Up against the wall, Motherfucker" in seven languages including body language. But since I had twenty thousand dollars in my pocket and had just clinched a half million dollar a year deal, I didn't feel all that inadequate. There was more to life than linguistics. "She's a cutie, Fuad, but she's not the cutie that I'm interested in today." The old rogue sighed with relief.

Fuad gave me the grand tour. Let me search high and low, and when I was done with my search I believed that the slavemaster was on the level and the Academy girls would not be found in his establishment. It was another strikeout, putting me one day closer to the return to road patrol.

I pocketed the cash and declined the offer of hospitality and green tea. I told Fuad to keep me informed on his stock of virgins, if any choice ones came in, and I'd be on my way.

I left him the engraved business card of Nurse Nancy, Mistress Melina's administrative assistant out at the Hazelwood Institute for Social Research. Nurse Nancy was all pro, I assured him. She'd give the patients tender loving care right up to the very end.

I was depressed as I walked into my digs at the Everglades Towers Condominium but when I heard what Crystal had to say I perked right up. The little minx came running up to me wearing only a skimpy bra and panty set and waving her latest copy of *Shocking Crime*. The byline was StarGlow Stuart's; the screamer headline howled: *Coeds Butchered; Thousands Flee in Terror.* A sidebar announced: *50 Thousand Dollar Reward for Clues.*

Crystal jumped up and down in merriment yelling, "We're rich, Dan! We're rich!" Crystal loved the role. Probably practiced it in front of the mirror while I was at work.

"How did we get so rich, pussycat?" I asked.

She looked at me as if I were a brainless dog. Then she smiled playfully and said, "Because we know who the Gainesville Slasher is, silly."

I blinked. "We do? Who is it?"

"It's that guy... you know, what's-his-name? The one you were chasing all over the state that time and I was going crazy with worry? The one who cut up all the girls? Slit their bellies and hung them up by their heels in the woods and cut off

their heads? You know, Dan! The one where you had to go up to Starke and see that writer who is the serial killer expert. Remember? He who told you about the guy they call the Butcher! It's him! It's the Butcher! I just know it is!" Crystal squealed and capered around the living room swinging the tabloid and doing a little dance. She could be a real nut.

As I remembered the Butcher case, I also remembered the StarGlow Stuart story that had followed it in the Exposé Galaxy rag *True Crime Classics*. StarGlow's headline was not complimentary. It read *Butcher Madman Foils Miami's Dark Prince*. The prose written by the tabloid queen told of my trek across the state, always one step behind the desperate killer who slashed the heads from young girls and wallowed in their hot guts.

The Butcher had escaped into the trackless wastes of the Steinhatchee Swamp after committing another ghastly rape and murder along Alligator Alley. I knew that one day the Butcher would be back seeking the blood of new victims. Crystal had a good point, maybe the Butcher *had* returned!

I chased Crystal down and snatched away her tabloid. I read the StarGlow story about the maniac that she had billed as the Gainesville Slasher. The M.O. was pure Butcher; I wondered if StarGlow had figured out the connection. The prospect of a quick fifty grand propelled me toward the telephone. I dialed the number given in the reward story. A dulcet female voice answered on the third ring. "Slasher hotline. Cathy speaking. May I help you?"

I told the telephone girlie just how she could help me. "I read about the reward for information on the Gainesville Slasher. I'm calling to collect it. Who do I have to discuss it with?"

The tolerant voice of Miss Chatty Cathy said, "If you know who the killer is, sir, simply give me the name and address where he is located and we will send a squad car out immediately to pick him up."

"I know who it is doing the killings. I wouldn't be wasting my time calling you if I wasn't sure. I want you to make sure that I am awarded the money. That I'm not cheated. I know how you media people operate."

"I understand your concern, sir. Tell me who it is and leave me your name and address and the money will be sent to you in due course."

"I want to talk to the honcho, the man in charge of this operation. Put me through to your supervisor immediately before I have you arrested for impeding a police investigation."

I heard a sigh, a click and a whir; then a mechanical voice came onto the line and said, "Thank you for calling the Slasher Hotline. Please leave the name and present location of the killer along with any important details about the crimes. Be sure to include your name and address so that the reward may be sent to you upon the arrest of the killer. A certified police detective will be contacting you soon."

I looked at the telephone in disgust. What sort of Mickey Mouse operation were they running up there in Gainesville anyway? I hung up. It was obvious that the Slasher Hotline was for armchair detectives and hopeless nut cases, little old ladies with visions of boogeymen under the bed. It was about what one would expect from a crime tabloid hotline.

I put in a call to the Gainesville Police Department and asked to speak to their

resident Slasher expert, Lt. Sadie Fennel. Sadie recognized my name from the detective magazines and deigned to speak to me in person; it wasn't every day that she could talk to a celebrity detective from Miami and she probably wanted to make the most of it.

"Dirty Dan Kelly! What a nice surprise! What in the world has prompted you to call all the way up here to our little police department?"

This Sadie Fennel was some smooth-talking broad, it was no surprise to me that she had wormed her way into some cushy public relations slot. "Listen up, Sadie, I have a line on the Slasher. Just picked up on it from a confidential informant." I looked over my shoulder and watched Crystal beam and preen.

"Dan, that's wonderful. Do you truly have a line on the Slasher or do you think your confidential informant is just another bozo trying to get their hands on that reward?"

"No bozo, Sadie. Not this time. Is it as bad as the papers say up there?"

"This town has gone bananas. People are running around forming posses, they're out there buying guns and anti-slasher devices; coeds are fleeing the area by the thousands. The media has everyone quaking with terror. It's good that people are staying alert but we could use some help. Can you give me a name and address for the killer?"

I glanced over at Crystal and shot her a grin. "Yeah Sadie, I've got a solid line on your Slasher, but tell me, what's the poop on the reward?"

Sadie Fennel clucked her tongue at me over the miles. "Dan, think of the public safety first. The rewards will all follow in good time. We are really in a jam up here, young girls are being murdered almost hourly and the killer is slicing off their heads... and molesting their other parts."

"Listen up, Sadie. Fuck you and your jams way up there in Ivory Tower Town. I'm in a wad of jams every day down here in Miami. You can't believe the jams that I get into... purloined corpses, missing virgins, fly-blown hookers and that screaming faggot Beau Morris mincing all over my city running after the Sex Beasts. You think you got problems? I get chopped coed for breakfast down here two or three times any given month. So what do you think about that?"

"We're just a small town, Dan. We've got small town problems. Date rape, panty raids, peeping toms and the occasional traffic ticket thrown in to keep me hopping. Nobody up here knows the first thing about catching a Slasher; our homicide bureau couldn't catch a cold on a wet day in January. I wish you'd come up here and help us; I'll make it worth your while; I'll owe you a big one!"

"Fifty big ones and your ass, Fennel. That's what I want!"

"My ass! What?! Kelly, you can't be serious!"

"As a heart attack in deep water, lady. You can put the fifty G's in an escrow account pending an arrest. The ass will be on call at my convenience."

"I've heard about what a lousy bastard you are, Kelly, and this certainly confirms it. The detective magazines are full of your rotten exploits and I've read about them all. I remember what you did to the poor misguided child, Janice Irwin."

"What was it that you heard, Sadie?"

"That you arrested her illegally and then cut the poor girl a deal that got her an

appointment with the Delaware hangman. And as if that wasn't enough, then you took a fourteen year old female juvenile delinquent up to the Delaware women's penitentiary to watch Janice Irwin dance. That's disgusting!"

"You ought not to dwell on the sordid side of life, Sadie. The JD needed some visions of what a future in crime can do for a lady... besides, she is a chickie who likes to watch. She'd go watch anything unusual; last week she asked me to take her to a traveling freak show to see a two-headed calf. Now she's been calling the squad room and asking me to take her up to Starke to watch the Black Widow fry on Old Sparky. The kid's a real comer."

"You're insane, Kelly; that's the most disgusting thing I've ever heard!"

"That's the same thing Pauline Tilly said about *Killer Fiction*. I don't know, I sort of liked it – reminded me of your so-called Gainesville Slasher."

I heard Sadie Fennel gasp. "Who told you about that? It's secret information! How could you know about the *Killer Fiction* connection unless you talked to the killer or unless... oh my God, I can't believe it!"

I heard Fennel screaming into the receiver. The stress was catching up to her. "What are you shrieking about, Fennel? Get control of yourself; explain this *Killer Fiction* connection business to me right now."

"How did you get ahold of that book, Kelly?"

"Our department has a copy we've been passing around. I heard they were using it at the FBI Academy too. As a text."

Sadie Fennel sobbed into the telephone receiver. "It's required reading for the Murder 101 course at the University. Or at least it was until this broke out. Those books are disgusting and pornographic, just like Pauline Tilly said! And decent citizens are going to rise up and do something about it or I'll turn in my badge!"

"This is America, Sadie. You can't stop a book from being published."

"This book is different! That killer tore pages out of it and laid them on the gutted corpses of the girls. The Slasher is copycatting the crimes in that awful book. A task force is drawing up murder charges against the author right now. It's all his fault! We're going to see him burn. You'll see."

Sadie Fennel's revelations convinced me that the Butcher had returned, this time known as the Gainesville Slasher. "Everybody knows that GJ Schaefer is a world-class pervert, but you can't charge a man with murder for writing dirty stories! Get real, Fennel!"

Sadie screamed into the phone. "We can and we will! These murders are all Schaefer's fault. He put them in his book and now they have come to life. A homicidal maniac got ahold of it and now look at what happened. Everyone is upset. Rush week at the university is ruined. The entire economy of Gainesville is a mess and it's all because of that beast Schaefer and his horrible book!"

"Hey, the funeral directors will be making out. Look to the bright side."

"What! What? That's disgusting! You call yourself a police officer? I can't believe you would say that!"

"I deal in realities, kid. Now how about the fifty grand? Do we have a deal or not?" I listened to the sobs of the flustered police hen trying to get her tattered emotions under control.

She growled like a cat preparing to deal the death blow to a worn out mouse.

"There is no reward. We just put that information into the tabloid so that people would call up and give us information. It's perfectly ethical. A legitimate law enforcement tool. We've got a lot of leads already. An arrest is eminent. We have suspects... more than one if you really must know...." Her voice trailed off in a hopeless whine.

"Call me when you get the cash lined up," I said, and hung up. I turned to Crystal. "Let that be a lesson to you, babes, never trust a damned cop. They lie. You can never believe a thing they say, especially when money is involved."

Crystal looked forlorn; flopped down on the sofa and began thumbing through *Shocking Romance*, another Exposé Galaxy tabloid.

I peered over her shoulder and eyed the story headline. It read: *Romeo Lawyer Steals Client's Wife; Killer Screams Frame-up!*

I chuckled. "I shouldn't be letting you fill your innocent mind with all that lurid trash, honey. Those tabloid writers make up those stories to sell their stupid magazines. That story you're reading there is a good example. It gives a girl like yourself a distorted sense of reality and God knows I've been trying to keep your feet on the ground and teach you what is going on in the city and the world."

Crystal grunted. She kept reading.

"You know, Crystal, the Bar Association would never allow a lawyer to violate legal ethics by marrying a client's wife after representing him in a trial. It's called a conflict of interest, moral leprosy and a few other things. Decent people would never tolerate it going on in their community."

Crystal huffed and snorted. "Dan, this story was written by StarGlow Stuart! She's my very most fave writer and I'm her number one fan. She'd never lie! And this story is so *romantic!* Listen. This poor young girl was married to a depraved cultist who was a corpse molester, but the police caught up with him and arrested him with human body parts under his bed. The defense lawyer says he had a hopeless case because all the details of the murders and this other gross stuff was written down in his diary and hidden in a closet, but the cops found that too. The lawyer really did try hard to defend him because he felt sorry for the beautiful young girl who was under the evil spell of the sex ghoul. Then during the trial the lawyer and the young girl fell in love. The jury convicted the villain and the judge him sent to prison forever. The evil spell was broken and the lawyer married the girl and they lived happily ever after! But now the ghoul is claiming that the lawyer framed him because the lawyer was after his wife. Isn't that interesting? I love to read these true romances!"

"It's all media bullshit, Kid. It damn sure doesn't happen that way in real life. There are ethical safeguards against it. If it really happened the way that nut case StarGlow has it written, then that lawyer and his bimbo would be out on the street collecting tin cans for recycling. That's the way it happens in real life, and don't you be forgetting it, Missy."

"How can they have safeguards against true love, Dan?"

I had to admit that I didn't have the answer for that one so I let it slide. I just stroked the chestnut tresses of the panting teenage romantic avidly scanning the doings of the lustful lawyer and his little princess. I imagined StarGlow creeping through the newspaper morgues; slashing away at genteel reputations with her

pen; whirling through the public records and probing into private secrets with her customary elán.

I remembered how her pink lace panties peeked out from under her Oleg Cassini suit as she sprawled unconscious on the carpet outside my front door, a delirious vision. And then this light bulb blinked on inside my head.

I walked over to the telephone, leaving Crystal to sigh over her silly romance stories. I dialed direct to Exposé Galaxy's central offices in Atlanta. I gave their operator the number of StarGlow's extension and she patched me through. StarGlow picked up her phone on the first ring. A plus for her. "Dark Prince here," I announced.

StarGlow squealed with obvious delight at the sound of my voice. "Dirty Dan, you old android, what have you found out for me today?"

"The identity of the Gainesville Slasher."

I heard the telephone fall to the floor as StarGlow toppled off her chair in a dead faint. The Exposé Galaxy paid well for their exclusives and I had a particular reputation for reliability with Mistress StarGlow. I made her an offer that she and her publishers couldn't refuse – not only would StarGlow have the exclusive identity of the Gainesville Slasher.

I would also use my considerable influence with Pauline Tilly to get the Queen of the Exposé Galaxy a rare and much coveted interview with GJ Schaefer, the reclusive author of *Killer Fiction,* who claimed to have crucial inside information on the moldering bones of little Adam Walsh, whose severed head had been found floating in a South Florida canal… information he had obtained from his cellmate, the arch-fiend Ottis Toole, whose granny brought him up to be the Devil's Child, and who joined Henry Lee Lucas on his nonstop killing spree. Who knows what else Schaefer might tell us?

There were arrangements to be made, people to lean on, and markers to be collected. And of course I'd have to pay another call on Schaefer. But for fifty grand I'd do it all quickly and well.

The check was Fedexed to me the next morning. StarGlow was ecstatic; Sadie Fennel was livid.

And the Butcher was gone – he must have fled Gainesville for his lair in the impenetrable Florida swamps. No doubt he would soon emerge again to terrorize the citizenry – severing heads, clipping nipples and emptying the viscera of slaughtered coeds onto the shag carpet.

Where would the slobbering maniac strike next? It was anybody's guess and every cop in the state was in the game. I hoped it would be Miami. I had a score to settle with the Butcher, and his ass was going to be mine, all mine.

"IT MAY BE THE GREATEST CRIME IN U.S. HISTORY"

A TRAIL OF BUTCHERED GIRLS

In a suspect's quarters police uncovered manuscripts detailing sex torture fantasies which may reveal over a score of victims

MEET THE SEX BEAST

In a suspect's quarters police uncovered manuscripts detailing sex torture fantasies which may reveal over a score of victims

MARTIN COUNTY, FLA. JUNE 25, 1973

Authorities claim:

Crazed killer's book tells how to commit murder!

It's only fiction, says author

SHERIFF'S OFFICE
MARTIN COUNTY, FLA.
4919 5-19 73

CHILLING CHAPTERS
FROM THE 'SEX BEAST' COP

SHERIFF SHAEFER,
DOING TWO LIFE
SENTENCES,
WRITES REALISTIC
RIPPER TALES

The Stuart News

Lurid tales a script for death?

The Palm Beach Post

Killer's book: Fiction or 'how-to'?

Ex-Martin deputy calls novel a product: 'It's not me'

TRAIL OF BUTCHERED GIRLS

"Find that fucking Butcher!" Chief Pork Shepherd screamed in Detective Dan Kelly's face.

Dan answered quickly, "Right, Chief."

"Do you have a line on the Butcher or not?"

"I've got a line on him, all right, Chief," Dan replied. "I'm on my way to Starke to visit the Florida State Prison. I'll have this case cracked soon."

"If you don't come back with the name of the Butcher, don't come back at all," Shepherd screamed, "Do you hear me, Kelly? Get out! Get out of my goddamn office!" Dan turned on his heel, closing the door behind him.

The Chief was having a bad day. Another couple of kids had been found slashed to death out at the University of Miami, and it had him upset. Reporters from the *Miami Herald* were asking questions he couldn't answer, and their bullshit detectors were flashing like Geiger counters at the core of an atomic power plant. It was enough to give the Chief ulcers. Dan sympathized. He hitched up his trousers and started pounding the pavement. He was on the trail of the butchered girls.

The Butcher liked to cut up women with a big fucking knife. Dan was going to find him and bring him in. He barreled out of the parking lot, and headed for the Florida state turnpike for the long haul north to the bleak prison known as the home of the most dangerous homicidal maniacs in the nation. There was only one man in the state who could I.D. the Butcher, and he intended to weasel that information out of him… one way or another.

Speeding along the turnpike, Dan made a mental effort to inject himself into the increasingly demented fantasies of the Butcher. Abandoning his own rapacious, greed-motivated personality for a moment, Dan felt reality sliding away as he descended into the psychic pit of black madness, the deadly nightmare that was the mind of the Butcher.

The Butcher had a name somewhere, and a face. He also had an insatiable hunger that swelled up and exploded like a festering boil spewing pestilential murder across the face of South Florida. Already there were over twenty gutted whores in Wilton Manors, just south of Oakland Park.

That name brought to mind the infamous Sex Beast case. This was the infamous campus Romeo in the sixties who lured young and innocent virgins away from their mothers, and introduced them to unspeakable acts of sexual depravity. Dan would never forget the impassioned letter from one of the maniac's traumatized victims, a plea for the capture of the Sex Beast. The terrorized ex-virgin had written, "Oh, my God! His dick was *HUGE*! And his stamina!" The list of victims had mounted to well over twenty in the Oakland Park area alone.

Detective Dan Kelly sat in the interview room of the Florida State Prison and looked into the blazing violescent eyes of the man alleged to be the greatest killer of women in the United States of America.

He felt the sweat break out on his back and soak his shirt. The sweat was from fear and from guilt. Fear, because the man across from him might very well jump

across the table and rip out his throat with his teeth. He had every reason to want to do so. Dan knew this for a fact, and that is where the guilt came in.

Dan was looking into the accusing eyes of a man framed for murder sixteen years ago, Gerard John Schaefer. Dan licked his lips and started in.

"Howya doin', John?"

"Fuck you, you stinking son of a bitch!" Schaefer responded with feeling.

"I came up here because I need your help."

"I've heard that line before, Kelly," Schaefer laughed. "I heard it when you wanted to put Allen Darrah in the chair for home invasion murders in Orlando. I heard it when you wanted to smash the international kiddie-porn ring run by Mervyn Cross. I heard it when you wanted a detailed, signed confession to the Adam Walsh murder from Ottis Toole. I've heard it time and again, and frankly, I don't give a damn."

Dan squirmed under the lashing. It was all true. Schaefer had solved the Orlando murders; he had destroyed an international kiddie-porn ring, and he had convinced Toole to give a detailed confession. Dan remembered how he almost vomited as he read the details of how the boy had been kidnapped, sodomized, murdered, and his corpse eaten by the man who called himself the Devil's Child.

"Look, I know you got framed," said Dan, "but what can I do about it? It was out of my jurisdiction."

"So what are you going to do for me this time?"

Kelly shrugged. "I ought to be able to get you some contact visits with StarGlow Stuart."

Schaefer leaned forward and lowered his voice. "Dan, Dan… sixteen *years*. I'm a big fan of the boys now, you know. Women don't have a thing I need."

Dan didn't know if Schaefer was pulling his leg or straightening him out about his bizarre sex life. It was always hard to tell.

"Well, what do you want?"

"I want a corrupt cop arrested."

"For what?"

"For aiding and abetting a felony."

"Oh yeah? What's his name?"

"Rick Mack, up in St. Lucie County."

"So what's your beef with him?"

"Rick Baby is as corrupt as a cop can be. A two-faced, ass-licking toady of whoever pays his bills."

"So tell me something I don't know."

"A couple of years ago I had a line on a fugitive from justice who used to sit on the Florida Supreme Court. Using my underworld contacts, I was able to contact him. I offered a deal to Mack. Deliver him to wherever Rick wanted him. Wanted some play as to witness protection and parole. But it didn't work out that way."

"Rick drop the ball or what?"

"Rick's boss pulled him off the case before we got going. Instead of going after the ex-judge fugitive, they told Rick to hang a couple of drug murders on me in retaliation for my snoopiness."

"Who were they?" asked Kelly with real interest.

"Couple of would-be dope dealers from Iowa that came down to St. Lucie County to buy some marijuana. Saved up a load of cash for a nice tidy buy. Rolled up and found a seller who was with a gang of cowboys. The two ladies were fed a load of buckshot by a dude name of Hacksaw. Now Rick Mack tries to sell the idea that I offed the dope-dealing bitches."

"That wouldn't be Goodenough and Wilcox, would it?"

"That's it."

"How do you know they were dopers?"

"A cop who was sympathetic to me ran them through the computer and found a sheet for drugs. Rick Mack tries to say they were little prom queens on a tourist junket who were massacred by the Butcher."

"Well, I know *you* ain't the Butcher anyway."

"Do you? How so?"

"Because the Butcher carved a couple of teenage girls down in Lauderdale just a couple of nights ago. That's what I came up here to talk to you about."

"I've got a pretty solid alibi, Dan. Don't try to pin that one on me too. Every fucking time a bone is found in the state of Florida, they start screaming my name."

"Look, John, I'll take a swing past this Rick character. Promise. I want a name from you, that's all. Just a name. I'll give you the facts. You give me a name to go with them. OK? Deal?"

"So we're all set on Rick Mack?"

"No problem. Cop's honor," Kelly swore, raising his right hand with a nod.

Schaefer gave a mirthless laugh and said, "Run it past me, Danno." His voice was cold as penitentiary steel.

Kelly suppressed a shiver and said, "This guy I'm looking for calls himself Jerry. Worked at a packing plant and came from the Rock. I figured that was Raiford prison. Huge guy, looks like Hoss Cartwright on TV. That's all I've got."

Schaefer looked at his gold Patek Philippe watch. "It's 3:00 P.M., Kelly. I want your ass back here at midnight. I'll let you know then if I can get you a name."

Dan got up and left.

The new moon cast a faint, eerie glow over the fields surrounding the Florida State Prison. It was 11:30 P.M. Dan stood at the main gate and listened to the inhuman howling floating across the bleak landscape with the moonlight. He was awed; never in his life had he heard anything like it. He turned to the fat, slack-lipped gate guard and asked, "What's all that screaming about?"

The gate guard spat a stream of tobacco juice and speculated on the nature of convicts. "Them's the screams of the condemned to death. They do holler a tad, I admit that. Decent folk drive past and they hear that noise and wonder, and then they forget it. Ain't no money in recollecting it."

"Must be the niggers doing it."

"Some say it's the niggers, but I've been on this gate for 21 years, and it ain't no racial matter a'tall. Them that howl are the living dead. Them howls have a certain tone to 'em and if you study on it, you can pick up the notes. You catch that deep bellow? That's your nigger howl there. The higher-pitched ones? That's the white."

Dan was bemused. "That one there sure sounded like a woman."

"Them high-squealers is the queens." The guard spat again, and the tobacco juice dribbled down his chin, staining his police shirt with the shiny badge. "True, that one did sound a bit like a woman. But ain't no real women in there now, though, not at the moment."

"At the moment?"

"Oh, we get 'em now and then. We kill 'em here. Them as is condemned for death by law. Can you see that building stuck out a bit there in the dark?"

Dan squinted, nodded.

"Well, that's where we kill 'em. Death chamber's in there. We got over 300 men in there waiting. That's them howling. Women, they are more on the order of shriekers and squealers. The bucks, they bellow."

"Is it always this bad?"

"Oh, it's a study on a warm night. The full moon stirs 'em up. You won't find no sane person in there. All raving murderous maniacs. It's a wonder the citizens tolerate it. Ought to execute the lot of 'em. My preacher was saying so at meeting only this past Sunday."

"You ever hear of Schaefer?" Dan ventured.

"Schaefer, sure," The guard laughed. "I read all about him in my detective magazines. Some correctional officers read pornographic trash like *Playboy* or *Penthouse* that show them naked

State Investigator Rick McIlwain says Schaefer had "the coldest eyes I've ever seen," and regrets charges could not be brought on the murders of Wilcox and Goodenough, whose ID and personal possessions Schaefer kept. "I believe his accounts are accurate depictions of what he did to his victims. He's writing about the crimes he carried out."

women. Not me. I read magazines that will help me in my work, like *Shocking Detective* and the new one, *Serial Killers.* I like to read them stories by StarGlow Stuart."

"Yeah, she's pretty good. Friend of mine."

"Really? She as good looking as her pictures?"

"Better, matter of fact. But what about Schaefer?"

"I do recollect when Schaefer was in every detective magazine in the country. Made the cover on most of 'em. There was pictures of his victims. The one I recall best was a pretty girl he hung up. Showed her photo. Flies crawling on her. Said he hung her up to die. Odd way to do a murder, I thought then; I still do."

"I remember that case," Kelly nodded. "That was in my jurisdiction."

"Then there was that business about him eating them young girls. Fried them in a skillet, I reckon. Purty little young-uns. Peggy and Wendy, I believe was the names. Gutted 'em like little piglets. Claimed they were right tasty too."

"They said that in the magazine?"

"Them detective books ain't gonna print no lies, now." The guard pulled a long face. "They'd get sued for libel if they did, wouldn't they?"

"Fuck if I know. I ain't no lawyer, but what about Schaefer?"

"Can't say that Schaefer is a bad sort. A bit of a jailhouse lawyer, calls himself the historian of the chain gang. Says he writes books, but he's probably lying."

Dan glanced at his twelve-dollar Timex. "I'd better get on in there and see him."

"You're cleared."

"Why did you have me come down here at midnight?" Dan asked the glowering convict. "It wasn't exactly easy to get clearance."

"I told you to come at midnight because now the Unit is on lock-down. The rats can't see us up here talking."

"So did you find out anything?"

"I'll talk, you listen."

So Dan sat listened as the convict told him the score.

"The name of the Butcher is Jerry Michael Squires. Guy's a dead ringer for Hoss Cartwright, and he has a bad attitude about whores, due to the clap he got from one years ago. He pulled 16 years on a murder rap he claims he didn't commit. He worked the packing plant killing floor at the Rock. He cut the head off a newcock name of Wilson who was put in a 20-man cell that was full. Swede Rankin was the cell boss. He took the heat, but Squires cut off the kid's head and pushed it out the bean hole. Squires is married to a pussy boy name of Ray Donato, a Cuban punk out of Tampa."

"So he hit Gainesville and Miami. You think he's headed for Tampa?"

"He was heading for Tampa when he got out. But his main job, the one he talks about the most, is to kidnap Christine Evert, the tennis girl. He said he's gonna kidnap her, ask for five million dollars ransom, and cut little hunks out of her and mail them in to Andy Mills until he pays up."

"Chris Evert is at the Polo Club in Boca. Maybe Squires is headed that way."

"That's what the snitches tell me. Could be true, could be bullshit. Willie the Weasel sent him to see two French experts from his string, and the whores ain't wrote him since. Willie wants his money. If Squires got near those whores, they're probably diced meat by now. Jerry always carries a blade in his right boot. It's his trademark."

"That was your trademark, too, wasn't it, John?"

Schaefer stood up. "This interview is over. Now get out of my prison."

"Your prison?" Dirty Dan was dumbfounded. "What are you talking about?"

"It's like this, Danno. This is a public institution, paid for by taxpayers, run by public servants, I'm the taxpayer, you're the public servant, I'm the public, you serve me. You are the one who comes slinking in here asking favors. I live here. This is my home. And I want you to get the fuck out. Now."

There was no arguing with the logic of the man with the blazing eyes said to be the top killer in the country. Schaefer spat on the polished floor as he watched Dirty Dan leave, then called for the shiteater to walk him back to his cell.

It was a new moon, but the howlers were going at it full tilt. You'd think the moon was full.

STARKE STORIES

MY TICKET TO THE SOCIETY OF FIENDS

The story in the *Palm Beach Post* on May 13, 1973 was about six pages long. The whole paper was practically devoted to it. That was the story Ted Bundy saw.

So he comes up to me and says, "I saw your face on the front page. I read the story." Turns out I am a *hero* to Bundy. You cannot imagine how I felt having the famous fiend in awe of me. But I *was* billed at one time on the front pages of newspapers and detective magazines as "The Greatest Mass Murderer of Women This Century," and that is no small statement. It's a real good ticket into the Society of Fiends.

But I don't brag. People say, "There's the great mass murderer," and I smile and say, "Oh, you read the papers, huh?"

He'd heard about the death diary that I was supposed to have kept. The thing is a myth made up by the state's attorney, but Ted believed it existed, so I'd tell him, "Oh yeah, that. Well, I never could keep track unless I kept a record and photos. The cops got over a hundred photos plus the diary." This would really get his interest.

My problem with Bundy, if you could call it a problem, was that he had a certain fascination with my own case. Any time I get questions about Bundy, I try to dodge them because I don't want people to say I'm telling tales which cannot be checked for verity. But essentially what the connection amounted to was that he wanted to outscore me. He had been reading everything he could get his hands on about me — most of which was complete nonsense. He was enchanted by all that, absolutely fascinated. He believed it all without question, and every time we'd be around together in a one-on-one situation, he'd be asking me for details on memorable kills… and then he'd tell me details about his own adventures.

One of Ted's first questions to me was about the number of victims I was al-

leged to have. He came right out and asked me about it — a very declassé move in here — and what could I say? My score is zero? I let him know in no uncertain terms that he was small time by comparison to me. He was really deflated but then he was in awe of me. Big smile every time I saw him.

I played it just a little aloof. I told him I had 34 kills confirmed in the media, and he said he had more confirmed than that. Then I'd go, "Yeah, but I worked three continents, plus a few trips to Canada."

And he'd go, "So you have some unconfirmed." And I'd go, "Private grave-yards, you've seen it all in print. You've heard about them."

Ted: Yeah, but how many would you say?
Me: You think I count them up on a tally card?
Ted: I was wondering who got the most.
Me: You and the FBI, Pal.
Ted: Gimme a round figure.
Me: OK. Figure I'm working this deal since 1963 and my last confirmed job was in 1973, so that's ten active years. I had me a nice sporty little boat. Cute little tourist girl hops in. Run her back in the mangroves and in less than two minutes she's got a mooring line tied around her neck, flopping on the deck like a flounder and peeing in her sunsuit. Mess around a little, then run her off shore and deep six her with a cinder block around her ankles.
Ted: *(Nods knowingly.)*
Me: Figure 28 confirmed kills in South Florida alone, plus my collection of heads.
Ted: Heads?
Me: Right. You obviously read about that.
Ted: I think I did.
Me: Well, first I started out with a little memento, like a ring or earring or brace-let. Cops got over a hundred pieces, so what does that indicate? They also got my photo collection, maybe 40 or 50 women, same as Glatman. Take her out in the woods, peel her down, photograph her, mess around, then *do* her. Of course, I always *did* them first, *then* took pictures. Confirmed. Then that gets old, so I decided to save heads. Why not? Bela Kiss put his girls in drums of alcohol, Hoess collected their panties. He had *boxes* of panties. Some even had little tags with the owner's name on it. A panty freak.
Ted: Hoess? *(Ted didn't know about Hoess.)*
Me: Yeah, but he was *official*. Not like us. So I figured I'd try heads. Collected two real nice ones up in West Virginia. College Cunt. Know what I mean? But they'd get wormy and smell.
Ted: *(Nods.)*
Me: So I just believe the cops when they say I'm the best this century. Green River, he's making a run on me but he's locked into hookers. Zodiac seems to have dropped out. You were good, Ted, but unless you can go over a hundred — *well* over a hundred — you're not in my league.
Ted: Yeah, well, I appreciate you telling me, Jerry.

Ted was very concerned with being a great killer. I'd take him down a notch by

talking to him like in this dialogue. It's fairly accurate in a basic way, but there was more sniffing around the issues than I wrote.

Bundy was always 100% respectful of me. I treated him as a supplicant, while others were hanging on his every word. He told me he had tried to copy my kills that he'd read about in crime tabloids. One tabloid ran a photo of a blonde and a brunette I'd allegedly killed, and so he tried to do a copycat. That would have been around July, 1973. He went out to some park in Washington and grabbed him a long-haired blonde like Susan Place, the victim he saw in the tabloid. He caught her in the morning and killed her, then went back in the afternoon and hunted a brunette in a black bikini to copycat Georgia Jessup, who was shown in an alluring black swimsuit. He selected the one he wanted and waited for her to go to the restroom, and then caught her on the way to the toilet. He took her where he killed the first girl and strangled her too. When he got the cord around her neck and pulled it taut she went off like a rocket. He told me that he'd put the seat of the VW as far forward as possible so the woman's knees would be jammed up under the dash. A large woman would be so cramped she couldn't move, but this one gal was on the small side and as soon as he yanked the cord she popped up and was half over the back seat. Her legs weren't tied and she was kicking so hard Ted thought she was going to kick out the windscreen. After that he'd tie the ankles, shove the seat full forward, then get in the back and get down to business.

He was annoyed that she crapped when he strangled her, and said he should have grabbed her coming out of the restroom instead of on her way to it. I used Ted's story about that kill when I described Cattle Kate in my story "Whores."

Both the women figured he had rape in mind. The blonde was some sort of social worker who promised she'd *help him* if he'd let her go. The brunette was sobbing and begging to be let go because of her widowed mother or something. Ted killed both on the same day, and he told me they were chosen because they looked like Place and Jessup.

He was simply trying to impress me with his various kills. I paid attention because it was fascinating to me what he had to say. I think a lot of people were fascinated by what he said, and I'm sure that the police are not revealing everything he told them. I'd make up a story and tell him, and then he'd tell me stuff like how he carried on with the dead women in Washington. He'd pretty them up with fresh make-up before the ghouling began.

He wasn't familiar with the basic chemistry of human putrefaction. I'd been a hunter, so I know how to prevent spoilage of meat in the field. I'd listen to him whine about how a girl would turn rotten on him so fast, then I'd clue him in on how to keep her fresh as long as possible. I told him to string the girl up by the ankles and cut off her head to exsanguinate her. Blood rots fast, and so do brains. So it's best to cut off the head and drain the blood. He wanted to know what I'd do with the head, and I said I'd put it on a stick so she could watch me make love to her body. He'd almost come in his shorts listening to this stuff.

Ted enjoyed killing women and experimented with different types of strangulation. He'd tie a cord around the captive's neck and then slip a length of doweling rod under the cord and begin to turn it slowly until the victim was strangled to death. He could control the pressure and would squeeze the windpipe closed, take the victim to the verge of death, then release the pressure. What I found most

interesting was his observation that when he would do this the victim's eyes would become glassy and vacant. She would be alive and breathing, but the life force would somehow be gone. As if there was a body but lacking a soul. I figured it was simply a catatonic reaction, but Ted liked to think he had an animated corpse to play with. He progressed to a point where he would kill the woman while he was fucking her. He told me that the Leach girl, who was twelve or thirteen years old, couldn't take his cock so he rolled her over face down and went up her butt with his dick while strangling her with a belt.

Ted was very sexually perverse. No way you could tell him that the lady didn't get off on having her neck wrung, because he'd tell you that the girls he strangled would have juicy slick panties when he finished with them. I knew it was bullshit because from reading commission reports on capital punishment, I learned that either gender will orgasm when executed by strangulation, and it's simply brain dysfunction, not a pleasure response.

All the years we were here together I probably only talked to him a total of ten to twelve hours, but he'd tell me stuff he would never tell other people — like about his car. We both had VW bugs and he wanted to know if I ever did any killing in my car, because he said the girls would always pee on the seat when he was killing them and it left a stale urine stink in his car.

There were times when he wouldn't even have the seat in his car. He said the cops were speculating that removing the seat was part of his trap, or that he was trying to destroy evidence. But it was just because the seat was being cleaned and aired to get the pissy smell out of the upholstery. I'd say, "I hated to do them in the car and get a lake of piss on the floor," and he'd say, "Yeah, I always had to clean the car when I did one inside."

I told him I used a plastic seatcover on the death seat, and spread newspapers over the back floormat so the pee would run off the seat onto the paper, which could be tossed away wet. He thought that was brilliant. And I'd simply tell him that such small things are what separate amateurs like himself from pros like me. He couldn't get enough of conversation like that. It was like he felt I knew for sure there was a real boring side to Deathwork, and it wasn't all raging sexual release, as the media likes to portray it.

I got on fine with Ted. He'd believe anything I'd say. He was keen to meet me because he'd read all the stories in the magazines and detective books saying I was The Best. It does no good to deny it. Denial is expected, so when confronted with someone like Ted — a fiend who is measuring you up as the top-gun — your best play is the modest insinuation that everything written was completely true and there's a lot more besides.

DEATH HOUSE SCREAMS

They call it the Death House because its purpose is human slaughter.

From 1972 until executions started up again in 1979, the Death House was like a little museum. Wardens would invite the budding social scientists from the University for this little tour. The climax was the trek down into the bowels of the death house, to the electric chair. The coeds plunked their cute butts into the chair while their pals snapped pictures and made *zzzzz* noises. It was a regular hoot, the most popular social science field trip. Best of all was when the little ladies got to meet real live criminal fiends: Murf-the-Surf, the Catch-Me Killer, and myself. More feral types like Ted Bundy were not allowed to mingle with the dollies.

In May 1979 all that changed forever, and it was the fault of one man — John Spenkelink. "Spink," as we called him, was a prison punk, a faggot — a product of the correctional system who couldn't quite get his sexual identity straight. He'd swish, but though he didn't mince or go about with a limp wrist, there was no doubt in your mind that he was a sissy.

Spink had shot a man in a Tallahassee motel room — an ex-con known to be a "jocker" — a bull faggot. To hear Spink tell it, the jocker had "ripped off his ass" (raped him) so Spink shot him. Mind you, Spink was not criticized for this amongst his peers. Had Spink done his murder in prison, he'd have just told the prison inspector that the jocker ripped off his ass so he killed him. He'd do ninety days in the Hole and that'd be the end of it. After all, prison investigators know what a young punk has to deal with. Jocker comes into the cell with a hard-on and says: "Put blood on my face or shit on my dick." The punk fights or he drops his pants and bends over. Spink had lived like that many a year in prison, and since he was a bit of a femme, his asshole was about like the entrance to the Holland tunnel. Maybe it still wasn't big enough.

Spink believed he had done the right thing shooting the rapist, so when the D.A. offered him a plea to Murder II he turned it down. Big mistake. He went to trial, and the good citizens of Leon County found him guilty of premeditated murder, which it was, and sent the no-good mad-dog murdering queer to Death Row, which was where he was on May 25, 1979, the day he loused things up for the rest of us with the tour chicks.

Day dawned and there across the road from the prison were the usual fields full of protesters and execution groupies. One field for anti-CP, another for those who enjoy the vicarious thrill of a good electrocution. Vendors abound: fried meat, drinks, souvenir T-shirts, miniature electric chairs that light up when you flip a switch.

We were looking out the windows at the show across the street. Signs on sticks, posters going up and down, everybody chanting and howling. Big party rolling along. That's when we heard the scream. It came rolling up the stairwell and under the door, and you just knew something godawful was happening.

In prison you hear a lot of screams. The one we heard was a scream of outrage, not a death scream. Not the kind you hear when someone gets a shank in his guts

and the killer rips open his victim's belly and his soul goes screaming off to Hell. It wasn't like that at all.

We all looked at each other. Nobody had to say, "What's *that*?" The question was in everybody's eyes. Even the old cons who'd been death house orderlies back in the sixties couldn't get a handle on that scream. We'd all heard the yarns the old timers would spin over a cigarette and a cup of joe. Good stories. You had to listen because the tales would sort of reach over and take you by the throat, or hit you like a guard's sap upside your head.

We heard of the men who spit in death's eye. And the craven baby-rapers who'd piss their pants and faint at the sight of Old Sparky on the upraised dais, all festooned with leather straps and buckles to hold them steady while they "ride the lightning."

They call it the three-minute electric enema: 2800 volts of blazing hellfire smack through your brain down your spine and out your leg. The executioner gives you that first pop of 2800 volts; it raises you right off the chair to strain against the straps; shit be slithering out your asshole like a big brown eel, eyeballs be hanging out on your cheeks, brain be boiling in your skull. Then the executioner draws back a touch and takes the current down to 1600 volts. Sets you smack down in your own slop. Then he runs it up the scale to 2800 again till your flesh smokes, slobber and drool be oozing, blood be running out your nose, your trousers be soaked in piss and semen. Cuts the current and you slump in the straps. Dead meat. Fried in your own shit.

We soon found out the story of Spink's death house scream. What infuriated Spink was the unexpected way the State violated his body.

Ladies of the media had been invited to the execution of Brother Spink. ERA time. Can't be prejudiced against women at executions; so here they come. All dolled up in their fancy go-to-execution ensembles, their sober skirts and blouses. Fancy hairdos, cheeks rouged, lips glossed, eyes shadowed, black stockings — nice touch there. We can all imagine the black silk panties riding tight against the perfumed cunt. Oh yes. Spectacles and notebooks and gold pens. Lordy, Lordy, Lordy! One old timer comments that the fancy ladies will soon be heaving up their home fries in the discreetly provided vomit bags.

The gallant gentlemen of the FSP administration, gracious fellows that they be, had decided that pretty media ladies ought not to be subjected to the baser elements of criminal execution. No unpleasant manure odors should offend those patrician nostrils, and urine on electrodes turns to noxious steam.

So to keep the execution tidy, the death strap squad held Spink down while a medical orderly stuffed cotton batting up his backside. Not just a few little cotton balls either. And when the orderly finished that unsavory task, he looped a surgical ligature around the base of Spink's penis and tied it nice and tight. Naturally the sissy screamed. Wouldn't you?

His scream when they crammed his asshole was so terrible that he went to the chair gagged. Prison Admin caught hell in the papers about the "brutality."

But at least Spink didn't scream in front of the ladies.

The medical orderlies have got it down to a science now. Nobody screams when

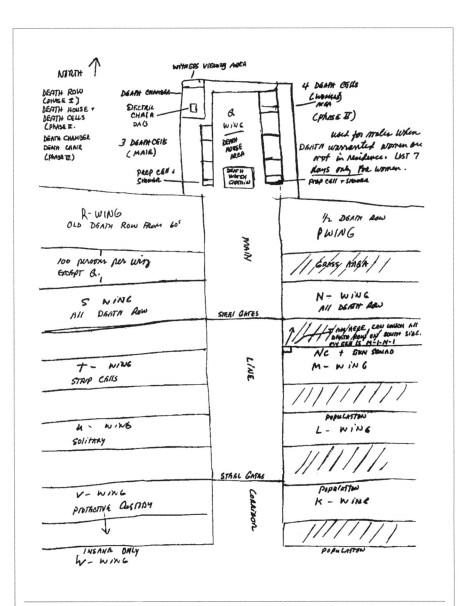

Floor plan of Florida State Prison drawn by G.J. Schaefer
for Sondra London on April 18, 1989

they get packed; they gag them *first*. After the business is concluded the gag comes off and he's hustled into the electric chair. People couldn't understand why Ted Bundy seemed a little unsteady on his feet there at the end. Maybe they shorted him on the Vaseline, who knows?

From midnight until they pulled the switch on Ted, the prison grapevine was buzzing with his every word, his every movement and attitude. All considered, Ted got good marks.

The all-time high for brass goes to Art Goode, who told the press his only regret was that he couldn't have a naked little boy sitting in his lap there in the chair. Truly fiendish. I knew little Art well. One of the nastiest psychopathic child killers imaginable. He was radiant with evil. Even on the Row, people shunned him like the plague. Bundy was a bore compared to Goode, so far as sheer evil is concerned.

Miss Andrea Jackson, the Queen of Florida's Death Row, is scheduled to burn soon. They have a nice roomy cell right behind the Central Control Station all ready for her. I've been in the women's death cell, swept it out. I've sat on the press bench where the women are held down for "preparation." Up behind Control is the infamous seatless toilet where they make the condemned woman squat before they take her down that polished, spotless runway for her date with Old Sparky. As she nears the door to the Death Cell, all eyes will be on her — but it will be the eyes of her peers, not the public. She'll be making chain gang history and every convict in the system will hear her legacy: the tale of how she went down the mainline.

The guards are talking southern fried cunt. Last night they told me they're bringing in *three* death strap matrons to handle Andrea. The medical tech is laying in an extra box of cotton for Miss Double Barrel. The cons are gonna watch her make her last mile, and she won't be brutally gagged. We'll all get to listen to her screams.

*E*ARLY *R*ELEASE

The bus crawled through the darkening Florida countryside, the soft hum of rubber on macadam floating up from under the wheels.

I was sitting in the back of the thing feeling edgy and impatient, smoking my RIP and contemplating the coming evening. I'd done sixteen years in the slam, straight up. One day the fucking warden says, "Pack your shit, Boy, you're being turned out. Early release. Prisons are full. Gotta push some of you oldtimers out, got too many newcocks coming in."

I packed my shit. It fit in the front pocket of my jeans. They gave me a hundred bucks and offered me a bus ticket to any city in Florida. I picked Tampa. What the fuck? One place is the same as another, ain't it?

I reached down and stroked the hilt of my shank. It was jammed in my boot convict style. I'd feel naked without it. In prison a man learns to rely on himself and the comforting presence of cold steel next to his leg on a hot summer night.

My shank had saved my ass more than once from the wolf packs of asshole bandits that prey on the weak after lights out. Only the fittest survive the brutality of prison with their manhood intact.

The only other person I knew on the Trailways was a baby-faced punk from Florida State Prison at Starke, known among the criminal brotherhood as the East Unit, or just the Unit. There is no tougher prison in the U.S. of A. — only Folsom Prison in California comes close in terms of murderous reputation. The only question in my mind was whether the slender boy with the shaved legs was a fuck-boy or a killer queen. The kid had himself a copy of *Hustler*, and was sipping liquor from a bottle concealed in a paper bag. I was feeling high with freedom and I needed to bat the breeze a bit.

I leaned over toward the punk and gave him a wolfish grin.

"Hey, boy. Whatcha got there inside that tote sack? Think I can't smell free-world hooch when it's uncorked?"

The punk had thick light-brown hair; he glanced up and over, blinking his watery no-color eyes. They were white trash convict eyes: guarded, fearful, ancient. Eyes that had known pain, and expected to know it again. The eyes of a prison fuck-boy. His answer was an apology.

"Sorry. I didn't catch what you said."

"I *said*, I want to know what's in that fucking sack you're sucking on, kid."

The punk shifted in his seat, quickly looked around, then offered me a sly, shit-eating smile. "This here is Jim Beam Whiskey. Scored it right at Big Bad Daddy's Lounge in Starke. Five finger discount."

"Stole it?"

"I gave that lonely little feller a new home, is all," he drawled in his cracker, grit-sucking voice. "He was just sitting there with nobody paying him a lick of attention, so I boosted him up under my arm and here he is. Besides, tastes better when you steal it."

"Think so?"

"Sure. Wanna try a little snort?"

"Fuckin-A on that, kid."

The wheels squeaked and hummed along the cement pavement, the tropical countryside oozed past. It was so green — a wondrous world of a million different shades of *green* after sixteen years of solid gray. I took up the bag, wiped the neck of the bottle with my hand and belted down a healthy slug.

"That's damn fine shit there. Beats plum wine all to hell and gone. Fiery. Sets the sparks to jumping, don't it?"

"You betcha," the punk said.

"Got me some Bar-b-Cue corn chips here. Got 'em at the Kash-n-Karry store. Walked right into the little joint. Ten thousand kinds of shit to choose from. I didn't know what to do. It made me nervous seeing all that stuff, so I grabbed the first sack on the rack and hauled ass. Paid my kash; and karried the shit away, just like it said up there on the sign. Little girl at the money taking place up front had tits out front like Jane Fonda in Barbarella. I stared right at 'em. She smelt like a whore. I liked to skeeted in my drawers." I passed the bottle back to him, my eyes automatically scanning for a guard as I made the pass.

"I'll slide on the munchies, Oldcock. I'd probably just puke those corn chips up. I'm aiming to get *drunk*." He took another pull on his bottle and gave me a grin. His eyes were already slightly tinged with crimson from the powerful 90 proof hooch. Niggers had been at him. It was in his eyes; it came off him like a bad case of B.O. He'd be a walking death factory full of AIDS. I knew that for a fact. Mess with a pussy-boy in the joint and it's like Russian Roulette. Hell, play Russian Roulette with a pistol, your odds are safer. I was looking at a walking dead man. I motioned to the magazine open on his lap.

"You read that pervo shit or just look at the pictures? That Larry Flynt is the sickest fucker that ever put out a skin rag; I never have understood his brand of humor."

The punk picked up the magazine and set it on his knee, leaving me to see his dick stuck up like a flagpole. He opened the rag to the centerfold where a bare-assed lady was showing her Vaseline-slickened tunnel of love. The punk bent over and ran his tongue over the page, leaving a wet trail between the model's legs. He made a growl like a hound dog and said, "I like it when the girlies show the pink. *Hustler* gets my blood moving around, heats me up, ya know: I don't read it — I don't look at the cartoons. I just stare at those titties and those gorgeous hairy cunts and jack my dick. Doesn't everyone? Ain't that the reason they show them in the fucking thing?"

I grinned back at him, wondering what an asshole bandit would see in a naked whore. Maybe the same as anyone else; who can tell what goes on in a faggot's twisted mind? I'd been around them for sixteen years straight now, and never could figure them out. "So it heats you up and now you're hot stuff."

The punk nodded agreeably and took another pull on the bottle.

I snapped my finger at him and he quickly handed the jug back my way. "Here you go," he said. Nice polite kid.

I drank his whiskey, felt it burn down inside me. It brightened me up, made me more aware of myself. Shit. Maybe stolen booze was better. I closed my eyes for a minute. Felt the sonorous hum of the bus all around me. Heard the snick-snack of the tires snapping across the expansion cracks in the rural highway. It was a pleasant sound. I was tense. I needed to ease up, relax a little. Too many changes too fast. I wasn't used to it. Riding this fucking bus with no mesh welded over the windows was making me nervous. I realized I could simply throw open the window and leap out. I had a crazy fleeting urge to do just that. I saw the big headlines: *Man Dies Jumping From Window of Moving Bus.* Nobody would ever know why. It would be another unsolved mystery. I smiled at the thought.

I opened my eyes again, glanced at the kid. His eyes stared at nothing. He was leaning back against the bus seat, his hand playing with his dick. He smiled in a self-contained, distant manner at visions only he could see. He scratched at his balls like a whipped cur. I wondered if he was insane. I decided to chat him up and see what sort of worms came to the surface.

"Hey, Boy."

He turned to me. "Yeah?"

"They give you that early release thing?"

He perked up. "Yeah. I got one of those. I earned day for day gain time working

in the broom factory. Maxed my nickel with a deuce, two months and six days. I kept close watch on it."

"Listen. You a street queen?"

"Naw. Bi."

"Niggers turn you out?"

"That's it. Turned my cracker ass out all right. First night too," the kid sighed.

"Bad shit there."

The kid giggled, a high screechy sound, his slim girlish body wriggling with grim recollection as I passed back his little jug. He needed a hit. Drank. Wiped his mouth with the back of his hand.

"Mama Herk comes up to me. The biggest fucking nigger I ever saw in my entire life. I figure I'm gonna die, right?" I nodded his way. "Mama Herk says, 'White Boy, I want to suck your dick.' I figured I'd heard the fucker wrong, like he wanted me to suck *his* dick, but no. He wanted to suck mine. And then I had to fuck him in the ass. You believe that shit?"

"Sure. Mama Herk is famous for it."

"He's a 280 pound queen."

"I know. I've *seen* Herk. I've been in sixteen fucking *years* and you want to tell *me* about Mama Herk? I've done more time in the *box* than you've done in the joint." The kid gave me a worried look.

"Herk turned me out, but I got protection too."

"You sucked nigger cock. Herk pimped you."

"OK, sure. That's it."

"What'd you get for two and a half years of swallowing black cock? AIDS? Clap?"

"I got half of everything."

"Niggers let you keep it?"

"Yeah. Herk made them let me keep it."

"Herk would be the only one who could help a little stringbean like you hold green money at The Unit."

"Oh, I made plenty. I made fucking plenty." He patted a fat roll in the front pocket of his jeans. "It all adds up, Oldcock."

I leaned back, enjoying the heat of the booze. What it added up to was AIDS. But for him, not for me. "So now you are one loaded white boy."

The punk giggled again. His face was flushed and almost trusting. "I got me a big roll of green, and I'm on my way to spend it. I tell myself I earned it. That's how I see it."

He obviously hadn't learnt his lessons at Starke. The first one is to keep your mouth shut — tight. The boy was no convict, not yet he wasn't. I mulled over the news about the fat bankroll while I squinted out the dirty window as the clapboard nigger shacks of drab, impoverished West Tampa slid past. Pest holes of crime. Nigger comes out of a place like that and prison life looks damned good by comparison. Steady meals, basketball, TV in the evening, some piss-ass job in a grungy prison factory, and all the white ass a coon can pump at night. Correctional officer asleep in a locked office and a dorm full of sex-crazed criminal perverts running wild all night. Rehabilitation. I felt the wheels swish along the pavement; the bus

swayed from side to side, rocking along at a steady clip. I looked back at the Kid and said, "Yeah. You might as well enjoy it while you still got it. You get the AIDS and you're through dealing." I waited for him to argue around that one.

"I know. I figure I've got those AIDS things swimming around up in me somewheres. But it takes awhile for them to breed enough to where they kill you. So I'm gonna hit that fucking Tampa on the run and I'm gonna get drunk and suck me some pussy, and then maybe I'll jump off the Sunshine Skyway Bridge right into Tampa Bay. Hey, I just don't give a fuck. OK?"

The punk gave me his best killer-convict-junkyard-dog stare. He looked like Garfield. I was trying not to laugh, so I said, "You ever sucked a pussy before in your whole damn life, Boy?"

He shrugged. "Never did, I admit it. Gonna start learning how to do it today. Heard me a lot of talk in The Unit about it, told myself I ought to give it a try. Hey, I sucked plenty of cock. Why not try a pussy?"

At least the kid had a sense of reality about life — or so it seemed. "How you figure to get ahold of this pussy? You gonna walk up to some lady and say, 'Excuse me, Ma'am, I'm fresh out of prison. Heard talk of pussy-sucking while I was in the joint, and figured I'd like to have me a try at it; would you be agreeable to lower your drawers and let me have a lick or three?' Or maybe you just knock her down, put a knife to her throat and tell her to fuck or die. About like that? Out where we're heading, Kid, is a thing called polite society."

"Just can't ask 'em flat out?"

"Well I reckon you can ask, but it's probably against the law to ask someone to commit a sex crime. Solicitation for criminal acts or something. I ain't no fucking lawyer."

"What's the criminal part?"

"Sucking pussy is a goddamned crime, Kid! It's called oral sodomy. You'd be right back there with Mama Herk in two shakes."

"You shittin' me? It's a *crime* to suck pussy?"

"No lie, Boy. It's a crime in the State of Florida."

I put the bag to my lips and sucked some liquid fire, let it trickle down my throat. I belched. Tasted corn chips at the back of my throat. I wondered if I could get AIDS from the neck of a whiskey bottle. Damn depressing thought. I dismissed it. Quickly handed the Kid back his bottle.

I watched him take a pull, then closed my eyes and suddenly I was back in the darkness of the Hole. I saw the big brown sewer rats come out of the toilet hole in the floor, heard the dry rustle of thousands of cockroaches, the screams of insane and desperate men. Seven years in the Hole. Then the bus began to slow down. I looked out the grimy window, saw the terminal, a big sign reading *Trailways*. End of the fucking line.

"I'm getting excited," the Kid said.

I knew what he meant. The feeling was as contagious as his AIDS. The kid closed one eye and peered into the empty bottle. "Dead soldier," he remarked as he dropped the empty. It hit the floor with a dull clunk. An old lady gave him a dirty look. Started to speak, but held her tongue.

I got to my feet. Ran my hand down the side of the Kid's face and gave it a

meaningful pat. He looked at me with new eyes, asking the unspoken question. He was borderline drunk.

"Got your heart set on sucking pussy, Kid?"

He nodded, "I did. Now I'm not so sure what I want to do."

"Yeah, but I know what to do."

"You do?" the Kid brightened.

"Damn right. Stick with me. I know Tampa pretty good. Worked armed robberies along Dale Mabry during the early seventies."

"You did?"

"Sure. And I've got phone numbers for a pair of cunts who done time down to Lowell. And you know what they fell on?"

"No. What?"

"Organized prostitution. I've got me a pair of whores on the line here. A pair is *two*, Kid. What do you say we call them up and I ask them to teach my homeboy from the Unit to suck honest-to-god pussy. I figure any girl come out of Lowell, she's got to be an expert at that happy pastime. Way I heard it, they don't do nothing else but lay around and lick each other's titties and suck those cunts. Now do you wanna tag along, or go to a motel and jack your dick?"

The punk gave me a look of gratitude. "Hey. That's OK! You really don't mind?"

"Hey. I done 16 years, Kid. I *dig* young boys, I just don't advertise it."

"What about the AIDS?"

"What about it?"

"...if you tell those girls I've been... you know."

"I ain't telling them double-barreled bags of shit *nothin'*. Are you?"

The punk smiled from ear to ear. "Fuck 'em!" he said.

"So what do you say?"

"I say *DO* it!"

So we hit the streets of Tampa running.

It cost me a quarter to get one of the whores on the phone. She said they were French teachers and could we meet them at the Blind Pig for our lessons? She said to look for her in a red dress with a big black flower at the waist. She'd bring her friend.

The next quarter went to call a cab. I didn't want to waste a minute getting to our first class.

The air in the Blind Pig was thick with the smoke of a thousand cigarettes. The people inside were loose and uninhibited. We stood just inside the door and watched everyone shouting and laughing. The lighting was subdued. Smoke swirled around the room, turning the air into a layered blue haze. The punk was agog.

"Outta sight!" he breathed.

We inched our way into the lounge and walked up to the bar like free men. Nobody tried to stop us. We weren't arrested or searched for contraband. Buying a drink without being searched for loose canteen coupons was a novelty. So was the selection. The faggot bought the first round. Dickel on the rocks. First ice cubes I'd seen in sixteen years. They were little tiny things, curved on one side and flat on the other. Sparkling and tinkling as I swirled them in the glass.

I checked out the Kid's fat wad of cash. He'd sucked him a lot of black cock to get that stash. I hoisted my glass.

"To survival, Kid."

He nodded. We clicked glasses and drank, glancing around the place and checking out the action. It was a honky-tonk kind of joint. Country music going wide open on the juke box. Cheap wooden tables with low benches. The room was three-quarters full and the conversation was roaring along. The tables were piled high with empty beer bottles and ashtrays overflowing with butts. The crap was falling onto the floor and being trampled underfoot. It was a real dump. It reminded me of the open dorms at the Unit. Sloppy as hell but as alive as an anthill. I decided I liked it. The punk loved the shit out of it. We'd been there 15 minutes already and nobody had cracked on him for some ass. For him, that was a whole new way of life.

But there was one thing at the Blind Pig that the Unit never had: real whores. Not chain gang pussy boys, but genuine double-barreled, ass-swinging cunts. There were whores wandering around the joint smiling at everyone. Big wide smiles to pull in them big stiff dicks. Same smiles you see on the queens at the Unit. A lot of them in red dresses, but I was looking for that black flower.

A bitch with a mop of tangled hair dyed three separate shades sauntered past with a bottle of Pabst Blue Ribbon in one hand and a pickled pigfoot in the other. She smelled real fucking sweet.

"Check out that real live snatch," I said to the queer.

"What about her?"

"She's trolling for dick. Down here at the Blind Pig twitching her fanny at us. That's your basic working girl. Needs to pay her rent same as us. Look at her move. You like whores, Kid?"

"I like 'em. I like how they move in those tight little skirts… Whooooeee! If she'd bend over a little, I could see clear up to where the sun don't shine. Maybe see the wet spot!"

"What wet spot?"

"There was this old con down on M-Wing. For some money or some canteen, didn't matter which, he'd tell about a gal he saw get 'lectrocuted up in Alabama. Told me all about it. He looked up her dress and there was a big roll of pussy up there and the crack part was wet. He said it was the girlie's wet spot and they all got one. Reckon she's got one up under there?" The punk seemed genuinely curious.

"That sounds like old Curly Bill's yarn."

"That was the guy: Curly Bill. A nasty old fucker with long yellow teeth, and not too many of them. I had to give him a whole jar of Maxwell House to hear his story."

"Was it worth it?"

"Hell yeah! Best story I ever heard."

"You heard some others?"

"Sure, plenty. I saw Ted Bundy, Murf-the-Surf, the Catch-Me Killer, and the Ghoul."

"The Ghoul?"

"Sure. You know, that cop that killed the 34 women down around Oakland Park. Cut 'em up. Drank their blood. Fucked 'em when they were dead."

"Go on! You saw this guy?"

"Walking around on two feet."

"Wha'd he look like?"

"Big ole scary looking fucker. Looks like Hoss Cartwright."

"You say he killed 34 women?"

"Men, women, kids. Nobody knows for sure. I read the whole true story in *Inside Detective*. It had pictures of two girls he ate, plus one he hung by the neck. That one was drawing flies."

"Showed a picture of *that*!?"

"God's truth."

"You talk to this Ghoul?"

"Are you crazy? I seen that fucker coming and I got the hell out of the way. I wasn't gonna piss him off and become Number 35. Know what I mean?"

I laughed. The Ghoul. I wondered who had come up with that one. Some media asshole no doubt. Last I heard it was the Sex Beast. Now it's the Ghoul. Christ on a *stick*.

I finished my whiskey; went up by the barmaid and ordered two more. We knocked them back. The night was young. The cigarette smoke and music swirled around us. The voices banged away at our ears. We took it all in, feeling right at home with the ear-splitting din.

I felt like talking. The booze was loosening me up, and the night was starting to glitter in my brain. I checked my watch, then felt foolish for wanting to see how long we had before count.

No count to stand at 8:00 p.m. Stand to attention, rattle off your number like a robot. No name, just your number. No nigger jive blasting from those black boom boxes. No prancing homos swishing off to the shithouse to suck black cock. The Unit — a place of rehabilitation. If the taxpayers only knew the truth.

I leaned closer to the pussy boy, put my elbow on the bar, and took a knock of bourbon. Damn good stuff.

"I done more than fifteen years, hard time. They bum-rapped me. I ain't no altar boy but you know a bum rap, it don't sit too well in a man. Festers in there like a cancer. A convict does his time. You get caught and you take the fall and you pull the time and you come out and you go back to work. You don't cry, you don't snitch for a plea. You've heard it said, if you can't do the time, don't pull the crime."

The punk nodded sagely into his drink. "What you fall on, Oldcock?"

"Murder! Bloody... fucking... murder."

"Jesus."

"Yeah. Chopped them up with a machete, they said. So when I get to Butler I go straight into Solitary. You know the drill."

The punk nodded.

"And for nothing, on the house, I get four years in the Box. Can you believe such shit?"

The punk's eyes widened as he shook his head in sympathetic understanding. "I

know a guy. He raped the Warden's secretary. He got two years in the Box. This other guy, he got caught with a .38 caliber pistol inside the prison. He did maybe five years in the Box. So if you get four years in the Box from jump street, I figure the Warden plain don't like you, or a buddy of the Warden don't like you. That's it, couldn't be nothing else."

"Good, you understand. So you can see how I might be tempted to get me a machete and settle a few old scores."

"I can understand the temptation."

"I ain't saying I'm gonna do it. But after that first four years in the Box, you could say my attitude turned a tad radical."

"But you did manage to get out of the Box, right?"

"Right. And here's what happened. Along comes this new warden, Braselton. Big fucking gorilla runs about 280. Lifts weights. Came down from Cook County. You know, Chicago. Me, I'm from the Windy City, grew up on the Northside. That was back when Old Man Daley was Mayor and the cops were real mean. Capone, he came out of Chicago. Word I got was that Capone had Cermak bumped off down on Miami Beach…"

"What? You lost me. Who's Cermak?"

"Mayor Anton Cermak. He got killed in Miami. They said it was an attempt to kill that Jew Roosevelt."

"Roosevelt? Hey, that was before I was born, Home. Tell me how you got out of the Box," the punk groused.

"Well I done a few short stretches at Statesville, one longer at Menard. Braselton knew me there. He comes down here to Florida and finds me in the Box. He takes a look at my jacket, sees I ain't got a single write-up, so he decides to give the homeboy a break. Gets me a transfer out of the Box right over to Union County, Raiford Prison. I go straight to the Rock. F-Floor. Nasty grungy place. Then I get assigned a job. Put me in the packing plant. Ever been in the packing plant, Kid?"

"Never was." He took a knock at his drink.

"Well it's a place you wouldn't forget. You know that bacon they serve in the chow hall with the hog bristles still in it?"

"Yeah. Not that you'd see me eating it. I do admit the niggers scarf it right up. They'll snatch it right off your tray if you so much as blink an eye."

"OK. That's the bacon I'm talking about. The packing plant is where that crap is made and the noise alone is enough to drive you fucking insane. Machinery crashing and slamming all day long. The squealing pigs."

"Is that four-legged or two-legged pigs?"

"Very funny. This is serious. Now pay attention."

"OK, run it."

"So Benny drives down to Avon Park for a truckload of pigs. Great big fucking sows maybe three hundred, four hundred pounds. He comes back and we run them out of the truck and into a pen."

"A pigpen."

"Right. Then someone gives 'em a jab on the ass with an electric prod and they go running up a narrow chute. They're lined up in there snout to asshole; squealing like mad, crapping all over each other, just like the poor slobs on their way to

Sparky. Same exact thing. Joe fastens some iron shackles around the rear hocks and this other fella gives the porker a pop on the noggin with a sledgehammer."

"Jesus."

"Yeah. Wham! Then they press a button and the hoist jerks the pig up into the air. The fuckers ain't even dead, just stunned, and they come to while they're hanging upside down. You never heard such screaming. The hog comes swinging down from the slaughter chute toward the killing floor and the thing is spewing shit and piss out its ass like a volcano."

"Gross."

"You ain't heard it all yet. Bobby Batson is there with this huge fucking knife and he slits their throats. The blood comes splashing out all over the place. They spray blood from the front and crap from the rear, and there's four hundred pounds of bucking meat writhing in the chains, gurgling and squealing and screaming like hell."

"So what was your job?"

"I gutted them. Slashed their fucking bellies open and got a snoot full of stench for my trouble. Let me tell you, Kid, there ain't no rehabilitation in the packing plant. Raw meat. Yellow tallow. Greasy coils of spilling guts. And the stench. I came out of four years in the Hole and walk into that. They told me it was supposed to be job training. Educational. Yeah, teach me the Work Ethic. The parole man would like it, they said. I'd have a skill to take with me to the streets. Make me a good parole risk. You've heard that story?"

The punk nodded. Caught the bartender for two more Dickels with ice. Good sipping whiskey. We sloshed them down. A whore rubbed her tits against the pussy-boy as she pressed through to the bar. He gave me a look. Big eyes, big wet smile. Thinking about a little cooze, he was. It was around. All around.

"Where are those French whores, Oldcock?"

"Don't cum in your drawers, Kid. They'll be around. You think you're the only stiff they got lined up to bury tonight? We got "call girls" coming. They ain't like some snaggletooth rummy you find in a tonk. Call girls — you call 'em on the phone, make you an appointment. They get top dollar. But you've got a wad of green to spend."

"Damn right. Top-notch pussy, that's what we want!"

"Yeah, that packing plant was a real trip. Every time I see a cop I think of it. Never could get the blood washed off me. It'd be under my fingernails, my toenails, between my toes. Slice one of those sows and she squirts blood and crap right in your face. It's in your hair, dripping down your arms, soaked into your clothes. August, September — it was hotter than hell in there. Sixty million flies buzzing around eating that liquid pigshit mixed with blood. We were drowned in that slime, Kid. We died. Our souls flew out and went away."

"Sounds bad, Home."

"You don't know the half of it, Kid. The old Rock was nothing but fucking madness. The noise and the stench alone was enough to drive any man insane. They built the place about 1920, so there's sixty to seventy years of sweat and piss soaked into the cement. August comes around and you can't hardly breathe for the stink of the place. We'd put in a day in the packing plant and then the screws

would herd us back to the cellblocks. F-Floor, H-Floor, G-Floor, all that was the packing plant crew."

"Big gang down there, huh?"

"Oh, hell yes. There was goddamned niggers in the cells too. Nasty fucking dirty black-assed niggers that never had a bath in their whole sorry lives. Filthy animals."

"Mama Herk was OK."

"Some are OK, some ain't. And that's a fact."

"Where are our whores? You think they'll be here soon?"

"Forget the whores for a minute. I'm getting to the part about when they cut off Newcock Benson's head."

"Cut the guy's head off? What was it, an accident?"

"Not exactly. Those niggers, you know they were bad, but at least they speak English and they understand when you tell them to hit the showers. Then we started getting them Cuban assholes, Marielito scum. Castro opens the door to his insane asylums and lets all the nuts go to Florida. Guess where they end up?"

"The Rock?"

"Fucking-A. And these are crazy insane fuckers, not convicts. No habla ingles. No comprendo. Let me tell you what they comprendo, is a big fucking knife. And even normal guys were driven mad by the stench and the filth and the blood-sodden clothes stinking up the whole cellblock. Guys were bugging up every day — regular white guys. You never knew when it would happen. It was a 24-hour red alert just to stay alive. Bad on the nerves, Kid, I can tell you that."

"What about cutting off the head?"

"Shit. Some guy would pull out a knife — a hog slasher, pig sticker, even a meat cleaver. And he'd start swinging. Slaughter guys in the cell just like they were pigs coming off the chute, hanging from a chain. Get the picture?"

"I'm seeing it. Living color."

"OK. One day we are in this 20-man cell and a shiteater name of Dennison comes along with this newcock to put him in our cell. Swede Perkins, who was the boss coon of the cell, tells Dennison we ain't got no more room, the cell is full. Twenty bunks, twenty guys: White, Nigger, Cuban. Dennison tells Swede the newcock is coming in as number 21, and we ain't got jack-shit to say about it. So Swede tells Dennison if he puts the newcock in the cell, we're cutting off his damn head. Dennison just laughs and opens the door. He pushes the newcock into the cellblock and walks away. An hour later he comes back for a security count and the head is laying out on the tier."

"No shit?"

"No shit."

"So what happened?"

"We didn't get more guys than bunks, that's what happened. Every other cell was stacked up with guys like they're sardines in a damn can. Cell H-4 had twenty guys, just what it was supposed to have."

"What'd the cops do?"

"Nothing. Every guy in the cell said he killed the newcock. Twenty guys. Twenty confessions. So the State said fuck it and put it under the rug. Called it a suicide or

some such shit. Suicide my ass. Dennison was *told*. He *murdered* that newcock. That was the old chain gang, Sonny. Pussy-boys don't have that kind of solidarity. No snitches stayed alive in them days. Ain't like now."

"What about the screw, Dennison. Did he get fired?"

"Dennison got fucking *killed*, Kid."

"Whaaaat?"

"Time goes by. The cons seen the cop who was responsible for the murder is still around. One day they caught him in the hallway and gutted him like a porker."

"But... *why?*"

"Because Swede told him, *if* you put the newcock in the cell he's dead meat. Dennison put him in. The newcock had to die. Real convicts don't run off at the mouth, Kid. Dennison killed him. The State should have fried Dennison same as they fried Aubrey Adams, that baby-raping pig from Marion C.I. Since nothing was gonna be done officially, it got done unofficially. A lot more of them shiteating DOC motherfuckers are gonna die before it's all over. You watch and see."

"Home, it sounds even worse than the Unit."

"It was." I took a drink and leaned closer to the Kid.

"Check this out: I lasted one week. Then I walked down to Classification, asked that old shithook Parks for a job change. Kitchen, laundry, farm squad, anything. Parks pulls out my jacket. He scans through it. Looks me dead in the eye and tells me his paperwork says I'm a butcher. I tell the fucker, 'I never done no butcher job on the street. Armed robbery, button work. That was my trade. Never done an honest day's work in my life, at least not in no straight john detail. What the fuck is this butcher trade crap?'

"Parks, that miserable shit, he says: 'Right here on your sheet, Boy, says *The Butcher of Blind Creek*. Got you some experience, says here. Hung 'em by their ankles and opened up their bellies. Figured you'd like it in the packing plant since that's your style. Heard it said them sows scream like real women. Hang 'em, gut 'em, listen to 'em scream. Talk about hog heaven, says right here you get off on that shit. Now get the hell out of my office.'"

The kid groaned. "Fucking Parks! I know him. What an asshole. Kept a bottle right in his desk. I went to a progress review with him once, and he was drunk on his *ass*. Parks. Sweet Jesus. Everybody hates that fucker."

"I seen it my own self, kid. I seen a lot. Parks and plenty more just like him. I don't know where the State dredges up the human shit they have running these prisons.... Someone must tack job opportunity notices up in gay bars. Half the staff of the Unit is faggot. The citizens say they want rehabilitation. I've seen their program. What it is, see, this rehabilitation program, it's a flip-flop deal. You flip into the system one way and flop out another way. You know? Go in straight, come out queer. Go in healthy, come out diseased. Go in normal, come out perverted. Flip-flop rehabilitation theory. An educated man could write a book about it."

The faggot nodded his agreement. How could he argue? His program might have been a little different, but he knew what I meant. The dickeater never had to ask a silly question about rehabilitation. He understood.

I watched his pretty-boy long-lashed eyes surveying the action. A covert ob-

lique swing of the eyeballs, always on the alert for the sudden move, the danger of the knife in the back. He slid up to the bar, copped two more bourbons, and paid for them. We slurped them down, the heat of the alcohol exciting our senses.

"Where's those fucking whores?" the kid moaned.

"Home douching out their cunts getting ready for two hardheads out on early release. They squirt perfume on their tits, powder their assholes, use cherry-flavored juice up in their pussies to make them taste nice when you suck on 'em."

"Cherry flavored pussy?" The punk was in awe.

"As I live and breathe."

"Real call girls."

"The McCoy. Call 'em and they come."

"Like a couple of bitches. Here, girl! Here, girl!" He was getting giddy.

"You got the picture, now hold it."

"I've *been* holding it. Now I want to stick it in one of them pussy rolls."

"Don't worry, you will. Tonight. Now listen to my philosophy."

"You make up a philosophy in the box?"

"I did. Now listen."

"Tell me."

"Blood," I said, "that's where it all starts. I was up to the Unit during the riot back in '79. There was plenty of blood to see there. The shiteaters came in on us with clubs and mace and spilled our blood. They broke our bones, bruised our meat. All you are to them, kid, is an animated bag of meat and blood. I seen it go down. I had a vision. Teeth were all over the quarterdeck. Smashed teeth. Step on them, they crunch like gravel. They'd run you down to Q-Wing and work on you with those clubs and cattle prods. Obedience training. Attitude adjustment. Rehabilitation. The beginning and the end of it is blood. The blood fills your mama's insides. She squats and squeezes you out her cunt like a lump of crap. You come sliding down her chute right between her piss and her shit. There's a cosmic message there, if you study on it. We eat shit and die. Just like it says on the back of the Scooter Tramps jackets."

"That's your philosophy?"

"That's it... blood. That's where it starts and that's where it ends."

"Makes sense."

"You gotta let it all out, kid. You can't keep it locked up in the box in your brain any more. To the public you ain't no more than a carcass on a hook. They don't know nothin'. They don't want to know nothin'. They think we live at some kind of summer camp. Tell Joe Six-pack what goes on inside a prison and he'll just call you a liar. But now we're out. First we're gonna have us some fun and then I don't know about you, but I've got some people to look up. A few folks who owe me."

I lifted my glass and realized it was empty. I started to order another round when I saw a hooker in a red dress come swinging through the door with a jaunty black silk flower pinned to her waist. She had her blonde hair up in a French twist. The other French teacher was right behind her, a brunette with fluffed-out hair in a shiny royal blue number. I gave them the high sign and nudged the punk, "Here comes our French lesson."

The two bimbos bounced over to a table and sat down. I took the cocksucker by

the arm and steered him through the crowd. We walked up to the women and sat down, just like free men.

The women were both obviously professionals, with painted crimson lips slick and wet. Their cheeks were rouged, their noses powdered. They were ready. I gave them a sharp, knowing grin. The women smiled back with avaricious eyes. They studied me and the punk, looking us up and down. I stared directly at their tits. They both had nice big ones. The punk snickered and sucked up some booze. His eyes were as red as a vampire's. His baby face was pink and greasy. He gave me with a callow grin. A full boner curved up toward his navel. He was a randy boy.

"I'm Jerry, and this my road dog, Danny." The whores looked at him and smiled to each other. They knew easy money when they saw it, and they were both licking their lips.

Danny gave up a self-conscious giggle. "You ladies the schoolteachers we called about private tutoring in French?"

"Oui-oui. I'm Candy," said the blonde.

"And I'm Tiffany," chimed in the brunette.

"You guys afford lessons?" asked Candy.

The kid flashed his roll and asked, "Can I buy you ladies a drink?"

"French champagne," Candy gushed. "The French lessons are two hundred an hour. *Each.*"

The punk blanched.

Tiffany arched an eyebrow. "Can you handle it, Big Daddy?"

"Sure — no problem." The kid put on a lopsided grin and shoved off toward the bar for a round of drinks.

"A couple of twenty-dollar hookers fleecing a lamb. Shame on you!" I grinned.

"Lambs were born to be shorn," Tiffany snapped.

Candy nudged me. "How'd you get our number?"

"Willy the Weasel."

"What'd Willy fall on last time — he tell you?"

"Murder Two. Willy has him a wart right here." I touched my finger to the side of my nose.

"So you know Willy."

"Sure. You think I'm vice squad?"

"Just being careful."

"Yeah? Willy told me you two pulled time at Lowell."

Candy groaned. "I did ten months on a bar-tack machine in the garment factory. Job training for the street, you know?"

"I know."

"Tiffany pulled a deuce at Broward. Armed robbery. She ain't as genteel as she looks. Where'd you pull yours?"

"Raiford — the Rock."

"Did you see Andrea when they took her up there?" Tiffany asked.

"Didn't see her but I damn sure heard her. Bitch screamed her lungs out. Took four matrons to get her down the mainline. It was a real show. I got the story from the Deathwatch Commander, Mr. Crowe."

The two hookers exchanged a glance and laughed.

"What's the joke?"

The kid came back just then with a fifth of Dickel and a big green bottle of champagne. He popped the cork. While he was pouring a round, I asked the kid if he was around the Unit when the Jackson bitch came up for a ride on the lightning. He said he was.

"Did she scream?" Tiffany asked.

"Screamed like she was being murdered. Everyone in the Unit heard her. The Captain told me there would have been a shit trail from the back ramp to the death cell, except they had her in sanitary briefs."

The two whores laughed some more.

"What's the joke?" Danny asked.

"My exact same question," I added.

"Tiffany saw when they put her on the transport van to ride her up to the Chair," Candy said.

"She was shrieking like a maniac," Tiffany giggled. "Old Lady Venziano, she's the warden down there, goes trooping down to Andrea's cell and reads her the death warrant and transport order. The goon squad is there with chains and locks. The nurse is standing by with the old-fashioned Kotex on a belt, and a green diaper."

"What's that about?" Danny asked.

Tiffany arched an eyebrow his way. "The electric chair is at Starke. The Women's Death Row is west of Lauderdale, out in a swamp next to the County Dump. It's a 6 to 8 hour ride to Starke. Maybe you think they'll stop and let her pee at a gas station?"

The kid shrugged, blushed a bit. "What they do is strap a piss sop to your cunt, honey, so you can piddle in it if you take a notion to go. The diaper is just in case you get real scared and start to shit. A girl on the way to the Chair might get the urge, don't you think?"

The kid obviously didn't know what to say.

"Any more dumb questions?" Tiffany huffed.

"Lighten up, babe," Candy quipped, then turned to the Kid and said, "She's only been on the street three weeks. Takes awhile to shrug off the stresses and tensions of that lousy joint. Women screaming and hollering, sex-crazy for a man, everybody angling for the cutest dykes and trying for early release. It's insane."

Tiffany's ire subsided. She said, "Andrea came back to Broward on a federal stay. She told us she took the mainline by storm. Went down with a tail-swinging strut and at least five hundred men calling out for her to fuck them."

"Her fantasy," I said.

Tiffany continued, "Then they gave her a cell next to that Adams guy and they talked."

"That part could be true," the punk said.

I nodded.

"Then they took Adams and burned him up in the Chair, and that was the end of him."

Candy said, "Then when she came back to Broward she was full of shit about

how she had charmed the whole Unit. True or false?"

"A little of both," I allowed. "The guards had the Unit on lockdown when she made her walk on the mainline. Crowe said she was crying and screaming. We heard that in the cellblocks.

"Lying damn bitch," hissed Tiffany.

We all drank up. The girls were originally from Atlanta and both were kicked out on early release. They were working the senior citizen trade at the condos. Lonely old men paid a mighty sweet dollar for juicy young snatch. Business was booming. I told them about the Rock. The rehabilitation. The packing plant. The early release.

The pussy was telling them about Ted Bundy, the Catch-Me Killer and the Ghoul. The drone of conversation hummed around us and the caustic smoke stung our eyes. We discussed the mindless violence, the bloody murder, the sexual slavery of men and women in prison. How their bodies were bought and sold to the highest bidders, unleashing the perverted lusts that gave hopeless men and women a reason to live from day to day.

The blonde put her hand on my crotch. Sighed with anticipation as she rubbed her hand along my ready shaft. Tiffany snuggled with the punk, her professional hands busy under the table. The sluts were already beginning to stink of rut. They gurgled and moaned, their minds clouded by the sexual business they needed to conclude. I looked at them with both contempt and lust. I slapped my empty tumbler onto the table and announced to the steamy group, "So let's get laid!" Everyone understood that. We got right up and off we went.   .

The fuck-boy was giddy. He couldn't believe his luck. We left the Blind Pig with the early release whores on our arms and lurched out into the humid warmth of the summer night. Nebraska Avenue was blazing with light. Cars with glaring headlights cruised up and down the Strip, their makes, models and styles all foreign and unrecognizable to me. Neon signs flashed and blinked, advertising places and products I'd never heard of. Music throbbed and boomed from the doorways of bars and clubs. The whole city of Tampa was a gaudy whorehouse catering to the pleasures of tourist flesh.

A stinking coal-black nigger in a dirty T-shirt rattled a paper bag in the shadows of a doorway. "White lady, white lady," he sang out, "Crack."

"Get fucked, nigger!" I snarled.

Candy giggled. The dope dealer retreated into his lair.

We turned off Nebraska. The side street was in darkness. The whores had them an old two-story flophouse trick pad. Danny was anxious to get it on. He was almost dragging Tiffany up the stairs. The stairwell stank of dry rot and stale piss. Familiar smells — prison smells. The stairs led up a landing. There were rooms on the right and left. Whores and transients.

Candy fished a key out of her clutch purse. She unlocked a door and flipped on a light. Hundreds of cockroaches fled, scuttling for the cracks. There were a pair of unmade ratty beds along the far wall, an aluminum chair, a Formica table strewn with Big Mac wrappers, cigarette butts and black ants.

"Home sweet home," Tiffany announced blithely.

"Fucking pig pen," I said.

"You don't like it, hit the road, Jack," Candy spat.

Danny toppled onto a bed. There was a half bottle of Dickel in his hand. He unscrewed the cap. Tiffany grabbed the bottle, drank up, handed it to me and began pulling off Danny's clothes. His trousers were hung up on his boner. We all laughed. I took a hit on the bottle, and passed it on to Candy. She drained it, tossed it in a corner and unzipped her dress. The cheap red fabric fell in a puddle at her feet. She caught it with her foot and kicked it into the same corner with the Dickel bottle. The bedraggled black silk flower was twisted and broken off its stem. It lay on the floor by the naked feet of the blonde whore. I watched her strip, burning with a puritanical rage as she shook her creamy udders free of her lacy black brassiere.

The punk and his dark-haired whore were wrestling on the bed. The blonde pulled off her black silk panty, put it to her nose and sniffed it, made a wry face and tossed it. She cleared her throat. "Straight French, half-and-half or around-the-world?"

"French for me," I said.

"Pay up!" the blonde said, holding out her mitt.

"You don't trust me?"

"Fuck no!"

I laughed. Fished out Danny's roll from his pants and paid the freight. The whore nodded. Put the four hundred in her shoulder bag.

Danny gasped and giggled on the bed. The dark-haired slut on top of him was naked. She had tapered fingers with the color of fresh blood glistening on the long enameled nails. Her hands fluttered around the boy's dick with professional skill. They knew what to do and were busily going about it.

The nude blonde stood there like a cow in a slaughter chute. Her eyes were bovine and dumb. She scratched absently at her pubic hair as we watched Tiffany work her magic on the fuck-boy's dick. What a pro. The queer was gasping. The slut was straddling his cock, her white legs spread wide. A lavish mop of dark pubic hair hung down between her legs. She took the punk's boner in her right hand and carefully angled it into her hole. She lowered herself with a grunt of pleasure. Danny's hands clenched the pillowy white buttocks, his fingers kneading the soft flesh. The impaled woman levered herself up and down on his pole growling deep in her throat. Her eyes were closed. A ropy tendril of saliva hung from her chin. We listened to the building tempo of passion, the wet smack of sweaty flesh meeting. The brunette kept sliding up and down Danny's cock until he arched his back and emptied his load, leaving her infected with the AIDS plague.

I unzipped my jeans, took out my own stiff boner, turned to the naked blonde and commanded her, "On your knees, bitch!"

The whore did as she was told. She took my root in her mouth and sucked on it. She'd done it before and was just fine. I let her work. I stood there and looked down at the dandruff on her head. It looked like she might have lice as well.

I listened to the slurping, sucking sounds she made as they mingled with the whimpers coming from Danny. I felt the head of my dick rub the back of her throat. I relished the slippery warmth of her spit, heard the gurgle and mewl of her efforts. I caressed Candy's blonde, dandruffed hair. It had a greasy feel. She hummed

as she sucked. It was a nice touch. I tried to pick up the tune, but couldn't recognize it. Must be a new one.

Outside there was the distant whoop of a police siren. Trouble for somebody, but not for me. The thought of being free was exciting. I speeded up my thrusts. Finally I held the blonde whore's head steady, shuddered and came in her mouth. She struggled to break free. I wrapped her hair around my hand and held her head tight on my cock. Danny was amused. He caught my eye as he giggled; probably remembering his own head locked on a man's spurting dick.

Tiffany wiped her cunt with a big wad of Kleenex and dropped it on the floor. "Ride 'em, cowgirl!" she yelped at Candy.

I felt the blonde's teeth close around my dick, and I shoved her away from me. It was the only thing to do. She fell back on the floor landing on her backside, gagging and heaving. She spat a gobbet of semen on the grimy floor.

"You motherfucker!" she shrieked.

I kicked her hard in the stomach and she doubled up. "Teach you to bite my dick, bitch!" Bloody vomit spewed up from her gut and splashed from her mouth onto the black flower on the floor. She retched and gasped. Her eyes were swimming with fear and disgust. Two tendrils of slick puke ran from her nose. "Like to bite my dick? I'll teach you to bite!"

I kicked her in the face. Teeth flew from her mouth. The force slammed her back into the wall. She bounced off and collapsed onto her side. Her head thumped the floor.

Tiffany screamed. Danny sucked in his breath and jerked upright, suddenly alert, his prison instincts overriding the alcoholic haze. The naked brunette made a lunge for her skirt. As she made her reach I drop-kicked her in the jaw. She spun around and crashed into the bedpost and flopped down to the floor into Candy's champagne-laced vomit.

I leaped in the air and came down full force on Tiffany's chest with my knees. Her rib cage collapsed under my weight.

She coughed, her chin slick with glistening blood. Gurgling rasps were her only sound. Her body stiffened slightly, and a thin bubbling sound came up from deep in her throat. The breath snagged and then stopped. Her legs began to jerk in spasms and a pool of yellow urine widened around her hips. The breath came back with a start. A few rapid gasps rattled in the back of her throat. Pink frothy lung blood gushed from her mouth, and she was dead.

"Jerry! Jerry!" Danny yelled.

"Fucking sluts," I growled.

The punk's face was fishbelly white. The gray eyes widened with sudden terror. I smiled. Pulled my knife from my boot. Strode toward him. Danny cringed back against the wall, his delicate fag hands waving before him. Cowardly little AIDS-ridden queer.

"Jerry! No! Please!" he blubbered.

I swung the blade in with a sharp upward motion. It glanced off a rib and sliced up into the faggot's yellow heart. I pulled the shank out and chopped it across his face. A fountain of blood erupted. He started sliding down the wall. I held him up with my left hand and drove the shank into him again. And again. And again. His

body slumped sideways, toppled over and hit the deck. I sank a kick into his balls. "Cocksucker!" I hissed.

He never heard me. He was dead.

The blonde whore had rolled onto her back.

Her face was bloody and broken, her eyes rolled in their sockets with the pain. Vomit and blood streamed from the corners of her mouth. Bloody bubbles formed and burst at her nostrils as she attempted to breathe.

I felt the pounding of my heart as the excitement fanned my rage. The coppery smell of whoreblood had me sweating and my nerves on fire.

The blonde bitch groaned.

The brunette was splayed across the floor in a ghastly pool of blood and urine and vomit. I walked over to her to get a closer look. Her open eyes were dilated. The blood oozing from her nose and ears was beginning to thicken. She looked dead.

I leaned over and punched the blade into her heart, just to be sure.

I picked up Danny's discarded trousers and removed the still-fat wad of cash from his front pocket.

I searched the pocketbooks of the two hookers and came up with a couple of C-notes, in addition to my own four hundred. Chump change.

I heard the blonde whore groan. She was still on her back, lips swollen, eyes puffy and blackened. I walked over to her. I could see the cheesy crack between her legs, with the cooties crawling in her bush. She wasn't a natural blonde. I examined her ruined face and noticed that somehow her narrow, aristocratic nose had remained unbroken.

I lifted the heel of my heavy boot and brought it down smartly on her snot locker, driving it up into her brain.

The whore didn't move and made no further sound. I set the point of the blade into the hollow of her white throat and shoved it in until I felt it grate bone. Then I twisted it. I picked up the sodden black flower and placed it in her evil mouth. It looked just right.

I opened the door to the flophouse flat. The hallway was dusty and empty. I walked down the rotting stairs to the street, with Danny's roll to keep me company.

I thought of Canada, the Bahamas, the coast of North Africa. Then I thought of the cop who had framed me for murder sixteen years ago. Within an hour I was on a bus to Miami.

Former State's Attorney Robert Stone convicted Gerard John Schaefer of the murders of Georgia Jessup and Susan Place, and connected him to several dozen cases, calling him "the greatest killer of women of this century."

"Schaefer ought to be in the worst possible prison in Florida," Stone said. "I want to be sure I am consulted before he is released."

"Schaefer is dangerous. I do not think he can control himself. He is a madman, and if he claims I'm trying to keep him in prison, he is right. If he got out, it would be like signing death warrants for a lot of people."

Note: Gerard John Schaefer specifically insisted that Robert Stone's statement appear as a sidebar to "Early Release."

NIGGER JACK

The warden of the Florida State Prison at Starke strapped John Spenkelink into the electric chair and fried his ass on May 25, 1979 and right away convicts began scheming for the job of death chamber orderly; that was because of a hooker named Sonia.

Sonia was the whore who'd murdered two cops down in Broward County: Trooper Black of the Highway Patrol and Constable Irwin from Canada. She'd shot them dead at a rest area off I-95 hard by Pompano Beach. A stinking scum-sucking rat by the name of Walter Rhodes had turned state's evidence and put Sonia's pretty young tail in line to fry on Old Sparky. She'd burn with her convict boyfriend, Jesse Tafero. It would be an event to see.

It all added up that Sonia would be riding the lightning. Spenkelink had murdered an ex-con rapo-faggot and the State had burned him, so there was no doubt that Sonia would be coming along to pay us a visit by and by. Everybody in the joint believed it would happen and almost everybody wanted to be on hand to watch — not because Sonia was disliked, but because she was prime pussy. She'd been a high-priced hooker on the streets, she'd blown away a pair of law dogs, she had great teats, and was the reigning Queen of Death Row.

The State would burn Sonia and some lucky convict would be assigned the job of mopping up her pee and emptying her knickers after the execution. The prison guards always have someone handy to dump the executed person's drawers before turning the smoking corpse over to the free-world undertaker, so we all knew someone would luck into the job of dumping Sonia's. It was a job to covet, and there was more to it than the chance to see real pussy. The job carried a guarantee of an endless income of coffee and cigarettes tendered by anyone wanting to hear the true story of Queen Sonia on her electric throne. Look at it as a form of chain gang Social Security.

We knew this to be a fact because of Curly Bill. Curly had personally watched a cunt sizzle in the Alabama electric chair in 1957. This unusual event occurred while Curly was pulling a stretch at the Holman Penitentiary, and for a small gratuity he'd sit down and tell anyone the whole story. I'd heard he told it well, so being of a curious nature I went down to the prison canteen, picked up a jar of Maxwell House Coffee and a bag of Oreos, and moseyed on down to Curly Bill's cell. I found him sitting on his bunk rolling a smoke.

I poked my mug in his door and said, "Curly Bill, if you're in a yarning mood I'd like to hear the story of the fried cunt." I took the jar of coffee out of the paper sack and tossed it on his bed. "Talking can dry a man out. I brought you a little something to wet your whistle while you talk." A flagrant bribe.

Curly Bill eyed the coffee. His tongue ran out and dampened the rolling paper for his cigarette. "Whole damn jar, all for me?" he inquired.

I shrugged. "Sure, why not? I heard you tell quite a story."

He lit his cig and took a drag. "What sort of story are you wanting to hear?"

"What kinds you got, Curly?"

He pursed his lips in thought. "Well, there's the kind I tell the Man when he comes snooping around. And there's the kind I tell the social science girlies from the university day trip every month. And then there's the true fact of what really happened the night the Captain strapped a Tutweiler cunt to Old Sparky and she rode the lightning down to the flaming pit of Hell." He cocked an eyebrow at me and said, "That pussy was so hot steam rose from between her legs. Now... what sort of yarn did you fancy, Jerry?"

"The one with the smoking hole."

Curly Bill grinned. "That's the one the free people don't want to hear."

"I ain't been free for awhile, Old Man."

He nodded the truth of that statement. He'd been seeing me on the yard for over ten years. He told me to come on into his cell and set my tail on a Number Ten can. I hunkered down while Curly cracked the seal on the jar of fresh mud and put a stinger in his cup to heat water. Steaming coal-black coffee, roll-your-own smokes, and all the time in the world. No place to go, nothing to do. Pulling a life hitch. May as well listen to an oldcock tell a tale of the way things were in the Alabama chain gang, not so long ago, not so far away.

Curly Bill was one of the slimiest human slugs ever to crawl out from between a whore's legs, but he was a good storyteller. He perched himself on the edge of his rack, took a sip of the smoking Joe and began his story.

"Her name was Rhonda Belle Martin and they'd drove her up from the Julia Tutweiler Penitentiary for Women earlier that day. She rode the prison death train north, a chained bitch in an unmarked van with a one-way ticket to the state Electric Chair. She was condemned meat, the kind the prison screws burn at Holman Penitentiary. They kept her in a cell right by the electric chair for a few hours, then Warden Hobbs got him a call from the Governor's Office at the State Capitol. The message was plain and simple: 'Fry the Bitch.'"

"Were they burning women regular back then, Curly?"

"More than these days, but not a passel. Now, a bitch figures she can get away with murder, but back then it wasn't such a sure thing."

"So they brought her up from Tutweiler, and then what?"

"It was a little bit secret actually. The first sign we men on the cellblocks had that she'd burn was when a death house screw come up into our living area to fetch Billy Mumford out'n his cell. Billy had the job to shave the condemned. Head and leg."

"What kind of job is that?" I wondered.

"That's special barber assignment. Before they take you and set you in the chair you got to have a body shave so the electricity runs all around you nice and smooth. Billy does the leg where the electrode fits on, and he does the head. They let a man shave around his own peter."

I gave Curly Bill a snort of disbelief. "I have my doubts anyone has to shave the hair around his peter for a ride on Sparky. What's the sense in it?"

"It's a rule. And if you don't care to believe my true tale you can march your dumb ass down to L-Wing and ask that nigger Jim Richardson about the body shave he got when they was making a practice run on him back in 1970. Body shave means they take every single hair off, even the ones on your nuts, boy."

"And a woman?"

"They skin her beaver."

"Hard to believe."

"I ain't asking you to believe. I'm telling you how it was and what I saw up to Holman when Rhonda Belle sat on Sparky." Curly Bill slurped some coffee and continued.

"So Billy went off to the Death House with the screw and later Billy comes back and tells us we won't believe it but there's a cunt from Tutweiler down in the Death Cell and they are fixing to fry her bottom real soon. He damn sure had our undivided attention when we heard it was a real female. Then we wanted to hear about the body shave. You know, did he shave her or what?"

"Well? Did he?"

"Billy told us he did shave her. He gave us the entire story. And it was his claim that when he was shaving her leg, her skirt was raised and he could see all the way up to where some brown pussy hair was sticking out from underneath the elastic around the leg hole. We were all asking him, 'Did she just set there and let you look?' and Billy swore that she didn't seem to mind his admiration of her charms at all. Now ain't that a treat?"

I bobbed my head acknowledging that it was indeed extraordinary and Curly Bill continued, "Billy told us she wore a white panty. Nothing fancy, just the plain kind the State issues to the gals at Tutweiler, but he could see a pelt of dark brown hair under the crotch part. And he truly believed that he could make out her crack right there in the center part, because there was like a little furrow where the panty indented and running along this groove was a wet spot dead in the center, right where her hole would be underneath the cloth."

"I'd have been looking my own self. Bet on it!"

Curly Bill hooted and slapped his knee. "And remember now in those days a gal didn't show her leg all the way up to her asshole like they do now. It was a real unusual sight for Billy to behold, especially her being alive and setting in a chair right smack dab in front of his face. We all wanted to hear more and Billy told us everything two and three times, and each telling got better as he recollected little details and related them to us.

"What sort of details do you mean?"

"Her name for one: it was Rhonda Belle Martin. Ain't that a lovely name — Rhonda Belle? Her eyes: she had these big brown sad eyes with long eyelashes. Her voice: it was a lady's voice. Southern and polite, and sexy when she answered a question. He told us about her bosom: a real nice big one, and when she breathed it moved. Billy was taken with her hair… long, clean, pretty brown hair halfway down her back, almost to her waist. And then to prove it to us, Billy reached into his jacket and pulled out a swatch of thick brown hair held together by a rubber band around one end. It reminded me of one of those Red Indian movies where they scalp a pioneer lady then run off with her hair and hook it onto a pole."

"They let this guy Billy walk off with her hair?"

"He's the special barber, ain't he? He cuts the air and hauls it off to the trash bin. Only this time he took him a little souvenir to show us in the cellblocks." Curly smiled a little, remembering her hair.

"We all smelled that long hank of hair. Put it right up to our noses and inhaled; it smelt real nice. Billy couldn't get enough of it. For a long time he would lay on his bunk, spread that spill of curly locks over his face, and jack his dick. For Billy, it was love at first sight between him and the cunt. He told us how he walked into her cell and right away saw she was no sweat hog. She was a sweet, pretty little woman. He had to tell her what to do. Take off your shoes. Peel down the nylon stocking. Put your foot in the bucket. She was shaking like a virgin and he had to calm her. Be gentle with her.

There he is, soaping her leg and it's trembling in his hands. Billy knows where she's going, so he tries to go slow to give her a few extra minutes. She's about to die, but he's making love to her with his eyes. Maybe she loved him back. He said she did. She cried when he cut her hair."

"Sounds like Billy was gone."

"Billy was speculating about that wet spot in the center of her crotch. He claimed it was love dew seeping, due to the way he was rubbing his hands up and down her leg. I reckoned it was plain old pee. I told Billy not even the horniest nympho at Tutweiler would be oozing love dew while sitting in the Holman Penitentiary Death House, even if Frank Sinatra was rubbing her leg."

"He took it pretty serious."

"Billy went all moony. We respected that. Didn't mention a word about the meat wagon from Bates Funeral Parlor that rolled in the back gate while he was down in the Death Cell sparking Rhonda Belle. Freddy, down by the gate, he saw it roll in and put it on the grapevine. I reckoned that gal from Tutweiler was thinking about something other'n Billy Mumford's passionate love while she was shaving the hair offen her own snatch. But I didn't tell Billy that."

"What did you tell Special Barber Billy?"

"We told him she'd get a stay from the courts. They'd send her back to Tutweiler and she'd write him fuck letters about what she'd do to him when he got out. What else?"

"Wishful thinking."

"Sure. And we were joshing Billy about it when Captain Scotty Crowe came walking up to the cellblock door. Captain Crowe ran the Death House. Enjoyed his work too. Got his name in the papers the time they burned that preacher's daughter from Anniston. Cute little blonde with big tits, killed her mama and her daddy. Told everyone the Devil made her do it. Maybe so. Then she come up to Holman and starts up that the Captain made an indecent proposal to her, so Warden Hobbs let him strap her cunt to the Chair. He did such a fine job they let him supervise every time a bitch burned. For all I know he's still up there frying those girlies."

"Do you think he made an indecent proposal to that preacher's daughter?"

"Bet your hairy ass he did. Told me so hisself. Said that little blonde was so fine it would give a man a hard-on just to look at her. One night he goes down by her cell and suggests he could fix it so's she'd die with a smile on her lips. She wanted to know how. He told her. She went off like a firecracker. Preacher's daughter. What the hell?"

Curly Bill took a long drag on his butt. Exhaled. Sighed. "So Captain Crowe

calls me over to the door and told me a white woman would be executed within the hour and would I go down to the death chamber and keep my eye on Nigger Jack."

"Who was this Nigger Jack character?"

"An asshole, a real asshole."

"I gathered as much, but why the need to eyeball the man?"

"OK, Nigger Jack was the colored boy they had to clean up the mess after each execution. 'Lectrocutions are a dirty sort of business; when it's done Nigger Jack unbuckles the corpse from the Chair and takes it back to a little room where it gets hosed off. He'd strip the cadaver down, turn the hose on 'em, and stuff 'em in a rubber bag for delivery to the folks from Bates Funeral Parlor. It was nigger work and they had 'em a real Nigger to do it. Sorry excuse for a human being. Yeah, Nigger Jack was about as sorry as they come."

This story was getting good. I broke out the Oreos, took a handful and tossed the bag to Curly Bill. "Well tell me, Curly, just how sorry was this nigger?"

Curly Bill dunked an Oreo in his coffee and crammed the whole wet cookie in his mouth. "When he first came on the yard he told us how he ran dope and whores. Had him a string of ten white ladies, he said." Curly Bill sighed.

"Every nigger's fantasy," I smiled.

"Right. We should have seen through that right away, but we didn't. What happened was that Sandy, the guy who cleans up in the Classification Office over by the Administration Building, found his commitment order from the Circuit Court. It was under a desk. Dropped by accident, I guess. Fact was that this Nigger Jack had worked in an undertaking establishment catering to the colored trade in Mobile. One day the owner of the joint comes walking in unexpected and there was Jack with his radiator hose up the behind of a six-year-old nigger baby that died in a car wreck. Jack wasn't just raping a baby, he was raping a *dead* baby."

"Pure fucking slime."

"You got the idea. So Sandy ran off some Xerox copies of this unusual rap sheet and passed them around the cellblocks and Carl Jones from Mobile happened to know the dead kid's family. So Carl walked on down to the machine shop and made himself a big fucking shank and set off to hunt down Nigger Jack. Carl was telling everyone how he planned to get ahold of Jack, cut off his johnson and feed it to him like a chow-hall donkey dick. Jack went screaming off to Captain Crowe's office begging the Captain to save him from Carl Jones and his sword of retribution.

"Now the Captain is a merciful man, and he has a sense of humor. So the Captain gives Jack a little private room right down next to the Death House. Gives him a job mopping up the shit and the piss, let him clean the crap off the Chair after each execution. Best of all, Crowe figures the Nigger can pump him some hot ass fresh out the Chair; after that, word on the yard was Nigger Jack takes a fancy to hot ass. *Smoking* hot."

Curly and I both laughed at that. He finished off his cup and plugged in the stinger for another round. He stacked three cookies neatly next to his cup and continued the story.

"So Captain Crowe had strong feelings about leaving Nigger Jack alone with a

naked white woman, even if she was dead meat. He was sure the Nigger would climb on her in a heartbeat. Figured a well-known cornhole artist like Jack wouldn't hesitate at real white pussy like Rhonda Belle. Fresh dead and still warm. Captain figured I wouldn't let a nasty thing like that go on, knowing how I feel about niggers. So I told him sure, I'd help him out. Stand around and watch the show. I had nothing better to do, and that's a fact. So the Captain opened the cell door and he took me with him on down to the death chamber. I'll tell you the truth. I wanted to have a look at this Rhonda girl that had Billy Mumford running around with cow eyes and a stiff dick."

"Did you see her?"

"Of course I saw her. Another cup?"

I passed him my empty cup. He tossed me the Oreos and I hooked out a fistful. Munched one down and said, "I've been thinking about trying for that Orderly job for when they fry Sonia. What do you think?"

"Good looking bitch. Nice tail."

"Better than Rhonda Belle?"

"I'd say so. They say Sonia sold her ass on the street. Jesse says it's true. She'd play Hide the Banana with Old Scotty, I'd bet that. Maybe scratch his eyes out for him too." Curly smiled at the thought of it. "Rhonda Belle weren't much actually."

"What did you think when you first saw her?"

Curly poured us our fresh cups and told me how it went down. "Me and the Nigger was standing off to one side when they brought her in for the Chair. I was figuring I might see me a cat fight. The sight of the Chair can fire a gal up, get her to scratching and biting and howling. I'd heard some women go out that way. Screaming. But luck wasn't riding with me on that pass. She was no screamer. It makes for a better story if I tell it with Rhonda Belle screaming and begging but you said you wanted the true story." He blew on his coffee. "What actually happened was that Warden Hobbs marched off into that room where the condemned wait for the call to the Chair and told her pure and simple it was her time. He gave her the usual choice; she could come strolling in like a lady or he could have her drug in by a couple of big screws on the execution detail. It didn't matter a lick to him one way or the other. Miss Rhonda chose to go peaceful."

"So much for the cat fight."

"Maybe. Maybe not. With a woman you never know. Captain Crowe used to say it was because a gal is a high-strung, emotional type of creature. Women can get hysterical fast. He told me he'd seen it happen."

"So she said she'd go peaceful. Then what'd she do?"

"Nothing much. The door from the holding cell opened and there she was. Two big bulldagger matrons from the Tutweiler Women's Penitentiary were with her. Big mean looking bitches in black uniforms. Rhonda Belle weren't no young gal, thirty years old if she was a day. Her big brown eyes were roaming around the room, flickering here and there taking everything in. She seemed a little shaky but not too much. I'd seen men worse."

"What was she wearing?"

Curly Bill thought on that one for a few beats. "She had a flowered scarf over

her head. Covered up her being bald. She was dressed nice. Ladylike. A black
dress. Sunday-go-to-meetin' clothes. Maybe like she'd wear to a funeral, come to
think of it. Nylon stockings. Black patent leather high-heeled pumps that made a
clickety-clack sound on the cement when she walked. There was make-up on her
face: shiny red lipstick, rouged cheeks, powdered nose. She was wearing nice
perfume. Back then a woman wore what she pleased to her own execution. Rhonda
Belle fancied heels and hose, plenty of Chanel perfume. You could see how Billy
had fallen for her. She was pretty. She smelt real sweet." Curly Bill licked his lips
at the memory.

"The two matrons had her by the elbows and steered her straight to the Chair.
Warden Hobbs asked her to take a seat, so she turned herself around and sat down.
She did it quick and smooth. She made a little squeak of alarm, like maybe she
figured she'd get a shock from the Chair. But when nothing happened she scooched
herself around and settled her nerves. She looked at Warden Hobbs and grinned
sheepishly. He asked her if she was comfortable, and she bobbed her head.

"Then Warden Hobbs turned to Captain Crowe and ordered him to strap her in
for the ride. She was looking a bit dazed, like maybe she really had been thinking
she'd be going back on down to Tutweiler where she'd sit in her cell and write
steamy letters to Billy Mumford at Holman and all of a sudden it dawned on her
that a stay wasn't coming after all. She was in for a big shock, compliments of the
State of Alabama. I asked the Nigger, 'Who'd she kill?'

"'Captain say her husband ate poison. Rat poison.'

"'Cold bitch to do that to a man.'

"'Fixin' to warm her right up, Curly Bill.'

"That was a fact. The pretty flowered scarf was gone and the Captain was taping
a strip of metal to the egg-smooth skin of her head. The Nigger explained that was
the primary electrode; he told me that at the pull of a switch, 4500 volts of electricity would boil her brain. Rhonda Belle sat in the Chair and quivered. The fat
matron with the dishwater blonde hair unceremoniously pulled up Rhonda Belle's
skirt and unfastened her nylon stocking and peeled it down her left leg, impatient
as a lover. The skirt was so high we could see the rubber strap holding up her other
stocking, and the white fabric of her panty rucked up in her crotch. Me and the
Nigger looked hard but didn't see the pussy hair curling out. I reckoned maybe
that body shave rule applied to Tutweiler gals after all.

"'Oh my God!' the Nigger sighed.

"'Amen, Brother!' I added.

"We could see everything between the top of her stocking and the white panty.
Meat the color of chicken breast at Sunday dinner. The tender, sweet kind. Rhonda
Belle was tender, and she was sweet. I couldn't believe they were about to kill her.
I had an impulse to step forward and tell them to leave her alone."

"Bullshit," I said. I just couldn't see old Curly Bill going sentimental on a condemned piece of ass. Curly cocked his eyebrow at me. It wiggled like a caterpillar
crawling across his brow.

"God's truth. I'd never seen a woman put to death. It stirred me, way down
inside somewhere." His eyes clouded and he looked away. The bastard seemed to
have feelings of some kind and I waited for them to subside.

"Anyway. They fastened another metal electrode on her leg just below her knee. Clamped it on real tight with a butterfly nut. Her stocking was in a little heap around her ankle. Then they took her ankles and set them in the wooden stocks and locked them in."

"Stocks? Why'd they do that, Curly? I mean she ain't going nowhere."

"Holds 'em steady so they get an even burn."

"Oh." That shut me up.

"Yeah, and when they fix the ankles that way it spreads the woman's legs. Opens them right wide, and when that happened we could see all the way up." Curly Bill clearly relished this part.

"What did you see, the famous wet spot?"

"Nope. Looked like a nice fat jellyroll wrapped in white cotton cloth. The Nigger gave me a little elbow and we were both straining our eyes looking up her skirt, but we couldn't see no wet spot atoll."

"So you really didn't see that much, did you?"

A smug look spread over Curly Bill's wide face. "We saw plenty, Sonny. Plenty. You ever seen a woman sit on Sparky?"

"Sure."

"You have! Where?"

"Right here on Q-Wing. Girls from the college tours sit on Sparky every month... used to anyway. They'd sit up there and some of 'em would show their panties. It ain't that much to see, unless you see one that ain't wearing no panty. Then it's worth a real hard look."

Curly Bill rubbed his crotch and eyed me like he wasn't too sure he was going to give up any more story. I'd have to prompt him.

"Well? What was Rhonda Belle doing in the Chair, Curly?"

"She weren't doing a damn thing but sitting there warming the seat — legs spread like some honky-tonk tramp looking for a boner. Her forearms and wrists were strapped down to the armrests on the Chair. There was a black rubber belt drawn across her belly and another one that ran under her arms just beneath her big ole bazooms; made it so they were pouched up like a movie star's titties. She was sticking them out like she was Jayne Fucking Mansfield on a casting couch. Bet you never seen no college girl wearing a set of death straps!"

"Well..." I shrugged.

"Damn right you ain't seen no woman's ass strapped to no goddamned 'lectric chair. When they lay that belly strap acrost her gut and snap it tight, the gal lets out a grunt like some stud just ran a ten-inch hardhead up her box."

"No shit! Why so tight?"

"Because, idgit, when she rides the lightning, she arches her back just like she does when she comes. They got to hold that stuff down in the Chair, boy, or it would be an obscenity. Decent folk don't want to see no whore with her cunt raised." He caught my look and quickly amended, "Not at an official proceeding at any rate."

"What were you and the nigger doing all this time?"

"Sheeeeit. We was standing right there looking at her snatch with our tongues hanging out!"

Curly stuck his tongue out and panted to give me the idea. I punched his arm. "Go on, man!"

"OK, once they got her body restrained, then they ran another rubber strap acrost her forehead. So she was pretty well immobilized. Warden Hobbs stepped up right in front of Rhonda so she could see him and read off the execution order from the Governor's Office. He read it slow and clear, so she wouldn't miss a word. When he was done Chaplain Curtis came in and read a few words from the Good Book over her."

"I wonder what she was thinking."

"I never found out. She had a chance to tell us but she was a quiet one. Warden Hobbs approached her and asked her real nice if there was something she'd like to say because if so she was welcome to speak up. She seemed to be contemplating an answer. I was thinking she might crack wise and ask Hobbs to hold her hand, or sit on her lap or something. But she just said she didn't have nothing to say about nothing. Very polite. Nice soft South'ren voice. The Nigger was real disappointed. He'd been expecting a speech, he said. Captain Crowe had told him some ladies get downright chatty at the last moment. Captain said the preacher's daughter ran on for more than twenty minutes about how hard liquor and sex was the cause of her trouble. She'd finished up her story by giving everyone a charming smile and going '...and here I am.'"

"Wow. What happened to the preacher's daughter?"

"Same as what happened to Rhonda Belle Martin. Warden Hobbs gave a nod to one of those big bull daggers that rode up from the Women's Pen and she walked right up to the Chair and commenced to pushing wads of cotton up Rhonda Belle's pretty nose.

"The fat matron went right to work at it. She'd take a wad of cotton out of a blue box and work it into Rhonda Belle's nostril, then jam it on up there as far as she could with her finger. Didn't wear no rubber glove or nothing. Stuffed that cotton way to hell up there too. Me and the Nigger couldn't hardly believe it when we saw it happening."

"What the hell was the reason for the cotton?"

Curly Bill gave me a look of disgust. "So her fucking brains wouldn't leak out of her nose, bozo. When they throw that switch and four or five thousand volts zap her in the head, the brain boils. And then it plain runs out your nose and down the front of your shirt. Or in this case, you'd see her sweetmeats dribbling down between her tits onto her lap." He leered at me. His eyes had the evil glint of a jackal.

"That's disgusting!"

"Happens all the time. You want to hear the story? Or maybe we'd better quit while we're ahead." He stood and hitched up his pants. "I don't want you puking up your Oreos, kid. Think you're up to it? It ain't no pretty tale."

"Naw, naw, Curly, I ain't no pussy. I came here to hear a yarn and I'm a-gonna set this one out. That is, if you're still pouring coffee."

"Oh you finished already? Well I guess you been drinking while I been yapping..." he was teasing me. "I reckon I could fix another cup, if you're gonna stick around."

"Yeah, Curly, come on and run the story. I want to hear it."

Curly settled the stinger for another round and continued. "The other fat dyke had an ass on her like a John Deere tractor. She was cramming cotton into Rhonda Belle's ears with the eraser end of a number two lead pencil. Sometimes the brains squirt out the ears too, you know?"

My mouth twisted with disgust. "How'd the girl react to all that poking into her head?"

"Howled like a fucking maniac is what she did. She was having a regular damn fit and shrieking 'What are you doing? What are you doing?' over and over like a busted Victrola record. The two matrons didn't pay her no mind. They were as busy as a son-of-a-bitch pulling cotton from the blue boxes and making it disappear into Rhonda Belle.

"While they were packing her, the two matrons were clucking and crooning, 'Be still now! Act like a lady! This don't hurt! This is for your own good! Behave yourself!' and happy horseshit like that. And I'll tell you something else what happened just then."

"What?"

"The Nigger leaned forward and lowered his voice. Muttered, 'Curly Bill' toward the floor. I leaned toward him to catch it. 'You reckon they'll pack her hole?' he whispered.

"The Nigger said that right there in the execution chamber?"

"Sure, he was a sex freak, remember?"

"Yeah, I see what you mean."

"I said I'd never heard of no such thing, but I kinda hoped they would, now that I got to thinking about it." Curly slurped his java. "What the Nigger said next was even more interesting."

"I'm on the edge of my can."

"Nigger said, 'If they put something in her hole, I'll be obliged to take it out later.' And I looked over at him and saw that he was serious. I could see it in his bugged-out eyes. His mouth was wet with spit because he kept licking his lips."

"Pure freak for that hot pussy, huh?"

"Hell yeah. By then Rhonda Belle was screaming and trying to wriggle out of the Chair. She wasn't getting nowhere, just howling like a bitch. Her nose was swole up with the cotton. She was crying. Tears running down her cheeks making wet trails through her make-up. She was a pitiful sight. We were watching it close, taking it all in. The Nigger whispered to me, 'That there be a real cunt, Man.' I gave him a look, trying to make out where he was coming from, and he came back real quick. 'Curly Bill, in here you can get a boy to suck your dick; you can bend him over and get you some shithole, but where you gonna get you some real pussy at Holman Penitentiary? Where else but right here?'"

Curly Bill paused and looked straight at me, waiting for me to say something.

"He had a point, I suppose."

"Bet your cracker ass he had a point. I told him I wasn't too sure about what he was getting at. I said Rhonda was wired for the electric enema, and that put me off my feed, so to speak."

"Did I miss something? They give her an enema?"

"That's what they call it when they hit you with 4000 volts and it blows the shit

right out your ass and down your leg. I had heard of it. There was a good chance I was about to see it. That is, unless the bull daggers put cotton up Rhonda's asshole. Now don't get me wrong. I like a boy to suck me off same as anyone in the joint. But I told the Nigger that dipping my wick in some whore's shit wasn't my idea of an afternoon delight. But the Nigger had an answer for that." Curly smirked and sat back.

"What was the Nigger's remedy?" I prodded, intrigued.

"The black son-of-a-bitch said the electric enema weren't nothing at all. He said, 'I've got me a water hose back there and I'll just spray some over her hole, wash it off real nice, and she'll be ready to ride. That juicy thing is gonna be as hot as a two-dollar pistol on a Saturday night.'"

"That makes sense," I commented judiciously.

"Damn right it makes sense. So I told that slimy fucker that maybe I'd go on back there and give it a closer look after he'd rinsed her off. Maybe hit a stroke or two. You should have seen those rubber lips smile. That boy was grinning like a weasel in a hen house."

"He knew he was gonna get him some white pussy now."

"Yup, sure as hell did," Curly Bill snorted.

"Did the prison matrons put cotton up her butt?"

"Nope, those bulldaggers didn't fool around with that. I figured they'd dive right into her panties and straight up her hole. But they never messed with her."

"Too bad, that would've been a sight to see."

"Yeah. There was nothing to look at but the panties, so I looked up at her eyes and they were like Billy had said: large and brown and wet with tears. And miserable. She knew she was on her way to wherever fried cunt goes, and she wasn't too anxious to take that ride. Those eyes. They were desolate. Then Captain Crowe covered her face with the rubber death mask and she started going, 'Oh. Oh. Oh.' behind the mask. The strangest sound you ever heard a woman make."

"Sounds like it took a long time to get her ready."

"Well, not really. The event moved right along. Everyone seemed to know just what to do. They'd had plenty of practice. They burned men regular at Holman. Women only came in once in a while but it went down smooth enough. When the fat matrons were done, Warden Hobbs walked around the Chair giving Rhonda Belle a close inspection. He checked the straps and apparently he liked what he saw. He thanked the two dykes from the Women's Penitentiary for their assistance and asked Captain Crowe to show them to the door.

"Back then the only woman allowed to see an execution was the guest of honor, and she didn't really see it. The two matrons took one last fond look at Rhonda Belle and waddled on off with the Captain. Warden Hobbs waited until the dykes were clear of the room, then he turned and looked thoughtfully at Rhonda Belle sitting there on the Chair making her funny little noises. It was so weird. She kept going, 'Oh. Oh. Oh.' over and over, and making a noise like a hiccup. She'd twitch, and she was sort of trying to wriggle around. She had the Warden's attention. He watched her for a minute like he was memorizing her reactions.

He pursed his lips and scratched behind his ear. Then he turned and gave a nod toward the black drape hanging off to one side."

"What's that for?" I asked.

"The executioner stands behind it, and when he gets the nod he pulls the switch."

"And he got the nod...."

"He damn sure did. One moment Rhonda Belle was wriggling around making squeaky noises, and a second later she was slammed forward into the straps so hard it made the leather creak. She came up off that Chair like a gymnastical gal trying to arch her body toward the roof." Curly Bill was checking me out, to see if I got the picture.

"She came right up off the Chair?"

"Damn right! They gave her a straight shot of 4500 volts and when the power took her, it lifted her up and tried to fling her right out of the Chair."

I could just see it. Curly Bill was smacking his lips, warming to his topic. "When those straps bit into her, she gave a grunt like someone hit her a punch in the belly, and at the same time she let go a fart. A real ripper, lewd and unladylike. And listen to this: a jet of pee squirted right through the white crotch of her panty like it was coming from a pressure hose."

"You mean it shot out in front of her? How far would you say?"

"A coupla feet at least. Came jetting right out. Made a little pool in front of the Chair and between her legs. Her butt was maybe six inches off the Chair. The pee wet her pants and dribbled. There was only that first jet that came through, when they put the juice to her. She didn't pee a whole lot, just that little puddle for her behind to sit in when it came down. Course, when the panty got wet we saw the crack. The McCoy. I recollect it perfect to this very day." Curly Bill was licking his lips, and I imagined that the bright look in his eyes was not too different from the one he had seen in Nigger Jack's.

"Is it true what you heard about the electric enema?"

Curly Bill sucked in his breath. "Oh, it's true all right. All the shit up inside Rhonda leaped right out her asshole and slithered around inside her drawers like a damn snake. The turd came out and coiled up in her pants. Made 'em sag with the load until they drooped down and touched the seat under her. The stink was vile. It rose up from under her and radiated around the room. There is no smell like it on this earth. Smoke was coming off her head. Her flesh was sizzling like bacon at the electrodes and her drawers were full of shit. The stench would gag a maggot.

"The Nigger's eyes were popped wide. He said, 'Curly Bill, that's what they call the electric enema.' I didn't know what to say. Then he said, 'Don't let it put you off none. All that washes off. I'll take care of that.' You see, he was coming on strong. He wanted that white pussy, and he'd do just about anything to get her. He knew I was standing between him and her, and he was working on me the only way he knew how."

"He was trying to work you up so you'd want a little piece yourself."

"Right. And he could see I was about to go a little green around the gills from smelling her frying flesh, so right away he started in on that."

"The smell?"

"Yeah. He said, 'Curly Bill, did you smell her perfume when they brought her in?' I gave him a nod while drilling my eyes on her body. It was changing color from white to deep pink. She was turning colors like one of them lizards that can

go from brown to green when they take a notion. Only she was going from white to red. Her leg where the electrode was around it was as red as a lobster in a pot above the electrode and white as a catfish belly beneath."

"She was changing colors while you were watching her?"

He nodded. "She was cooking between the electrodes is why. A big ole burn blister rose up on her leg just above the electrode cuff. It swole up with liquid and then it popped and smoke rose up from it. The watery stuff soaked down into the cuff and hissed like a snake. Steam came up in a white cloud. Smelled so awful I could feel my dinner coming up on me."

I stared at him. He was really into the story. His lips were curled up in a grimace as if recoiling from the stench of frying flesh.

"Curly Bill. Didn't the Nigger say something about her perfume?"

"Oh yeah," he sniffed unconsciously. Maybe that cleared out the memory of the death stench, because his face relaxed. "Nigger Jack told me she put perfume on her tits and in the crack of her behind."

"How'd he know?"

"He watched her through the security mirror."

"What's that?"

"It's where the prison officials watch a woman when she's naked. They watch her when she takes off her prison uniform and puts on her execution clothes."

"The men watch her?"

"Sure they do. That's security. Suppose she jumps on those matrons? Anything could happen in that room. She could kill them two matrons in there and who'd know? They got to watch."

"Makes sense. But it must really embarrass the woman."

"Well they do it in a polite way, so she don't feel embarrassed."

"Who watches?"

"Oh, the Captain and whoever else he lets come in to see the strip show," Curly Bill chuckled. "He would have killed the Nigger if he knew he was watching the white woman, but Nigger Jack slipped his sneaky black ass into the room while Captain Crowe was off checking on the death straps and had himself a nice long look. That Nigger, he got him an eyeful, and he was giving me an earful."

"Wanted to get your cock up for Rhonda."

"That's it. He said he'd watched the white lady shave the hair off her cunt. She squatted on the toilet and soaped it, then she shaved it, washed it by pouring water from a plastic cup over it, and patted it dry with a paper towel. Then when she was done she stood up and the fat matron handed her a little bottle of perfume and Rhonda Belle put some on her finger and went up behind her ears with it. She dabbed a bit on her neck, then ran her finger down smack between her teats. Lifted up each titty and put a dab under each one. Finally she rubbed some between her legs and reached around and drew her finger up the crack of her ass. The Nigger told me he took out his cock and jacked off into his bandanna just from the sight of her."

"Think he was lying?"

"Nope. I saw the look on his face." Curly Bill took out a cigarette paper and sprinkled some Kite tobacco onto it. He rolled it, licked it and fired it up. He puffed away at it, recollecting Rhonda's perfume.

"Nigger tell you anything else he saw?"

"They took away her brassiere. Made her go to the Chair without it."

"That's weird," I remarked. "Why?"

"No metal is supposed to be between the electrodes. None at all. The brassiere she had been wearing had metal fasteners and stuff on it, so they confiscated it from her. They made her wear special underpants too."

That got my interest. "Special in what way?"

"The Nigger knew all about it. He told me the panties the state issues convict women have elastic at the waist and leg. The elastic melts when they cook the gal, so before she comes up here, they sew up a special panty for her, one with no elastic. It's got drawstrings like one of them bikini suits Brigitte Bardot wears.

"So after Rhonda Belle was shaved and perfumed, the matron tied the bikini on her ass. They knotted that sucker up tight too. We had to slice it with a razor to get it off."

"So you did get to see her pussy!"

"Saw it? Damn right I did. I saw it snuggled up in her panty when she was alive. I saw it squirt pee when they ran the lightning through her. I saw her raise that pussy up off the Chair like a woman ready to fuck. And I saw it bleed—"

"What do you mean, bleed?"

"What I mean is… she was arched up in the straps and turning red as a cooked beet. Her hands were curled into grotesque claws with her fingers angling out in every which way. She was shaking so hard her shoes fell off and her toes were curled up like she was coming hard. She was sizzling like a pan of fried meat. Up inside her belly some female part of her must have burst, because the blood rushed out from her. It gushed from her hole, it soaked her panties dark red. Made a pool on the Chair and dripped onto the floor."

I took a deep breath. I was trying to think of some reasonable explanation. "It must have been her time of month, Curly Bill."

"Nope. For that they put the woman on the rag. She wasn't on her period. She just busted up inside and the blood ran out her cunt, that's all."

"That is totally fucking gross." Curly Bill's story was starting to get to me. I started to tell him to stop, but I figured it couldn't get any worse. Curly Bill looked like he was in another world, like he was actually seeing the whole disgusting spectacle and couldn't tear his eyes away.

"Now you know why they don't let ladies come in and see the executions. Even a girl reporter might be upset by a sight like that."

"You can bet the women will be here to watch Sonia Jacobs when she cooks."

"Yeah, and you can bet Sonia will have more cotton stuffed in her than a teddy bear. This ain't like the old days. Sonia won't get no 4500 volts neither."

"What will she get?"

"Not more than 2800 volts, about enough to just knock out her eyeballs. Damnedest thing you ever saw, eyeballs popping out of the head and hanging on the cheeks by the optic nerve. Happens every time. Why do you think they make them wear a mask?"

"I guess I never thought about it, Curly Bill. Or at least, not enough."

"Sonia will have it easy compared to girls in the old days. They'll stick cotton

up her cunt, up her butt, let her wear a ministration rag to pee on, and give her plastic pants to boot. Then they'll tickle her to death with a measly couple thousand volts." Curly Bill spat out a shred of tobacco on the floor.

"1800 volts will kill you."

"Sure. After awhile, so will these RIP's." He blew smoke at me. "But Rhonda Belle, they ran the power through her for three minutes, then quit. Rhonda Belle went limp in the straps, sat down in her own fucking pile of slop as dead as anyone you ever did see. Doctor Garcia, the prison sawbones, was called in to examine her. He told everyone she was dead. Captain Crowe said, 'No shit, Sherlock?' and the sawbones scuttled on out of there. The stench was so thick you could almost see it; and it wasn't Rhonda Belle's Chanel we were smelling. That smell is really something. They ought to bottle it and make juvenile delinquents take a whiff every time they get to feeling ambitious." Curly chuckled at his own little joke, and I urged him on.

"So the fried lady was sitting there…"

"Oh yeah. Well, Warden Hobbs yelled to Nigger Jack, 'Git this damned mess out of my 'Lectric Chair!' and the Nigger comes back, 'Yes sir, Mister Warden, sir!' He unfastened all the straps and buckles, then loaded her onto a metal gurney and wheeled her away to the back room."

"Where were the screws?"

"The screws were fucking gone — long gone. The show was over and the audience cleared out fast. Like I said, the place was stinking so bad, people were ready to puke. It's a real bad smell."

"So nobody was around but you and Nigger Jack?"

"Me and Nigger Jack — and Rhonda Belle." Curly Bill grinned like the very Devil himself. "We took that cutie into the back room and the Nigger got to work cleaning her up. He pulled down those nasty panties, cut the knots with his razor, and slid them off her ass. It was like he promised, exactly. He had his hose and he played it all around her hindparts. Steam rising off that hot ass, swear to God. Got after her with the lye soap. The mess came off her and went down the drain. He stuffed her soiled clothes into a bag. He poked her eyeballs back into their sockets and stuck a piece of adhesive tape over them to hold them in."

"Why was he going to all that bother?"

"That part was his job. He has to fix her up for the free-world undertaker. But soon as he was done with his job, he took her and draped her over a nail keg. He put the garter belt back on her and attached the stockings. Her head was down and her bottom was up. There was a big smile on those nether lips. Smooth as a baby's behind, and bright pink. The Nigger ran his hand over the full round ass end of her. His hands real black against the bright pink of her behind.

He took his fingers and dropped them down to the center of her pussy and spread the petals. It was a gentle gesture. Nigger Jack was very tender with Rhonda. He asked me, 'When do you figure she last had a man, Curly Bill?'"

"You stood there let that Nigger handle her that way?"

He shrugged. "Hell, I had my eyes on that pussy. You would too. That stuff looked real good — pink and soft. And there was no more nasty smell at all. She

was nice and clean from the soap job the Nigger gave her. I got up a little closer to her, and I caught a whiff of her perfume too."

"She was dead."

"Fresh off the Chair, Sonny. And still hot — about 106 degrees and cooling fast."

"But she was dead, Curly Bill, *dead!*"

He paused a beat. "More like dead drunk, actually. She weren't stiff, and she didn't smell bad at all. That Chanel on her neck…"

I licked my lips. Puffed out my cheeks. Held my peace while I waited for him to come back.

"It was the Nigger that did it. Had him a hard-on from sticking his hands in Rhonda's privates to clean her. He started to rub on it, then opened his pants and took it out. He spit in his hand and rubbed it on his dick. Then he just turned around and stuck his johnson right up her poop chute."

"Cornholed her?"

"As I live and breathe. I watched him."

"What did you say to the black bastard?"

"I told him I had first dibs on her cunt," he answered with a straight face.

"First dibs," I repeated. "Then you fucked a woman who just got off the Electric Chair?"

"I never said that," Curly Bill disclaimed.

"Was it good?"

A look at Curly Bill's long yellow teeth was my only answer.

I got up off the buttcan and stretched. "I think I'll get moving, Curly Bill."

"Oh? What's the big rush, Sonny?"

I looked him in the eye and said, "I'm going down to see the Death House Captain about an orderly job."

"Figuring you might get that job?"

I nodded. "Sonia. I've seen her picture. I'm in love. Hearing what you say, I'm ready to give it a try my own self. I know I'll never get me no more live pussy. So what the fuck."

"You can forget Sonia," Curly Bill said, a little smile curling one side of his mouth.

"Oh? Why is that?"

His curious smile became an outright leer. "Because the job's been took already. They gave it to the only convict in this joint with experience handling a burnt woman."

"*You!*" I whispered.

"Yup. Me. And when it's done, come on down and I'll tell you how she was." Curly Bill gave me a big wolfish smile as I turned on my heel and went back to my own cell.

*G.J. Schaefer tries to scare Sondra London
at Glades C.I., Belle Glade, Florida, 1990*

*Guard tries to stop Sondra London from photographing
Schaefer at Glades C.I., Belle Glade, Florida, 1990*

Actual Fantasies

The stories and drawings in this section were among those seized by police from a closet in Schaefer's mother's home, and used to convict him of murder in 1973.

Murder Plan

I n order to remain unapprehended, the perpetrator of an execution-style murder such as I have planned must take precautions.

One must think out well in advance a crime of this nature, in order for it to work. We will need an isolated area, accessible by a short hike, away from any police patrols or parking lovers.

The execution site must be carefully arranged for a speedy execution, once the victim has arrived. There will be 2 sawhorses with a 2x4 between them. A noose is attached to the overhanging limb of a tree. Another rope to pull away the 2x4, preferably by car.

A grave must be prepared in advance away from the place of execution.

The victim could be one of the many women who flock to Miami and Ft. Lauderdale for the winter months. Even two victims would not be difficult to dispose of, since women are less wary when traveling in pairs. In any case it may be more preferable to bind and gag the victims before transporting them to the place of execution.

Then again, depending on what torture or defilement is planned for them, other items may be useful.

Bars of soap & water. These are useful if you would want to wash a woman before her execution. Induce her to urinate and then wash her.

Soap provides an excellent lubricant for anal intercourse.

Beer is useful to induce urination and make the victim groggy and more cooperative. Soap can also be forced into the rectum to induce defecation if the victim has no particular desire to relieve her bowels. Possibly she may want to defecate, since people generally have a desire to do this when they are scared.

A douche bag may be helpful in degrading her further, and is also useful for a soapsuds enema which would be a great indignity, especially if one victim was made to urinate or defecate on the other. This would be a gross indignity.

Nylon stockings are useful to tie the hands and feet of the victim. The victim should be made to strip at least to her underwear. If stripped completely nude an attempt can be made to excite her sexually. This effect would be especially interesting if the victim had her neck in the noose and hands tied behind her back.

A *white pillow case* should be placed over her head and her mouth *gagged*. Her panties should be pulled down enough to expose the genitals, and clitoral stimulation applied. During the height of her excitement the support should be pulled away and she should dangle by her neck.

She may be revived before death if desirable and subjected to further indecencies. After death has occurred, the corpse should be violated if not violated already. The body should then possibly be mutilated and carried to the grave and buried. All identity papers should be destroyed and the place of execution dismantled.

Into the Mind of the Ghoul

I walk into the bar and look around. There is something special that I am looking for, or should I say someone special. A woman with that look about her, that look of wildness, uncaring, a willingness to do anything for a price. A whore or someone like one.

I have to be sure she is the right one because one blunder could be the end for me. When I find the one that I'm looking for, I have to be sure through conversation. I'll make sure that no one notices me and then I'll make my offer. And if she accepts she has signed her death warrant.

Everything has been arranged long before in preparation of this event. I take her for a ride. I am cordial enough and make no threatening motions. I give her no reason to become alarmed. I drive out to the place that I am going to leave my car, a place I have left it many times before, so as not to draw suspicion. I could be an ordinary traveler out of gas or taking a nap on the side of the road. Nobody would think differently, not even the police. That is important.

I pull over and casually say that we are here, and for her to get out. Maybe it is then that she starts to worry because of the fact that we are in the middle of nowhere. Maybe it is then that I have to show her the gun and remind her of the consequences for disobedience. If she knew what lay in store for her, she would gladly choose the bullet.

I have traveled over this trail before so the darkness is of little hindrance. The trail is well hidden. No one has ever been down it before, because of the desolate location and the thickness of the jungle around it, but with little difficulty I know where the trail is and where it goes.

Deep in the swamp is a huge tree with limbs strong enough walk on. It is completely surrounded by jungle. This is the place I seek. I have been there many times before, only those times it was in rehearsal and there was no victim, only the fantasy of it all. But I do know what will be done and how to do it step by step.

The woman is by this time very frightened. This is good, because the more frightened she is, the greater the thrill for me. I tell her to strip, but I let her leave

her underwear on. I tie her to a branch and gag her if she is too noisy while I go about the business at hand.

I bring over the white sheet and a pillowcase to go over her head. I explain that I am going to hang her and she might as well accept the fact and cooperate. The gun is persuasive and there is always hope, so she cooperates. The limbs are arranged perfectly for the deed, all the right height and distance apart. It has taken a long time to find the right tree and the right person, but I finally did it.

I arrange the rope and the noose and I dress the woman in the white shroud, place the pillowcase over her head, and then if I feel like it, sit down and entertain her with a bit of my conversation. Terrorize her. Give her my ideas on what she will look like while she is hanging there, fighting the rope that is slowly choking the life out of her. Make it as real as possible for her, so that she is petrified with fear. Make her know that she is going to die.

The noose is arranged so that she will strangle slowly, and she sits on a board between two limbs with a long rope leading off into the jungle. When it is time, I will go off into the jungle and pull the rope and she will hang.

Then I will go home to have something to eat, and bright and early the next morning I will be out hunting. I will find the body hanging from the tree and only then will I really notice it. Maybe fondle it and maybe even have coitus with it. I will notice the expression on the face, the position of the body, explore every nick and cranny of her, maybe mutilate her and delight in the smell of any urine or excrement that she may have passed while hanging there.

I leave and then return so it will be unbelievable to myself that I did the deed. I will not be able to remember doing it. Funny isn't it.

Then after many hours I will dispose of the body in a place that has never been seen by man, and it will soon rot away in the tropical heat, with the help of the bugs and vermin, the rats and raccoons that abound here.

This is what I intend to do, but I do not know why.

There is a drive within me so powerful that it completely takes over my sense of reason and values. I am at the mercy of this insane maddening drive to commit the ultimate crime of horror, and only when it is done will I be at rest. I have to fight off this desire every day of my life. Why? Why? That is the question. If I could understand what causes these emotions then I might be able better to combat them.

I do positive things to prevent this happening. I stay away from bars, the beach, dances, anywhere that I might come in contact with that person that might put me over the edge. Twice this has nearly happened, but both times my senses prevented disaster before I had gone too far.

Once I picked up a girl at the beach and took her to a place that I had picked out for just such an occasion. She stood beneath the limb that she was going to hang from and somehow I just prevented myself from exposing what it was I had in mind. She was really frightened, and I was so nervous that I could barely speak. This was accompanied by violent headaches, and even as I recall this information to put on paper, I am plagued by headaches and a ringing in my ears.

I have been tempted to do away with other women too, usually ones that I am sexually attracted to but do not know personally. One girl whom I almost killed I

later became good friends with and drove her to the airport to fly up north. It was an experiment to see if I still wanted to kill her after I got to know her, and I didn't. In fact, I am still rather fond of her.

Once while in high school I playfully strangled a girl into unconsciousness, and have longed for the feeling it gave me ever since. I have always liked the idea of strangling women. But I never do, because I am afraid I will be caught and confined. The idea of confinement is horrifying to me. I don't mind death, and have often thought about suicide. But it is the idea of confinement that keeps me from doing anything on the spur of the moment.

Often when I was sexually attracted to a woman and wanted to kill her I would steal her clothes and dress up in them, and then hang myself instead. This is a little risky, but I have only been caught at it twice by strangers, and I managed to wiggle out of it both times. I used to have piles of women's clothes that I stole, but it got to where I didn't have anywhere to keep them, so I have to work with a minimum amount now. There was a time that I had wardrobes of clothes in trunks out in the forest, but then one day a forest fire destroyed the area, and I had to start all over.

Hanging seems to be the most exciting way of dispatching a victim, but in a pinch I would resort to strangulation. I can't explain why. The experience of imagining a woman hung produces intense sexual excitement. It is always the same thing: the preliminaries to the woman being hanged, and then ejaculation as she vanishes through the imaginary trap.

Recently I have become seriously emotionally attached to a girl and she to me. We have experienced coitus together on several occasions. I always feel for her a deep and strong love, and will marry her if all works out in the future. But I am not completely emotionally wrapping myself up in her, so in the event that something does happen I won't do anything foolish.

When we make love, it leaves us both feeling terrific and unguilty. But the only way that I can experience an orgasm is to think of that woman going through the trap and hanging there. I can make love all night and never lose the erection unless I think of that hanging woman. I merely wait until my girl is beginning to climax, and then I think of the woman hanging and I automatically climax myself. This bothers me but it doesn't take away the deep and intense feeling that I have for the girl that I make love to.

It has long been known that men ejaculate when hanged. A favorite method of self-gratification, used in the Middle Ages and still today, is what might be called do-it-yourself hanging. The sensation of choking produces an erection that culminates in a violent orgasm, sometimes during the dying process. This stimulation has not been lost on the sexually perverted, who constantly cast about for more intense pleasures to replace whipping, self-scourging, biting and the like.

The maniacal rapist murderer represents the unholy marriage between sex and death. I wonder if he understands his act. I don't understand it, even though these same feelings are occurring within me all the time. I would like to be able to free myself from this world, because it inhibits my creative ability. My mind cannot function properly when it is preoccupied with averting a social calamity and a personal tragedy. It is trying to fight the urge to relieve these terrible cravings. I am sure that there must be an answer somewhere, and some day I will be cured.

This is mainly a European method of execution by hanging. The woman is pulled up while on a dais. The hangman controls the strangulation. The woman is pulled up until she loses consciousness, then lowered in order to regain her senses, then hauled up again. The procedure for men convicted of high treason in England was to be hauled up naked and strangled to the verge of death, causing the culprit to have an erection. The man was then castrated and disemboweled. The bowels were burned before the prisoner in a brazier. The brazier here is marked RIP.

This sketch shows a pre-disembowelment hanging for a German woman during the 18th Century. Instead of disembowelment, Englishwomen were publicly stripped, slathered with lard, hanged on a stake and set afire.

Naturally nobody bothered to ask me what this doodle means. I suppose the police figure the executioner is me and the woman is one of my alleged victims. Or maybe they just like lurid depictions of State-sanctioned violence.

POWERLINE ROAD

We drove out Powerline Road. It was about 9 a.m. She was making with the small talk and I was attempting not to appear nervous.

I was wondering who she had told and how much she had told. I was pretty sure she had blabbed to someone because that would be just like her. We turned off onto a dirt road. I knew where we were going. I asked her to put on a blindfold. She was nervous. Said she was scared and had an uneasy feeling. She said it was because of all the killings recently and such. I told her there was nothing to worry about which was a lie, and we drove off into a field.

When we got to where I wanted to go I stopped and we got out. She still had the blindfold on so I helped her. We walked about ten yards and I said to stand still, because I forgot something in the car. I went back and got a sack filled with lead weights, walked up and hit her on the back of the head. She was stunned a little and I hit her again.

Then she started to try to protect herself and fell to the ground screaming "Don't hit me. Please don't hit me." I was shaken because of her pleas and didn't hit her. I helped her up and said I was sorry and that I had been instructed to put her out. She had messed us up once before and now we didn't trust her.

I asked her who she had told and she said nobody. I said we know she had told someone, and she became a little worried but still would not admit telling anyone.

She was sitting on an orange crate and when I put the pillow case over her head she complained so much that she couldn't breathe, I took it off. As she sat there she kept complaining about being dizzy and feeling faint. I would just tell her to shut up.

I tied her hands behind her and put a noose over her head that I had put up the previous afternoon. It had rained that day and the rope was wet and didn't tighten properly. I tightened it as best I could but the noose wouldn't slip. I would pull the rope up occasionally to hear her beg.

She must have been really scared. She was sitting in the sun and sometimes she would forget about her legs and let them come apart, giving me a good look up her dress.

She finally asked what had probably been going through her mind for some time. "Are you going to kill me?" I told her that I didn't know, that it wasn't up to me and the people responsible were deciding her fate right now. I said she had made too many mistakes and her mouth was too loose and we had people watching her constantly. It didn't look good for her. There was silence for awhile. Then she asked me "Is it quick?" and I asked her, "Is what quick?"

"Hanging. Aren't they going to hang me? They're going to hang me aren't they?"

"No," I lied. "I don't know what they're going to do." At that point I didn't know, because I was beginning to feel sorry for her. Then she said, "I have to go to the bathroom."

"There isn't one around, you'll have to wait."

"I have to go bad. Couldn't you just let me go back in bushes?"

"No. I have my orders but I'll let you squat right here if you want."

"No. I couldn't. I'd be too embarrassed."

Ho! I thought to myself. You embarrassed. No chance.

"Then you'll just have to do it in your pants. What do you have to do anyway?" I was hoping she had to shit.

"Never mind," she said, and that was that.

I went to where I said a man with a radio was and left her sitting on her aching bladder. When I came back a rain squall started to fall. The rope wouldn't come loose from around her neck and I said I'd have to back up to get some slack. She thought I would haul her up then and begged me not to. The rope was tied to the bumper of the car. I finally worked the rope loose and we sat in the car all wet.

I told her they had decided to kill her. She was really scared and begged me to help her escape. I said I would do what I could. The rain stopped and I told her I was to take her to a grave that had been dug for her. I said she should fake a faint and I'd carry her over to the grave area. I wanted to force her to pee her pants with my shoulder in her gut. I carried her over and set her down.

I let her see the hole I had dug for her. She really got scared then, and I was afraid she might panic and start fighting since she was not tied around the legs and only loosely about the hands. I told her to lay down on the ground and I would try to think of something.

She said if I let her go that she'd pay me all her savings, leave town, never say a word to anyone, give me anything I wanted. She was desperate. Almost in tears.

She said, "I don't want to die. I think I'm pregnant. I love Buddy and I want to have a baby." I told her to shut up. Then I told her to strip.

"Why do I have to strip?"

"Because it's the way we do things. We never kill anyone and leave their clothes so they can be identified by them. We make 'em all strip. If you don't want me to help you, forget it. We'll strip you after you're dead."

I cut her hands loose and she began to strip out of her clothes.

"I'll shoot a hole through the dress and show it to the other guy and he'll think I killed you."

She was stepping out of her white waitress dress. "Get off the slip too," I said. She stepped out of it too and was standing there in her brassiere, pantyhose and bikini panties and shoes. Her jugs were big, almost popping out of the bra. "Kneel down," I said. She knelt.

I put the gun next to her head and shot a hole through the dress. I thought she might shit her pants in fear, but she didn't. I said, "I need blood," and she wanted to cut her finger, but I decided the hole in the dress would look good enough.

I told her to lay on a sheet I had brought and she did, stomach down, her big ass sticking up. Very sexy. I told her to wait while I checked with the other guy.

I walked around, still undecided whether to kill her or not. I could see her and then she did the thing that sealed her doom. She picked up the blindfold and looked around as she lay there. I decided then for sure she couldn't be trusted, and I would have to kill her. I didn't know if she could see me or not.

When I got back I told her the other guy wanted to see her body and take her valuables. I told her to give me her jewelry. She took off two rings and lay back down. I told her the other guy was coming, so she'd better play dead or she would be dead. Then I went to the car and took out the pistol and cocked it so she wouldn't hear it.

I went over near her and aimed the gun at the base of her head. I aimed a long time. Then I closed my eyes and pulled the trigger. When I fired I ran.

I ran around to the car and then worked my way back as if I was going to discover her body. She was still laying there with no visible sign of injury. Her body was still and one leg was a little drawn up. I couldn't see her breathe, but her head moved slightly and I felt repulsed, horrified and ashamed all at the same time.

I quickly raised the gun and shot her twice in the back of the head. This time blood spurted out and I turned away. I covered her head with a sheet so I didn't have to see the blood, and went and got several crates. These I arranged to stretch her out on.

I went to the car and stripped down. Came back nude and grabbed her around the ankles and pulled her up onto the crates. I then slipped my hands under the elastic of her hose and panties, and pulled them down to her knees. The white cheeks of her ass no longer held tightly together by the panties slumped apart and I saw her purplish-pink colored asshole, which was open so wide I thought it was her cunt hole. I mean she had one hell of a big ass hole.

I stuck a finger up it to see if there was any shit in her rectum. There was none. I stuck two, then three and I could almost stick four fingers across into that giant asshole. There were a few blonde pussy hairs growing around it. Not like one asshole I had seen with hair so thick around it you couldn't see it. No, she had a beautiful hole.

I pulled off her shoes, thinking it wasn't right to cornhole a woman with her panties down around her knees and a bullet in her head with her shoes on.

I mounted her like a horse and let my dick go right into the open hole. It was hot in there and I humped a few times and shot off long and hard. I had soaped her hole and she was slippery and wet which made it more exciting than ever.

I fucked that hole as long as my dick would stay hard and then just sat on her big ass warming my balls in the crack of her backside.

Then I felt like I had to get rid of her fast, before somebody should come along or a plane should see us. I unhooked her bra and reached down and squeezed her giant teats and then slid off her. I grabbed her by her ankles and pulled her off the crates, noticing her gaping hole and tightly stuck together cunt. I wondered why she hadn't pissed. Her panties were a little wet but not a lot. Probably a few drops squirted out of her when I carried her.

I dragged her body to the open grave straddling it as I pulled her toward it. Her head was down and her arms were outstretched. When her chest was at the edge of the grave, I gave a jerk and let her feet go. She dropped to the bottom of the pit with a terrible hollow thump. Her legs went up over her back because the hole was too short for her. She lay there with her head down and her feet and legs up, one arm beside her and the other stuck straight up as if she were reaching up to get out.

I then threw the bloodied sheet over her head and tossed in her shoes. Her pant-

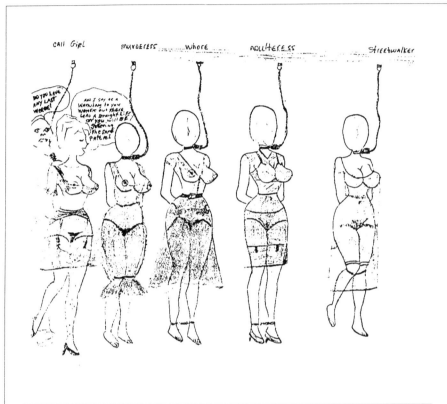

This type of platform scaffold was popular circa 1800 — 1860. The one on Newgate Street, London, could accommodate 27 prisoners per drop. The annotations across the top refer to various categories of capital crime.

Generally, women had the privilege to wear what they pleased to the scaffold. Fashion and style was set by the condemned; the hangman regulated the suspension. A pre-hooding speech was expected.

Platform scaffolds were also used in the United States; a single drop executed 38 men in Minnesota in 1860, and mass platform hangings were common at Blackwell's Island in New York City. The largest platform scaffold in use today is at Pretoria Central Prison in the Republic of South Africa. Curiously, the scaffold is one South African public facility available for use by all races equally.

This sketch represents a mass hanging of French partisans by Nazi Germans. Women were often stripped to their underwear or hanged nude with a short cord. Death comes by means of slow strangulation, since no drop is used. The maximum anguish is intended to have a deterring effect.

The word gallows comes from the word gala. Mass executions were treated as festivals in England until 1869. They were called Tyburn Fairs and were recognized as holidays in the City of London.

English hangmen were public celebrities. Albert Pierrepoint as Hangman for King George VII and Queen Elizabeth II executed notable criminal fiends and ran a pub in his spare time.

Expecting Dinner

S he was expecting dinner, but instead was driven down a deserted road.

She was asked to get out of the car and submit to a frisk search. Then the handcuffs were locked around her wrists and the blindfold placed over her eyes. She was then led away into the dark to the place of execution. She was assisted in mounting the ladder and sat down on the top of it. The hangman's noose was placed over her head after a pillow case was dropped over her face in a hood arrangement.

She sat there very composed and ladylike while I adjusted the rope. She obviously had no inclination of what was about to happen. I told her some stories about Vietnam and then told her I had to make a radio call. I warned her if she made a sound that she would be hanged immediately.

I went back to the car and had something to drink and then brought the car up. I got out and tied the rope to the bumper so that if I pulled away it would pull out the ladder from beneath her and she would be left hanging.

I went back to see her and asked if she were comfortable. She replied that she was getting bored and would I please hurry up with whatever business I had to attend to. I said I would, and before I went back to the car I made sure that the rope was tight around her neck.

I wanted her to stand up but she was afraid, so I let her sit. She sat there in a black chiffon dress with her hair done up and black pantyhose and high heels. She was wearing perfume and was very sexy.

I went back to the car and finished off the bottle of wine and then promptly at 9 P.M. I started the car and after allowing it to run for a few minutes I threw it into reverse and backed up quickly. I turned off the car and got out, straining to see if the branches were moving in the trees or hear if there were any other sounds. There were none.

After fifteen minutes, which I judged to be a sufficient time for her to die, I went slowly forward into the grove of trees where the execution site was arranged.

It was nothing more than a road with a hangman's noose over a limb dangling above the ladder where she was to sit. I had a light but I almost didn't want to see what I was responsible for. I approached in the dark and could make out her body turning slowly, suspended from the tree.

I went forward and turned on the light. I was a little shocked. There was a considerable amount of blood staining the white pillowcase hood that was over her head. The noose was pulled tight around her neck and her head was tilted to one side because I placed the noose beneath her left jaw. When I was within a few feet of her body I could see that where her feet had been tied tightly, she had broken the bounds obviously in her violent death throes. One of her shoes was off. I was probably shaking as I slowly ran my hand up under her dress just above her knees and began to work it upward. I felt a big hard-on growing in my pants as my

hand traveled up her legs, still warm and very much alive to me. The inside of her thighs were wet where she had urinated in her panties. Her underpants and pantyhose were soaked. She was wearing her pantyhose over her panties that were white nylon mesh and very skimpy. I lifted her dress and her wet slip and pulled down the pantyhose over her backside just leaving her panties. I slipped my fingers beneath the rim of her panties down near the front of her cunt and moved them slowly back toward her asshole, fully expecting and hoping to find a nice pile of shit.

My fingers found the hair of her ass and inched toward her hole. Her hole was open and my finger easily slipped into her hot rectum. There was a small amount of excrement littering the crotch of her panties and some more clinging to the area around her asshole but there was not nearly as much as I hoped to find.

I went back to the car and stripped and then returned to the grove. I then stripped off her dress and slip and pulled down her panties and hose to around her ankles. I then draped her body over a crate that I had brought along for that purpose and fucked her up her asshole. I shot off almost at once and then felt very sorry for her.

Oh, before I took down her body I forced myself to lift up the pillowcase hood and look at her face. The face was swollen and a little mottled. The eyes were closed and swollen at the temples. Her mouth was open and her tongue was visible but not protruding much. I was sick at the sight but I left the hood off because of the blood which I didn't like. After a few minutes I got on her again and fucked her ass some more. It was still hot in there and I shot off quickly once again. Then I stripped her and threw her clothes into a pile.

I then carried her body over to where I had rigged up a toilet seat between two crates and I sat her limp body on it. I then went down beneath the seat and stared up at her cunt and asshole, playing with them and fantasizing that she was in the act of shitting or pissing.

After a while I got tired of this and left her body on the toilet seat and went back to the car where I think I slept. After a while I went back to her and when I fucked her asshole again, for the first time noticed that she was getting cold on the outside but was still warm on the inside. Then I left her nude body sprawled out on the ground with her ass sticking up in the air, sort of like she was kneeling.

I went back to the car and went to sleep again feeling sick to my stomach. Later I woke up again and got out and went to her and stuck my prick in her ass again. This time I noticed that not only was her body getting cold, but it was also getting stiff too. I woke up cold and went to the car leaving her in the pine needles after humping her hiney and then passing out over her dead nude body, some time before.

The next time I woke up it was nearly daylight, so I went and took her body which was becoming stiff down in the joints of the arms and legs, and dragged it over to the rope. I replaced the noose around her neck and hauled her up to see what she looked like in the gray daylight. She was too difficult to haul up very far so I took her down and hauled her up on a lower limb where I could support her body as I was pulling it up. For the first time after removing her handcuffs I noticed that her wrists were very bruised, most likely from where she tried to get out of her predicament just before she died.

Earlier I had lain beneath her and looked up her dress with a flashlight, but now with her hanging there naked she was not too stimulating. I went to the car and got a woman's slip and put it on her, then as she was suspended from the rope I stood on a crate behind her and screwed her ass from behind. But it was hard to keep her still on the end of the rope, because she kept wanting to swing out. Her body was cold by this time, and it was exciting in another way being able to fuck her cold corpse.

I got off in her ass once more and then since it was getting light, I took her down and wrapped her up in a white sheet, and took her to the car. I dumped her body in the trunk and picked up her things and wadded them up all except her panties, pantyhose and slip, which were soaked with her piss. I wanted to save these for souvenirs.

I drove to another deserted spot and took her corpse out of the trunk wrapped up in the sheet. I half-dragged, half-carried it a good 200 yards into the bush along a dike. She was very heavy now and it was real work just to move her. When I got to where I decided I wanted to dump her corpse, I opened the sheet and rolled her out, noticing now in the full daylight that she was still wearing one earring and a gold chain. These I took and threw into a canal. Her clothes I also threw into another canal, and then I rolled her corpse down the side of the dike into a palmetto thicket. In the daylight her corpse was very cold, stiff and grotesque. She had large bruises on her legs from where she probably kicked herself during her death throes. This together with the distorted face and her bruised wrists made her appear very unattractive.

I propped her up as best I could and stuck it in her asshole again and then turned her over.

For the first time I really noticed the auburn V covering her cunt. I forced her stiff legs apart as best I could and screwed face to face, which was not easy, since she was very stiff and a little tight from the rigor mortis between her legs. I finally got my nuts off in her and then I was exhausted.

I sat for awhile and then decided to dump her body in the canal. I pulled her body down to the water and pushed her in head first. Her auburn hair swam around her as she began to slip beneath the hyacinths. Finally the water came up over her butt and went into her asshole. I let her feet go and she sank beneath the water.

I went back to the execution site and cleaned up any traces of our having been there. Then I went to a rock pit, where I dumped her pocketbook and the sheet and a few rags and things. Then I went to Lum's and had lunch on her money, and didn't enjoy it too much.

About two weeks later I was curious as to whether she had floated to the surface. I was horrified when I went to where she was dumped and saw her body swollen and bloated, tight-skinned, floating there. She was face down and her hair was covering her shoulders. Her ass was sticking way up in the air and I was looking right at what had been her cunt and asshole. The maggots had evidently been at work on her, because there was a big hole from her cunt to the top of the crack of her ass, and she stunk to high heaven. She was really putrid with all the flies buzzing and landing on her too. I poked her with a stick trying to get her down under the lilies, but ended up having to pile lilies up on top of her to hide her

corpse, which was a funny reddish color.

Another few weeks and she was out from under the lilies again. I tried to sink her with a few blasts from my shotgun. I would almost puke when I got a whiff of her corpse. It was that bad. I would always go there and beat off toward her, just out of range of the smell. Eventually she began to rot away and every now and then when I could stand the stink, I would drag her body out and try to mash it up with a stick. It seemed even the maggots didn't want anything to do with her after a certain point.

Finally I managed to break up the body and make it sink. I took the skull and let the ants eat her brains out, if she had any, then I pulled out all the teeth and scattered them over the county. The lower jaw I buried and the rest of her skull with the face smashed in and the teeth out, I put into another canal some ten miles from the rest of her body. All in all she is probably scattered over some thirty square miles, and I hope that she will continue to remain among the ranks of the missing, even though there is no possible connection between us.

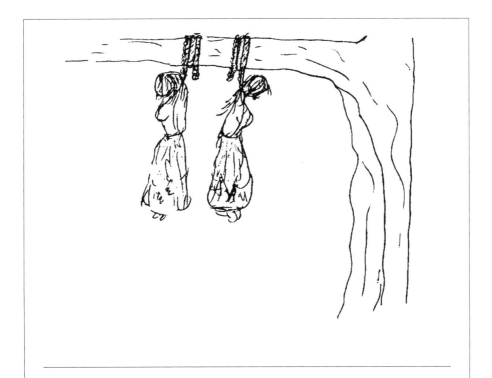

This drab, morbid sketch was done by G.J. Schaefer for Sondra London in 1991.
He suggested it be used for the cover of this book.

This modern-style trap-drop gallows is designed with a glassed-in viewing port to accommodate the required witnesses. The glass insulates the witnesses from the disturbing sounds and odors associated with execution by strangulation.

This sketch is loosely based on the execution of Eva Dugan at Arizona State Prison in 1919. Modern socially-conscious prison administrators are cognizant of feminine modesty and dignity: condemned females may be provided with a long gown with ribbons attached. Once on the trap, the ribbons secure the skirt to prevent billowing at the drop. Brassieres are not worn at trap-drop hangings due to the downward force of the plunge breaking the straps.

Modern nations retaining capital punishment employ prison officials who strive to ensure that executions are perfectly humane, decently sanitary and suitable for viewing by mixed company. Obscenity is not tolerated.

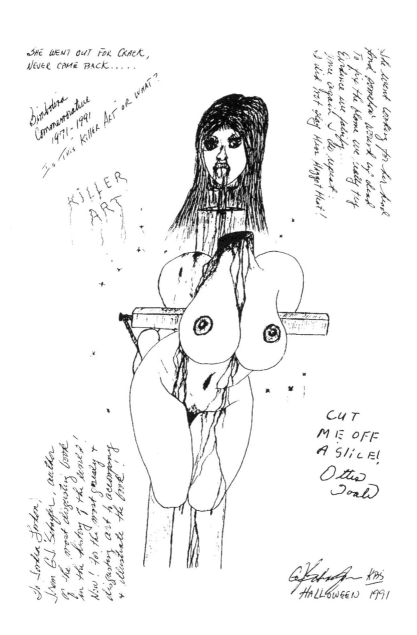

G.J. Schaefer sent this gleefully macabre sketch to Sondra London in October of 1991, after having it autographed by serial killer Ottis Toole, who cracked, "Cut me off a slice."

BEYOND KILLER FICTION

BEING CALLED GHOULISH

EX-SHERIFF ASESINA
MAS DE 30 JOUENES

T here's nothing to fire up one's interest in ghoulism like being called ghoulish.

Some years ago I wrote a story called "The Girl Ghouls of Galveston," which was a true tale about the monster hurricane that flattened that city in 1900. The story was about the expedition of New Orleans prostitutes sent to Galveston to do relief work. These women quickly turned to organized corpse robbing and were caught by the military when the Army arrived on the scene.

This entire boatload of whores was tried under martial law and executed by the Army, and their corpses were burned. The women were tried and executed as *ghouls* — in this case, corpse-robbers.

When I was accused of being a ghoul, I had to look the word up to get a clear meaning of ghoulism — which is defined in law as either robbing corpses or feeding on corpses. I wanted to clarify the distinction between a ghoul and a cannibal.

I might mention that Ted Bundy took a pretty good bite out of that girl at the Chi Omega house. Bundy bit off the girl's nipple and ripped a hunk out of her buttocks. I confess to wondering why he stuck a Clairol bottle up her butt. Was it a "sexual attack" or simply a matter of plugging her up because he was gnawing on her buttocks and she began to shit in terror? Rip a hunk out of her ass and she's going to bleed plenty. Did Ted relish the taste of blood?

Was he a cannibal or a ghoul? Out in Washington they found this corpse with fresh lipstick and recently painted fingernails, but she'd been dead for several weeks. She was rotten and decomposing. Ted admitted to doing her up on a regular basis. What he was doing, having sex with rotting corpses, is incomprehensible.

Oh, I've met guys in here who enjoy sex with a fresh young girl's corpse. They are quite frank about it being perfectly OK with them. These fellows are usually caught in funeral parlors or working as ambulance attendants, and get busted humping a car wreck victim or such as that, but Bundy liked them nice and juicy, rotting and stinking. There's a guy in here by the name of Giles who has the same quirk. Pick up a chick, strangle her, set her out in the sun to ripen and then climb aboard!

I was talking to another serial killer in here the other day named Jerry Stano. He said he got more kills than Ted Bundy. I told him I had more than him and Ted put together. He could only blink his eyes and make a little "o" mouth like a whistle pucker. It hurt him.

I told him he was a pussy to stab a hooker, and the only real way to do it is the way the "Bow Boy" did them: tie their nylons around their necks and smell the perfume behind their ears while they turn blue. Fucking Stano. With Ted gone, I've nobody to razz but him and Giles... who likes them dead. No reason except he enjoys rotting pussy.

I was accused of the exact same thing in 1973 on the front page of the *Palm Beach Post*. I cannot imagine a nastier accusation. Believe me, it's very hard to defend against such charges — especially when they are made in the media but not in court.

I wasn't accused of being a rapist/killer, it was specifically an accusation of fucking rotting corpses.

I couldn't even confront it objectively until about 1980. I'd read it and go into a mental fury. I mean, that's *ME* right on the front page of the Sunday paper that Jack Nicklaus probably read. But eventually I got up the intellectual fortitude to research the actualities of that accusation, and I did.

It's a well documented historical fact that a number of world leaders in African nations have practice cannibalism: Jomo Kenyatta, Idi Amin, and Jean Bokassa are three names that readily come to mind. While I've seen printed references to their cannibalism, I've never seen one called a *ghoul*, so perhaps there is a distinction. The "savage cannibal" of Africa or Amazonia feasts on human flesh as a matter of choice, not of necessity. The major difference is in how the local social structure perceives the custom.

Albert Fish, an American gent who enjoyed eating little girls, was tried and executed for murder — not cannibalism. Interestingly enough, it is not in violation of law to eat human flesh in New York or Florida. Mr. Fish had a taste for human flesh and went out and picked up children as if he were selecting vegetables at a greengrocer's stand. He slaughtered them, dressed them into select cuts and cooked them up in accordance with his favorite recipes. Nothing too fancy... a basic cutlet sautéed with onions. I'd expect the Africans would serve up a spicy repast. Bokassa favored a young girl, prepubescent if available.

Fish was caught dicing up little Grace Budd, also a prepubescent girl, so it does seem that the preference is not necessarily cultural. Maybe the older ones are tough. Pullets and hens are both chicken, but I'd prefer a pullet... more tender and juicy than a stewing hen. Apparently cannibals see things in a similar light.

Human flesh was Fish's meal of choice, and the motive for the murders he committed was called cannibalism. In New York, such an act is regarded as deviant but not insane, and is socially unacceptable.

Compare the Ed Gein case. Gein murdered women and ate them. He also dug

up fresh female corpses and ate them. Dressed them out like deer into appropriate chops and steaks and roasts, and put them into the meat locker. Gein was regarded as insane and after he was caught, spent the rest of his life in an insane asylum in Wisconsin.

These two cases are very similar, yet in one state the murderer/cannibal was executed, and in the other he was hospitalized as insane. Both cases involve fellows who simply enjoyed a dish commonly unavailable in our society.

Then there's another well-cited case, that of a butcher shop owner who murdered prostitutes and turned them into fine sausage and sold the meat to customers. He had a fascinating operation, and sold tons of human sausage. Made a lot of money. As I recall, he was busted because his product was noticeably superior and the local authorities decided to inspect his premises — a sanitation check. They found several women in cages awaiting slaughter and the story came out.

This fellow was also executed. However, I don't cite this case as ghoulism or cannibalism, but rather murder for profit.

Does it make me ghoulish to wonder about the reasons behind a crime? Even if it does, being ghoulish isn't criminal, or even dangerous.

The moral of this story is, if you're going to call me ghoulish, you'd better be able to back it up. I haven't been charged in a court of law with eating a corpse or robbing a corpse or screwing a corpse, and nobody has found anything on me that came off a corpse.

So tell me, why am I being called a ghoul?

Gerard John Schaefer's passport photo
taken June 8, 1970

Jesse in Flames

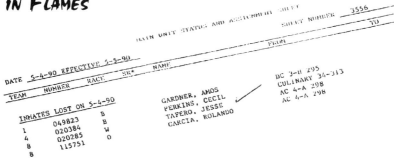

S tate killings are a spectator sport in Florida. Tickets to these events are always much in demand, and the atmosphere is surprisingly festive. There is a sense of expectation as if fascinating secrets are about to be revealed.

The electrocution of cop-killer Jesse Tafero at the Florida State Prison on May 4, 1990 promised to be no exception. Political dignitaries from the Capitol were on hand; representatives from police agencies pushed and shoved as they angled for the most favorable viewing positions behind the thick glass windows that allowed an unimpeded view of the death drama.

Jesse Tafero was a vicious criminal in his day. He topped off his career in burglary, robbery and rape with the murder of two fine police officers. There were some doubts about who actually pulled the trigger on the lawmen. Jesse claimed it was his rat partner Walter Rhodes and his hooker companion, Sonia Jacobs. After all, Rhodes pleaded guilty to the murders and became a witness for the State. Rhodes' testimony guaranteed both Sonia and Jesse one-way trips to the Death House.

I remember the day Jesse Tafero came to Florida State Prison. The first thing he did was scream for someone from the law library; I was a law clerk. Officer Campbell, the librarian, sauntered over to my desk and said, "The cop-killer Tafero wants to see a law clerk. I'm assigning you to handle it." Campbell laughed and turned away, amused by his own sense of irony. There was no way I could refuse the order. Life had thrown me another curve, so I picked up my legal pad and left the library.

I walked down the polished corridor that led to the death cells... the infamous "last mile" walked by men and women fated to die sizzling on the death chair. I've walked it year after year, never failing to thank God that at the conclusion of my visits to the condemned that I could turn my back on the grim portals of the death house and walk back to my job in the law library. But on the day I was scheduled to meet Tafero, my feelings were in turmoil. He had a reputation for violence.

A tobacco-chewing guard escorted me into R-wing and opened the security gate that gave me access to the death house cell blocks. As he opened the iron

gates he laughed and said, "If you have any trouble, give me a call and I'll have the goon squad come pick up the pieces."

The man had good reason to be amused. He was putting me into an area with seventeen condemned killers, men facing certain death at the hands of prison cops. Me, an ex-police officer, now an inmate; facing the collective wrath of men adjudicated savage beyond redemption.

I sucked in my breath and entered the cellblock and walked to Tafero's private cell. I stood in front of his bars and said, "I'm Jerry Schaefer, the law clerk assigned to help you."

Tafero took one look at me, picked up his television set and slammed it into the concrete wall. I stood there as the TV exploded into a thousand bits and made no comment. "I know you!" He screamed, "You're that ex-cop who killed 34 women! Aren't you!?"

"That's what the prosecutor says," I deadpanned.

Tafero cocked his head at me and howled, "But I'm in here for killing cops!"

"You killed two lousy cops. I've got thirty-four kills. You've got a little catching up to do, don't you?"

Jesse began beating his fists against the walls and yelling, "I don't fucking believe this!"

Three hours later we were on a first-name basis and he was showing me photographs of his bimbo, Sonia. She was fine, and I told him so. I didn't mention that the guards were already talking about what fun it would be to watch them both fry. It was their fondest fantasy: the double execution of the pair of cop-killing lovebirds. John Spenkelink had yet to make his historical debut on the Chair, but for the prison guards at FSP the frying of Tafero and his whore was something to live for, to speculate upon, day after empty day.

The death house guard who let me off the row said with a sense of awe, "I don't know why you ain't dead, boy."

"Jesus loves me," I told him, and it wasn't a joke.

One of the most powerful inmates in any prison is the skilled legal clerk, and before the public funding of lawyers for death row inmates, "jailhouse lawyers" literally held the power of life and death over men whose death warrants had been signed by the Governor. Thousands of executions have been blocked by a timely filing of a petition for the writ of habeas corpus to a United States judge. The key to saving the lives of the condemned is legal knowledge and articulate representation of constitutional issues.

I learned this skill as though my very life depended upon it, which in fact it did. Within one week of entering FSP, I was under the tutelage of an imprisoned union boss and labor racketeer who needed my literary skills to draft his motions to the U.S. District Court in Jacksonville. During the next four years of my imprisonment, I studied law during every spare moment and by 1977, I was regarded as one of the foremost legal minds at Florida State Prison.

I was sought out by some of the most virulent criminals in the State, and learned prison lawyering from ex-judge Joe Peel, who was serving a life sentence for his

part in the double murder of Palm Beach County Judge C.H. Chillingsworth and his wife. Jesse Tafero was damned lucky to have me assigned to help him research his legal issues, but as I told him after reading his trial transcripts, it would only be a matter of time before he'd ride the lightning.

Jesse Tafero was a professional criminal with almost limitless unsavory connections in the prison system. He spoke well of me to his associates, telling them of my research efforts on his behalf and my unquestionable integrity concerning confidential matters. His esteem for me as an adherent to the Convict Code of Silence was so strong that I was the person he chose to deliver the death message to his former partner, Walter Rhodes, late in 1979.

I will not reveal what that precise message was, but it was the driving force behind Rhodes rescinding his trial testimony and swearing he'd earlier committed perjury, a tactic that delayed Tafero's execution for almost six years.

I sat down with Walter Rhodes and coached him about what to say. I opened law books and showed him that the rescinding of his testimony would not change the outcome of the case, only delay it a few years. Rhodes was slated for a prison rat's death. His execution contract was given to one of the most feared prison gangs of the eighties. Rhodes was reduced to quaking jelly, knowing full well of Tafero's ability to reach out from death row and be the instrument of his doom.

Rhodes called the Broward County State's Attorney's office pleading for protection. I was standing beside him when he made the call. The police establishment had everything they wanted from Walter Rhodes in the way of testimony. They told him that they could give him no special protection; they implied that he was being thrown to the prison wolves, and Walter Rhodes lived in deadly fear for his life. I watched that fear eat away at him.

Such is the power of prison crime syndicates, and the indifference of the police to informants, once the snitch has been milked for everything of use to them.

I met with Tafero again in late 1989. He looked good, healthy and handsome, bedecked in gold jewelry and chains. He saw me and smiled like a Mafia Don bestowing a favor on an underling. We spoke of serious matters, of life and death. I suggested he turn to Jesus, but he told me he was relying on Bruce Rogow, a respected constitutional lawyer from Ft. Lauderdale.

Tafero ran down the issues that were being considered before the Eleventh US Circuit Court of Appeals in Atlanta. I told him he was riding a loser, that the decision would go against him, and that he'd be dead meat in 1990.

"I'll never quit filing petitions," he smiled.

Tafero was good to his word. On Monday, April 30, 1990 the law clerks spent an entire day helping Jesse file his last-ditch appeals. He'd fired his lawyers and returned to the inmate law clerks. But for Tafero it was too late… two lawmen had been riddled with gunfire and left in a lake of blood on the roadside.

Somebody was going to pay for *that*.

On Friday morning, May 4, 1990 the Warden ordered a full prison lockdown in anticipation of general rioting as a prelude to the Tafero execution. No chance would be taken that a revolt might disrupt the course of Justice.

From my cell window, I looked across the fields of spring wildflowers toward the State highway. Beyond the road I saw the media vans, and fleets of police car bubble lights blinking festively in the early morning. The crowds of morbid curiosity-seekers and anti-death penalty demonstrators milled in adjacent pastures. I stood at my window and took it all in, measuring the emotional tone of the event.

Bundy drew a larger crowd but the pulsing emanations of hate flowing from the mob were no less intense. There was no attitude of even-handedness to be applied, only an amorphous surge of unrestrained violence and projected enmity that flowed from the crowd toward the prison and those within its walls.

Less than fifty yards away from my cell Jesse Tafero, devoid of smiles and gold chains, was showered, shaved and diapered, and led to Old Sparky. It was 7:00 a.m.

Within five minutes Tafero was strapped to the oaken seat and at a nod from the Warden, the Executioner threw the switch, and fire leapt up from Jesse's head as if Satan himself had come to claim him. The Warden let Jesse burn alive for thirty seconds before ordering the electrician to cut the flow of current.

Officials tinkered with the mechanism of death while Tafero writhed in agony on the Chair, and smoke from his charred flesh drifted toward the ceiling. A few minutes later the Warden gave it another try. Once again, flames burst forth as Tafero's flesh ignited and was consumed.

The Warden stopped the execution once more, leaving Jesse to squirm in desperate pain. The electrician continued to fiddle with the wires and electrodes. At ten minutes past seven the Warden, seeing that Tafero was obviously still very much alive, ordered the switch thrown for the third time.

Five minutes later Tafero was pronounced dead by the prison doctor. It had taken the State of Florida almost ten minutes to kill the man.

I observed the laughter, the self-satisfied smirks of the prison guards who regarding the burning alive of a fellow human being as great sport, an entertainment akin to hog butchering. They clearly relished the idea of the cop-killer stripped of his gold and his dignity, writhing against the death straps with flames curling up around the metal skullcap.

I returned to my cell early that day, reflecting on the Jesse Tafero I had known: a man of many passions, not all bad — and not as evil as many who would live a long life. I was there when he walked through the front door, and I was there when his roasted corpse went through the back gate in a hearse. For Jesse it was over, but for others it was just beginning.

I sat down on my bunk, opened the bound trial transcript of another condemned man, and began to read — searching for the legal challenge that could save his life.

GREEN DRAGON TONG

The life of a master criminal is fraught with danger and uncertainty.

And we were engaged in some unusually risky business. So when the parcel from my niece arrived I couldn't be completely sure it didn't contain a bomb, yet I couldn't ignore the insistent squawk of my door buzzer. A decision had to be made.

I removed the stolen Model 1911 Army Colt .45 semi-automatic pistol from the leather shoulder holster and held it down next to my leg, slightly behind my back. Then I called out in a gruff voice seeking the true identity of the unknown person lurking on the other side of the plywood door. It could have been anyone, but it turned out to be a fat black woman delivering mail for the United States Postal Service.

The postal person pushed the carton through the open door with her large foot. I looked down upon it, observing the colorful Malaysian stamps franked in the capital city of Kuala Lumpur. I didn't know exactly what was inside the sealed package, but I had an idea. Hopefully, it was a shipment of the finest refined hashish produced in the Burmese People's Republic and trans-shipped over jungly trails to a destination within the Sultanate of Penang, a political unit within the Federated States of Malaysia.

The Customs police in Asia and, apparently, their counterparts within the United States seemed to have no interest in opening for inspection a carton marked "Human Remains."

Only a few days earlier I had received an airmailed letter from my niece Melanie, advising me that my father had died of a stroke while patronizing a sing-song girl establishment on Victoria Street, and that his cremated remains would be airmailed back to the States for interment forthwith. Now here they were before me on the living room rug, and the uniformed person was demanding my signature on the postal registration slip. Was it a postal police trap that would earn me fifteen years in a federal slammer or was it my ticket to prosperity?

I eyed the negress. She smelled of sweat and fried mullet. Was it part of a clever disguise or was it her usual condition of odorous dishevelment? There was only one sure way to find out.

I signed the green registration card and watched the smelly mailwoman turn on her heel and waddle away on her appointed rounds.

Setting the parcel on a coffee table, I withdrew a knife from my boot and carefully cut away the sealing tape, then I slit open the heavy cardboard packing case and pulled back the paper lid. Tucked inside, taped under the cardboard flap, was a handwritten note from Melanie, stating that the contents of the weighty ceramic funeral urn contained the earthly remains of my dearly departed daddy. The top of the urn was sealed with a plug of jade green wax, inscribed with an array of Chinese characters and a small fierce-looking dragon. The urn was carefully nestled

in a protective cocoon of thick Styrofoam to protect against rough handling and breakage.

Wasting no time in getting to work on the wax seal, I quickly dislodged it with the point of my black switchblade knife. What I found within the confines of the urn made my heart skip a beat. No familiar odor of pure gummy hashish assailed my nostrils. What I found was a container of pure brown heroin! My mind raced. What was that crazy bitch Melanie up to now? I could sell the shit for millions with one quick call. Could it be that my sister's opportunistic girl had made a big-time connection? And if that was the case, why hadn't she tipped me off to it? A mystery!

Suddenly the door buzzer began its annoying rasping again. Now what? I carefully opened the door just a crack, keeping one hand on the pistol just to be on the safe side. I took a quick look. A tall blonde with a pair of knockers like honeydew melons and a single braid of thick, gleaming hair stood in the hallway. Her emerald eyes were deep-set and sparkling with unconcealed fear. I'd seen that look enough to know it well.

She turned her eyes to me and asked, "Are you Melanie's uncle?" I gave her an almost imperceptible nod, thinking she sure didn't look like any cop I'd ever laid eyes on. Then she squeaked, "Help me! Please! They're after me!"

She was the sort of earthy woman that any red-blooded male would be after constantly, so the idea that she was being pursued seemed reasonable.

"Who's after you?" I inquired, "Cops?"

She pulled a wry face. "No, a hit team sent by the Green Dragon Tong. They're right behind me! They've been on my trail all the way from Kuala Lumpur. You've got to save me — I'm Melanie's best friend!"

Almost immediately I heard the tread of footsteps echoing in the stairwell from the end of the hall. What was this craziness about the Green Dragon Tong? I knew they were the criminal gang that controlled the dope trade in Hong Kong, but what did that have to do with her?

Suddenly the door to the stairs flew open and there they were, a pair of Orientals at the end of the corridor — a stocky man and a slender woman. The woman yelled, "There she is! Kill her!"

And then in slow motion, as if in a dream, I watched the man raise a pistol with a bulbous silencer attached to the muzzle. With a small puff of sound, a bullet hole appeared in the wall next to the blonde's head. That was enough for me. I yanked the girl into my apartment and closed the door, but I could hear the patter of shoe leather rapidly approaching. Suddenly a jagged line of bullet holes splintered the wood of the apartment door, shattering furniture and smashing glass throughout the entire living room. I snatched up the urn full of primo dope and pushed the terrified blonde toward the bedroom.

"That guy has a silenced Uzi!" the girl whispered with a quaver of true terror in her voice.

"No shit! Now get out the window and down the fire escape! Don't even think about anything else, it's way past time to be hauling ass!" I heard the sounds of someone kicking down my front door as I levered myself out the window onto the metal platform of the fire escape. I tucked the .45 in my belt and the urn under my

arm, and scooted down the stairs after the blonde. The deadly whine of a ricocheting 9mm slug hurried us on our way.

Garbage cans clattered as the mysterious blonde and I leaped from the fire escape ladder and barreled down the filthy alley toward the busy street. The girl had a rental car parked nearby. We piled into it, she fired it up and we sped away. I fished a pack of Marlboros out of my jeans and fired one up. "Christ, that was close! Who *are* those maniacs? And who the hell are *you*?"

The blonde cut her eyes toward me for a second and then returned them to the traffic. All we'd need now would be a fender bender with yours truly sitting up front with a stolen pistol and a ceramic pot full of class-A narcotics. The blonde said, "I'm Helga Sorensen, Melanie's best friend. Surely she's mentioned my name to you?" I couldn't recall Mel mentioning any Helga, so I just shook my head in silent perplexity. The blonde continued, "I bring you bad news. Melanie is dead."

That stopped me. All I could manage to say was, "What... what happened?"

Helga gave a world-weary sigh. It was a raid by the Kuala Lumpur police. The special anti-narcotics unit. Something like your SWAT teams. There was a huge gun battle. The cops blew her right out of her Reeboks. Gunned her down in the street like a *dog*. Melanie and four other European women. It was a massacre. I'm surprised it didn't make headlines over here."

"What — dope? The cops seize it by the ton these days. A gunfight in Malaysia isn't going to make the news back here." I took a long drag on the cig and gazed out the window vacantly. "That crazy Melanie. She should have surrendered."

Helga hawked and spat out the window — an amazingly vulgar gesture, I thought. She almost growled, "Surrender for what? She'd have a speedy trial and an even speedier appointment with a Malaysian hangman. Melanie would rather go out shooting, fighting for her life, than strangling at the end of a rope."

"Hell, we could have bought her out of it! The Cartel would never let Melanie swing — never! She wasn't some ignorant little bimbo with a couple of ounces stuffed up her snatch. Melanie was their top woman in Southern Asia. It just don't make sense... Mel getting herself in a lousy gunfight. We could've arranged a nice payday for that judge. Convict her, fine. Reverse it on appeal and deport her ass after the heat mellows out. Happens every day."

The blonde frowned. "Maybe it used to be that way, but those days are long gone in Malaysia. Singapore too. Listen. In Penang it's the Sultan himself who controls the narcotics trade, and anyone caught messing around in it is promptly tried and hanged at Pudu Prison. They hang you for *possession* in Malaysia. It's no joke, Mister. Where you been? The Sultans of the Federated States are cleaning up their own drug problems. Now they're regulating — and I mean *strictly* regulating — narcotic exports. What do they care if Australia is in a heroin stupor? It's business, babe! Big business!"

She wasn't telling me anything new. Dope had always been big money. Melanie was in middle management, with her home office right in beautiful downtown Bogota. She'd gotten her start as a courier; spent six years faithfully muling coke and heroin packed in her intimate cavities. Never a bust. Not even a close call. Three years alone on the Bogota-to-Paris run. She was a pro, not the type to fuck up and get wasted in a gun duel with police or government stooges anywhere.

"It can't be that rough, Helga. Money talks. Given the choice, would the Sultan rather have a nice hefty bag of Gold Pandas or Melanie's ass on a rope? He's a rational businessman. He'd go for the gold."

Helga shook her head. She was wending her way through heavy traffic and keeping her eye on the rearview mirror. "Courier work is getting too risky these days, Mister. Smart women aren't going into that line of work any more. What stone fox from North America or Europe is gonna risk her neck for a lousy ten thousand dollar courier fee? I'll tell you. Very few. It's an unacceptable risk."

Yet the dope had to move. "Tell me, Bright-Eyes, who mules it today? Somebody's got to be out there."

Helga turned left and headed west across the city. She seemed to know where she was going. "In Southern Asia, it's all controlled by the Tongs. They use bar girls, diseased prostitutes from the slums. Women so desperate they'll do anything to get ahead of their poverty. Eighty percent of the women hanged at Pudu Prison are Chinese. The police can't get them all, but the Tongs guarantee them 10% of every run. Ten out of each hundred couriers that make the Hong Kong-to-Kuala Lumpur run are betrayed by the Tong."

"You mean to tell me those Chinks are ratting on their own people?"

The blonde eyed me and nodded. "You got it. That's exactly what they do! They consider it the cost of doing business. Overhead. That ten percent is tried and hanged. Makes the police statistics look good, and gives Malaysia an international rep for death on drugs, but it's all a fraud."

"Except for that ten percent. No fraud there!"

"True. Those ladies are dead meat — just like you and I are gonna be if those two hitters from the Green Dragon catch up with us… and they probably aren't far behind!"

I pitched my butt out the window and lit up another one. "Yeah, about those Green Dragon people. What seems to be their problem? Somebody needs to tell them this area is sectioned out between the Bogota and Medellin Cartels. We don't have no beef with Chinks from Green Dragon or any other dragon."

Helga inhaled deeply, and released her breath slowly as if she were about to deliver some crucial message. "Heroin — that's their problem, my friend. Melanie and I pulled a little switcheroo, and unless I miss my guess, the proof of the caper is right there in your lap… and since the pigs wasted Mellie, I guess her share goes to you. There's 10 kilos of pure uncut brown heroin in that pot, and it's a 50% share. That ought to put you in the millions, but the immediate problem is how to keep it. Are you man enough to hang onto it?" She cut her eyes toward mine and I nodded. "I'm betting my life you are."

I understood the dilemma perfectly. Melanie was stone cold dead and Helga was on the run with a quinella of professional killers in pursuit. It was certainly shaping up to be an interesting day.

Helga had herself a fancy flat on the west side of town. The address wasn't particularly posh, but the chick impressed me with the key to the penthouse suite. Helga claimed to be Melanie's best gal pal, but for the life of me, I couldn't recollect her mentioning this Swedish delight… nor had Melanie ever been inclined toward any rip-off actions. Seemed out of character to me, and for all I knew Mel

might pull up in the next taxi, or maybe she was really dead in a hole in Penang. But the current problem would still be to stay alive.

Helga double-locked the front door. We were twenty stories up, so I didn't mind when she opened the sliding glass doors that led out onto a sun deck and terrace. The place seemed to have it all, including a giant rubber tree that grew to the apex of the cathedral ceiling. A selection of pricey modern art graced the walls. Helga seemed to be laundering her cash through real estate and art.

"Let me take your jacket and box of goodies," Helga said. I shucked my wind-breaker and handed over the urn that had everyone going crazy, and watched as she stowed the stuff in a closet. The blonde drifted off into the kitchen and re-turned with a pair of cold Pepsis. She said, "I could offer you something stronger, but I suspect you want to keep your wits about you. Am I right?"

I agreed. Snapped open the top on the Pepsi and helped myself to a long cold draught. Helga followed my lead and opened her can, and sipped daintily at the cold drink. "I really like you," she purred. She gave me the once-over with those green eyes that glittered like a set of precious gemstones in her finely chiseled face. She arched her back in such a way that her teats threatened to burst through the fabric of the cotton *Six Flags* T-shirt she was wearing. The big Swede was hauling around a nice set of jugs, they were enough to take my mind off my troubles for a moment or two... but not too long, because I was looking at Big Trouble with a capital B.

Then suddenly with no forewarning, Helga was on her knees before me fum-bling at my crotch with singular determination. She yanked down my zipper and took my cock in her well-manicured hand. Her green eyes brightened with femi-nine lust, as she savored my quickly elongating erection. She was obviously no stranger to hard cock, and stared at it with an undisguised hunger.

Helga moaned with contentment as she slipped her spittle-wet lips around the swollen head of my penis and began to nibble her way down the shaft, licking her way toward my balls. She hummed with her exertions and the overheated musky scent of her wafted upwards to my nostrils. She smelled hot and sexy.

When she had my boner up and twitching to the manipulations of her tongue, she released it from her mouth with a wet, slurpy *pop*. She giggled girlishly and in a single graceful movement drew her *Six Flags* over her head and tossed it onto the coffee table, revealing her glorious breasts — the pink nipples standing at attention with erotic excitement. She unfastened her skintight designer jeans and slid them off her backside, along with a whispery bikini panty. She was wonder-fully naked, and reclined on a large velveteen sofa like some modern naked Maja waiting to be serviced.

She cocked an eyebrow my way in unspoken invitation. The big juicy bitch wouldn't need to ask twice; I try not to keep girls like that waiting. I shucked my own duds and climbed into the saddle. I stuffed my boner into her box and got to work stroking her hole until the clawing filly reared back and whinnied with a hip-grinding orgasm.

I'd been so involved in the monkey business that I had failed to realize that Helga and I had an audience. The Oriental couple were standing nearby inscruta-bly observing the impromptu sex show. The front door was still double-locked,

and I wondered how the little creeps got into the living room. What did they do, fly in from the sundeck?

When I looked at him, the chunky Chinese gentleman said softly, "Don't make any sudden moves!" The silenced Uzi cradled in the crook of his arm made the statement more than a request.

Helga began to shake and sob, and drew me fiercely to her bosom, as if my body could shield her from the spray of red-hot slugs that she seemed to be expecting. She wasn't faking it, she was peeing all over the couch!

I looked down at her in wonder and disgust. She closed her eyes and began to gnaw on her bottom lip. It looked like she might bite a hole in herself.

"Where's the heroin?" asked the slender but unusually well-stacked Chinese lady standing beside the chilling visage of the hired Green Dragon Tong killer. She had long, thick hair the color of the bottom of a coal mine at midnight, hanging straight to her shoulders. Her eyes were the color of wet anthracite, deadly and promising *no mercy.* The eyes of an unusually cold killer. The overall effect was enhanced by the curious black silk pajama suit she wore.

Embroidered over the breast on the left side was a Green Dragon, the totem of her secret criminal society. The talons of her Dragon were capable of reaching halfway around the world.

When I didn't answer, the Chink bitch glared at me and spat, "You give us heroin! You give it now! You not give, you die plenny quick!"

I was in no mood to die plenny quick or even a little bit at a time. I looked down at the shaking Helga and said reasonably for all to hear, "Hey, do you know what these two characters from Central Casting are babbling on about?" The naked woman beneath me whined piteously and shook her head back and forth in abject denial. What could I do, call her a liar? I was in no position to argue.

"My lady friend here don't know nothing about no heroin. Now why don't you burglars haul ass on out of here right now and we won't even call the law about this home invasion outrage. Don't they teach you manners where you come from?" What the hell, if they're fixing to blow us away, might as well fish for time, and maybe get an unexpected opening to settle their hash before they settle mine.

The stocky Chinaman laughed heartily, but I noticed his little lotus blossom of a partner didn't crack a smile. "Do not be fooled by this common prostitute, Sir! That one knows very well why we are here, for she is a thief. We have come to retrieve for our Master that which belongs to our Tong. What we seek is somewhere in this apartment. Our property was shipped to you in the name of your dead niece. You speak to me of manners! Frankly, we are quite astonished that you now consort with the very woman responsible for her sad and unnecessary death."

I felt a ripple of involuntary terror course through the lovely body beneath me; then the big blonde began to shiver in earnest. I looked at the Chinaman with sincere interest all over my mug. "That's one hell of a yarn. Why don't you explain to me what's going on here, before you get carried away with that 'die plenny quick' shit?"

The Chink spoke as reasonably as a banker's lawyer evicting a widow and seven starving kids from their home.

"The shameless harlot is a confidential informant for INTERPOL. She befriended

your niece Melanie in Kuala Lumpur, then betrayed her to the Penang police for money. She led the police to your niece and was present when she and her associates were taken captive. It was on the suggestion of this Helga, who is now beneath you, that the North American and European women were summarily shot. Now the same woman who was the betrayer of your own flesh and blood befriends you also. She is a very friendly woman, is she not? I believe her intention is to have you arrested... or perhaps even murdered by the lawless police of the DEA. You are very well known to the DEA, are you not? It would pay well if you were able to be, how do you phrase it? Put out of circulation?"

Could it be that I'd been a chump for a pretty piece of tail once again? The Chink wasn't lying. His voice carried an underlying tone of righteous anger, as if he were a victim of the lousy cops himself. I looked down at the now wide-eyed Helga. "What do you have to say about all that, lady?"

She didn't say a word. She immediately dissolved into a series of mindless sobs and hiccups. I slowly climbed off the Judas bitch feeling dirty and full of unspoken rage. The Chinaman had me covered with the Uzi. I leaned over the whore and hissed, "What about it, cunt! Is he telling the truth? Or not?"

The naked informant sat up on the urine-soaked sofa and nodded with hopeless resignation, admitting her guilt. She tossed her braid back over her shoulder and said defiantly, "You're nothing but dope-pushing scum. You and those two little niggers. You're committing crimes against humanity. There's a war on drugs and you're the enemy. You deserve to *die!*"

I listened thoughtfully to her tirade. When she was finished I asked the Chinaman, "What are you planning to do?"

The little black-eyed lotus blossom piped up, "Do you know where our heroin is?"

I admitted that I did.

The Chinaman swung the Uzi toward Helga and fired a quick burst into her chest directly between those lovely rubbery boobs. The blast of 9mm lead blew a fist-sized hole in her back, along with a spray of shredded flesh, blood and a white hunk of her spine.

She bounced off the back of the sofa and flopped forward face down on the shag carpet. She had not uttered a sound or asked to be spared. She knew when her number was up. A scarlet pool began to form around her. Her tapered fingers opened and closed; her legs jerked and twitched with little spastic movements.

Then the Chinese woman turned her hefty Baretta 9mm semi-automatic pistol toward me and said in a no-nonsense tone, "We require the heroin at this time. You will give it to us now."

"Whoa! And what happens when I cooperate? Does Charlie Chan here blow me away the same way he just aced the pretty cop?"

The Chinaman spoke right up. "The Green Dragon Tong has no evil intentions toward you, sir. You are another victim of the wicked betrayer. You heard the words from her own mouth. There is a war being fought. The governments would empty the rice bowls of our starving children. We are business people. Honest capitalists who just supply the demands of our customers. We only wish to protect our investments and live in peace. You will suffer no harm from the Green Dragon

Tong. However, should you wish to dishonor us by attempting to steal that which belongs to our people then my lovely associate will have to give you a lesson you would not welcome. The choice is yours, of course. We are civilized people, are we not?"

The Chink was a genial son of a bitch. I wasn't really interested in experiencing any artfully applied Chinese tortures. There was no choice but to give the suckers what they wanted and hope they'd be good to their word. Hey, I was a victim! Hadn't they told me so themselves?

"Yeah, look, man, your dope is right there in the front closet. As soon as I saw the little green seal I was afraid someone had fucked up. I was expecting some hash actually... for personal consumption of course."

"But of course!" The Chinaman nodded somberly, then hustled off to check out my story. The little lady smiled maliciously as she pointed her Baretta autoloader at my still-wet dick and said in a conversational manner, "If you lie to us, then I shoot that thing off you plenny quick. I make bang-bang and then you no more number-one stud, eh?"

Eh, indeed! I wasn't about to tell that pair any cute stories. I'd put on a kimono and serve them green tea and fortune cookies or call out for hot chop suey for plenny-quick delivery, all they'd have to do is ask. I took my cock in my hand. "Nice looking Suzie Wong like yourself might like to take a ride on this here magic dragon some time. Think so?"

She smiled mischievously and said, "Oh! Very yes!" But she didn't drop her deadly aim from my nuts.

"Mind if I put my pants on now?"

She frowned. A big decision. "Is OK. I never mind."

She watched with undisguised feminine interest as I jacked my ass into my jeans. Whoever spread the story that ladies don't like to look was a damned liar. She was looking for all she was worth.

"Too big for a little delicate Chinee girl like yourself, doncha think?"

She muttered something in Cantonese that probably meant something like "go fuck your mother," and suppressed a wry grin. Then her partner called to her in the same dialect and she turned on her heels and ran to him. I had no inclination to reach for my gun.

The Chink unlocked the penthouse door and turned and gave me a small bow. His doxy made a feline sound and bequeathed me with a smoldering look. Another time, another place, that one would be a handful.

They politely closed the door, and left me to contemplate my fate and clean up the mess the whore had made of herself.

Gator Bait

T he locals called the place Johnny's Bass Hole, but the big attraction was not the bass. It was the monster alligators that could be seen sunning themselves on the spoil bank across the canal from the little boat dock.

People came to Johnny's for bait, tackle and cold drinks. There was a fish cleaning table right next to the dock. Fishermen would clean their catch out behind Johnny's and fling the guts into the water and the gators would come scrambling. The regular anglers who'd clean their catch at Johnny's would call up the gators from the cattails by tapping the handle of a fish-skinning knife on the boards of the table.

Go out there and make that tap-tap-tap noise, and you could rouse a couple of fourteen-footers along with the old 16-foot bull gator they called Captain Crunch. He was particularly fond of the unwanted kittens and puppies people would carry out to Johnny's. They'd fling them into the canal and Captain Crunch would gobble them down.

There was a big *NO SWIMMING* sign by the dock. Yankee tourist kids needed to read the sign, maybe ask about it. But locals knew better than to go swimming in Johnny's Bass Hole.

The only person ever eaten alive by an alligator in Broward County was taken off a levee within a mile of Johnny's. Big old monster come up out of the hydrilla, chomped down on that boy's leg, and drug him off into the canal. The boy, who'd been dozing by a cane pole set out for catfish, was chewed into parts and swallowed. His friend had seen it happen and reported it to the sheriff.

The sheriff called the Fish and Game Commission and a posse took up the hunt. By and by, some of the officers put a hook in the gator, dragged him out of the canal, shot him, cut him open, and there was the boy. In parts, of course, but perfectly identifiable.

Pictures were taken of the dead gator and the chomped-up boy and those snapshots were posted on the walls at Blackie Hinkle's Bait & Tackle on State Road 84, and north of the floodgates on US 27 at Johnny's Bass Hole. I saw those pictures many times over the years they were posted. That's where I got the idea.

I figured that if a gator could gobble down a big old boy like that, that a whole passel of gators would have no problem at all with a particular soft-bellied whore lady who'd dragged me away from my accustomed path of righteousness right down into Satan's Hell.

I was an athlete. Kept in shape running, never missed doing a couple miles a day. One day I came to notice this damned woman out in her front yard sunning herself. Remember the song about the itsy bitsy teeny weeny yellow polka dot bikini? Well, the one she had on was akin to that, only smaller, and white. I later came to know it was a French make. I read it on the label the night I was going through her bureau drawers, waiting for her to come home so I could kill her.

I'd go jogging by, and she'd be laid out all greasy with sun tan oil there on a plastic chaise lounge.

I did look, and what I saw wasn't decent. I saw her pussy hair spilling out around the elastic by her crotch. Imagine her laying there with her legs open, the skimpy fabric pulled up tight so I could see the cunt crack underneath, pubic hair all falling out everywhere. Showing her cunt in public.

If she was sitting up reading when I happened by, she'd smile and sometimes lean forward, showing me her titties pouched up on those half-cups.

I looked. I did. Sometimes she'd smile and lean forward a bit more, let me see the nipples. I knew what she was up to: seduction. She was an occasion of sin, and I had to do something about it. I began to keep a close eye on her.

On weekdays she'd watch the eleven o'clock news in her living room, then come into the bedroom. I'd watch her through the half-open drapes in the bedroom windows. Her routine rarely varied. She'd undress; a messy woman, she'd leave her clothes strewn about.

Then she'd go into the bathroom and squat on the toilet. There was a metal magazine holder beside the toilet. She'd do her business while flipping through the pages of Cosmopolitan or Vogue.

Occasionally she would stare directly at the window as if she sensed my presence. The toilet face the bedroom window. I watched her for months, kept notes. I knew her bedtime routine. She'd spend ten minutes on the pot with her magazines. Then she'd turn off the light, come out into the bedroom, take clean underpants from her bureau drawer, step into them, and go to her bed.

She never wore a nightgown, she slept naked except for her panties. The bed was just to one side of the window. I could smell the whore lying there.

I knew where she kept her hide-a-key too. It was under a brick near the front door.

She was a party girl, a weekend boozer. She'd come in late on Friday and Saturday nights, leave her date at the front door, and then go through her routine. I made up my mind to visit her while she was tiddly. I chose a moonless Saturday night. Watched her leave with her usual boyfriend, let myself in with her hide-a-key, looked around for a good place to wait. I had plenty of time.

I went into her bedroom. It was familiar to me. I took in the view of the window from her angle, and noticed that when the bedroom light was on it was not possible to see outside. I went to her bureau drawer and helped myself to a handful of nylon stockings. I stuffed them into the pocket of my cutoffs.

It was summer and I was wearing nothing but my cutoffs and a leather knife sheath that contained a Rapala Finnish skinning knife. I prefer the narrow blade of the high-quality Rapala product. Honed to razor sharpness, the knife can be angled in under the ribcage and up into the heart in an instant.

I waited in the darkness of an unused bedroom. Just sat there in a chair fingering the knife and wondering if I'd have the nerve to take the whore to visit Captain Crunch. I had it all worked out in my mind. There was rope and cement blocks in my car. There would be plenty of time to drive her out to Johnny's and dice her up before the first fishermen came around. She'd be gator shit on the bottom of the Everglades by Monday morning.

The slut came home just past midnight. In the quiet of the house, I heard her say her nighty-nights to her date and close the door. She went into the fridge for something, and I heard the clunk of its door shut. I heard her heels clip-clop on the terrazzo as she made her rounds, checking her doors. I knew she wouldn't enter the unused bedroom; it wasn't part of her routine.

I saw the light come under the door. She walked past, just on the other side of the door from me. I could hear the rustle of her skirts.

I fingered the blade of the knife, smiled to myself, and sat perfectly still, hardly daring to breathe. I listened to her undress, visualizing the actions I'd watched at least a hundred times before. I could hear her urinating in the quiet of the house; I waited. I heard the toilet flush after ten minutes. She was right on schedule. Soon the light would go out.

I watched her in my mind's eye. Heard the bureau drawer open. Fresh panties for the whore's ass. There was a rustle of bed linens and the light went out. She'd need time to settle into sleep. My watch told me it wasn't even one o'clock. I had time to give her. Plenty of time. I decided to wait until half-past one.

I walked into her bedroom on silent bare feet, my eyes well adjusted to the dark. The whore was on her back snoring, a rhythmic purr. I stood over her taking in the dim outline of her nakedness, absorbing her essence. She was sleeping, secure in her own home, safe in her own bed. I smiled in anticipation of her coming surprise, and considered for a moment that it might be easier to simply put the knife into her while she slept.

I decided against it. My preference was to do whores in a standing posture, punch the slender blade in under the left ribcage and angle it up into the heart. Stop the heart and there is very little bleeding. There's a special pleasure in watching the eyes as the soul departs. One moment they are alive with an all-consuming interest. Then, as the knife cleaves into the heart, they become suddenly vacant, dull and… lifeless.

I had carried a pillow in from the other bedroom. With my left hand I put it over the woman's face, and with my right hand I put the point of the blade against her throat. I felt the slut come awake.

I said in a growl, "Scream and you die. Move and you die."

I pressed the point of the knife into her flesh to underline the threat. Then I said, "Close your eyes and roll over on your stomach." She did so immediately.

I set the pillow over her head, pulled her arms behind her and tied her wrists with one of her nylon stockings. I warned her again, "If you open your eyes I'll kill you," and then I removed the pillow and gagged her with two nylons.

I took the pillow out of its linen case and drew the case over the whore's head, then tied it firmly in place with a stocking. The bitch was secure. I sat down on the bed next to her and said nothing, allowing the fear to build.

My heart was racing and my cock was hard. I took in the scent of her alcohol-laced sweat. She opened the game with hitching sobs, the female first line of defense. I'd seen it before. Crying brings on a runny nose, and before you know it the bitch has snot all over her lower face. The inside of the pillowcase tends to get slick with it. Tears are the harbingers of hysteria.

I reached over and jerked her head back with my left hand. With my right I set

the long blade of the knife under the whore's chin. The acrid stink of terror-in-duced sweat rose from her to assault my nostrils.

"Silence," I hissed, and let her head drop back onto the bed. She whimpered and sneezed twice into the pillowcase hood.

I was in no hurry. While the minutes dragged by, the whore lay there on her belly breathing raggedly through her gag and snot-obstructed nostrils. I let the blade of the skinning knife wander down the knobby spine to the elastic waist-band of the white nylon panties. I turned the knife over on its side and let the scalpel-sharp edge slice through the elastic and part the fabric down the cleavage of her buttocks.

She understood.

I set the blade in the cleavage and put a bit of pressure on the inside of the fleshy cheek. First a little pressure to the left, then a little to the right. She silently spread herself for me as a good riding mare responds to the touch of the reins. Whores know what to do.

I let my fingers trace the path of the blade. The whore was greasy with sweat. My finger touched her anus; I felt her clench her sphincter. I pushed my finger against the hole; she tightened it even harder. I removed my finger, stood up, leaned over her and spread her buttocks with my left hand. With my right, I set the point of the blade against the puckered opening. She began to shiver as if in the throes of a chill. I smelled her wet the sheets.

Sat back down on the bed. Shucked off my cutoffs, set my knife on top of them, stood up and masturbated. I came almost instantly, spraying semen over the woman's buttocks and back. She twitched and squirmed with alarm as the gobbets of semen landed on her.

I instantly felt an overwhelming sense of guilt. I was still young then, and unac-quainted with the parameters of power and rage in the unholy union between sexual release and death. I pulled on my cutoffs and knew in my heart that I could not carry through with the plan. Captain Crunch was going to have to wait.

I sat down on the woman's bed again, took another nylon from my pocket and tied her ankles together, then I stood up and took out my penis and urinated over the whore's buttocks and back. She lay on her belly shaking. I stepped to the front of the bed and urinated on the pillow case over her head. She gurgled and wheezed as the urine soaked her.

I leaned over and slid my hand up under the wet pillow case and found her throat. I could feel the blood pounding beneath my fingers. The room was hot and stinking. The excitement and lust were coursing through me. I drew myself down close to the whore's head and spoke close to her ear. I told her, "If you tell anyone what happened here tonight I'll find out. I'll come back and slit your throat. Do you understand me? If you do, nod your head."

She bobbed her head rapidly against the sheets.

"Good. I have a key to your house. I got it from your ex-lover. Better change your locks, hear?"

Her head bobbed again.

My fingers closed around her neck, pressed the rapidly pulsing carotid, closing it. She went limp, the oxygen cut off to her brain. I released my hold on her neck,

felt the blood come surging through the vessels under my fingers.

I stood up, turned on the light. Found her purse, cleaned out her wallet. Cash only. A tube of red lipstick caught my eye. I recalled reading about a killer in Chicago who wrote messages with his victim's lipstick on the wall. I opened the tube, brought up the lipstick, and looked at the naked back of the unconscious whore.

I stepped to her and wrote *WHORE* across her back. She'd never have the nerve to show that to the police. I took a last look around, feeling disappointment that my plans were in ruins, but then turned out the light and left.

The woman was up and about early the next day. I saw her supervising the locksmith as he changed all of her locks. She had a tasteful scarf around her neck. I never saw a police car at her house, but she had floodlights installed at the corners of her property and kept them on all night. I sometimes wondered which of her former lovers would be the object of her enmity.

She continued to sunbathe in her little bikini, but she stayed in the back yard. Now and then she'd look my way as I jogged past on my daily run. I sensed that her passions were subdued.

G.J. Schaefer: Once accused of 34 murders, widely regarded as a criminal mastermind whose alleged plot to escape prison and murder the State Attorney of Florida's 19th Judicial Circuit made newspaper headlines in 1985, now rocks you with a literary punch that will leave you reeling.

[KF LOGO] ... Jolts the reader like a ride in the Electric Chair! Authored by G.J. Schaefer - ex-cop convicted of gunning down two narcotics informants in 1972 - KF deals with the reality of crime and punishment today.

Killer Fiction: A unique literary statement that enters forbidden territory. Don't miss it!

Starke Stories: As fascinating as a fatal traffic accident and twice as bloody. G.J. Schaefer rips away the benign mask of the Florida Corrections System and exposes the Executioner's mask beneath. Spawned in the same cesspool of State Corruption that gave birth to Donn Pearce's "Cool Hand Luke", G.J. Schaefer takes the reader one giant step beyond into the depravity of prison life in Florida today: Prison politics. Sexual Slavery. Young boys beaten, robbed and anally raped. Serious: G.J. Schaefer takes you behind the super-secret gates to the State Death House where condemned men and women are brutally degraded: Penis tying, anus packing; where women are dragged to their deaths wearing a diaper. Writing as sharp as the Guillotine's blade; delivered with the sting of a slavemaster's whip.

FALSE CONFESSIONS

> Everybody always wonders how it begins, The
> Serial Killer Madness; all the hot shot researchers
> have their theories. But that's all it is, theory.
> None of them really know for sure, and maybe
> it's not the same for everyone. I can only tell you
> how it was for me. I was one of the best in
> the world, maybe THE BEST, and it all started as
> a sort of accident. I'll tell you about it, after all
> that's why you bought this book isn't it? You
> went to read about the murders ...

First Kill

I t was the spring of 1962 – spring break, as it happens – and I had just turned sixteen. Had my driver's license and the use of the family car, a green '57 Ford station wagon.

I drove down to Ft. Lauderdale Beach one evening, prowling for beer and pussy. That's what I told myself. The best I could brag on was what we called "heavy petting" and that wasn't solving any sexual release problems of the kind we all have at age sixteen.

I parked the wagon at Bahia Mar – it was still free back in those days. I walked across the street to the beach parking lot that had been roped off to create a dance area. At night, the bands would play and the couples would mingle. It was supposed to be for the college kids only, but every high school harry in Broward County was hanging out at those beach dances. Spring break was always a wild event in Ft. Lauderdale.

I was there early, well before sundown, and spied myself a lone girl hanging out. She was leaning against a palm tree next to a picnic bench minding her own business, probably waiting for the dance to crank up same as everyone else. I went up to her and said, "Hi."

It was no big deal. I was still a virgin. I had no idea how to put the right moves on a girl to let her know I was after sex, so it was all very non- erotic and innocent.

This girl was rather ordinary, a bit on the short side but with a nice figure and certainly under 25. She had brown hair and wore a blouse and walking shorts. We had a nice chat, the usual bullshit, and decided to take a walk down the beach to kill some time.

Back in those days south of Bahia Mar there was the Yankee Clipper, and then a fairly deserted stretch of beach running all the way to the Port Everglades jetties.

A hike down to the jetties and back was a real nice stroll. So I said, "Let's walk down to the jetty," and she was all for it.

It was twilight by the time we got down to the ship channel. Not a soul around. All the people were a mile north, where the dance was going to be. On the way down to the jetty the little bitch was rubbing and pushing her boobs against my arm, sending her make-out signals, so by the time we actually arrived at the rocks, there was a certain sexual tension between us. We got down to the jetty and next thing you know, we were making out.

No doubt this was a very romantic scene for the girl: the sunset, the handsome young man, the passionate embraces along the lovely secluded beachfront. She gets her little taste of fantasy: the french kisses, the boob massage, the feel of a hard dick in a man's pants pressing against her belly. And then suddenly she decides she's had enough. She breaks the embrace and dances away with a merry giggle.

She was wearing a silk scarf. You don't see them much anymore, but in the early sixties, the girls would wear them to the beach to keep their hair from being wind-blown. When she turned to bounce away, I grabbed her and caught her scarf. It came away in my hand.

She turned around and I flipped the scarf over her head and pulled her back to me. In the same motion I made a knot in the scarf and pulled it tight. Just a quick jerk in a playful manner. You know, flip it over her head and pull her back. A game.

But the silk scarf went deep into her soft neck flesh. She opened her eyes wide; it was almost a comical expression. Then her eyes rolled up into her head and she collapsed like a boneless doll. Her legs twitched for a bit and then she was still.

I thought she was horsing around. I went right to her and untied the scarf. The smell of her made me ejaculate. The smell cannot be described but it triggered an already powerful horniness into climax. Her shorts were urine-sodden. She had fallen forward on her face, and when I rolled her over she was soaked, and a slimy drool was all over her mouth and chin. I was shaky and agitated, but I did have the presence of mind to know that before me was trouble with a capital T.

So I stripped down to my jockey shorts and pulled her into the water. There was only a gentle swell, and I paddled out the length of the jetty, made a swing around the east end of the thing, and swam her about thirty yards out into the ship channel. The tide was just turning and the current took her seaward. Her shoes and clothing caused her to sink slowly, her arms outflung, her little clutch purse tucked into her shorts.

I swam back around toward the beach, got dressed and walked back to the dance. I can't even recall what she said her name was. Maybe Linda, but I can't swear on it. Nobody stopped me or questioned me or looked at me oddly. I was just another college kid on the beach. Most interesting of all, I wasn't struck dead by a bolt of lightning. But everything had changed.

After a while it was as if it had never happened. I did think on that event for a long time. There was an enormous power involved in the thing. I'd been terribly horny to begin with. The make-out session had held me on the point of orgasm, and then I did ejaculate all over myself. Remember now, this occurred well before

I'd had any genuine normal vaginal sex with a female, so there was some abnormal imprinting there certainly.

What had me amazed was how quickly the little bitch had collapsed. Certainly that was due to the constricture of her carotid artery. It was completely inadvertent, but also fascinating, and a very clean kill compared to most.

Once I began to take murder seriously I always had to remain aware of cleanup, and since I always hated having to clean up messes, I experimented with ways to avoid making the mess.

After that initial kill in 1962 there was, of course, a lot of guilt. I had to make a conscious decision as to whether I wanted to experiment with a second girl. I finally decided that I did, and in order to prepare myself I read every book and magazine I could find on the topic of crime and murder.

Eventually I came to see that if one plans carefully one may kill with minimal risk. There are basic rules to follow if one is to avoid apprehension.

In 1962 and 1963 I concentrated almost exclusively on transient hitch-hikers. One of my favorite hunting grounds was the Jo-Der Truck Stop on State Road 84, just west of US 441. Women would hit the Jo-Der for coffee and then come out on the parking lot apron to thumb a ride west. It was a 20-mile run to Andytown and I knew every isolated side road over that twenty miles. Believe it.

Another early pickup point was the junction of US 27 and SR 84. From the roadside park I could watch for transient women going in any direction – south toward Miami, east toward Lauderdale, west toward Naples, or north toward Clewiston. I would examine the women from a distance with binoculars and make my selection from a quick observation.

My usual approach to these hitchhikers would be to make the pickup and start a conversation. Once I'd determined the woman was not a local who'd be missed, I'd proposition her for sex. "Hey, would you like to screw? I'll give you twenty dollars." About 80% would give a positive response. Most would agree to accept money in exchange for oral sodomy. This suited me, since my interest was in killing whores, not innocent women who were just down on their luck.

The actual sex was always limited to the preliminaries, the kissing and breast fondling. My intention was to get the female "hot" so she would orgasm during strangulation. This was a misconception on my part, due to my inexperience.

My source material was marriage manual sex books that stressed foreplay. I could talk about sex knowledgeably and recognized female orgasm when I saw it, felt it, smelled it. Always the back would arch, the victim would tremble and convulse, and the eyes would roll back. It's a most distinctive reaction. And when she'd have her climax, I'd have mine. I never felt guilty about killing them when I'd paid good money for their services.

I'd sometimes experiment with how long the woman could hold her breath. I'd lay her on the front seat of the car, her head in my lap, and then I'd clap one hand over her mouth and squeeze the nostrils closed with the other hand. I'd take her right to the edge of death and then let her have some air. Then we'd talk about it.

Death on Sex

I had killed seven women before I ever had normal sex with a girl. Looking back on it there was a sexual element involved even at the beginning. I found myself erect during the killing, even though I was purposely engaged in murder, and not rape or sexual molestation. The victims were *WHORES* and the correct thing to do was to destroy them.

These women left somewhere and were never known to arrive at their destination. During this time I always selected single victims. Later for variety I did double and triple victims.

I discovered very early that the average female on the prowl in a bar or on the street was interested in sex in one form or another. The buzzword in the late sixties was "Wanna get high?" Those girls got a high that had nothing to do with drugs.

I rarely had anyone turn me down. I was sixteen or seventeen, and a fine hunky kid. I'd pull off SR-84 at any one of a number of places, and first thing I'd do would be pull a pistol, and then I'd handcuff the woman so that her wrists were behind her back. Nobody argues with a pistol. I'd say that most of these women understood instinctively that they were in serious trouble.

The killing shed was on private land. The roadway leading to it was arranged with light test fishing line. If the line was disturbed, I'd abort the killing to a second area.

After the victim's wrists were handcuffed behind her back, a dyed pillowcase was pulled over her head. The hood was merely to prevent her from seeing the necessary preparations. A noose was prepared using whatever type rope I was experimenting with at the time.

I'd toss it over the grooved beam, then remove the victim from the car and take her into the shed. I'd set the noose, then take up the slack by tying the rope to the car bumper. Then I'd get into the car and back up. I kept detailed notes on the victim's reactions.

It was all done quickly. Hooding to hanging in perhaps fifteen minutes at most.

Those early days were training in the techniques and dynamics of death. The sexual element was there, but the nastiness was counter-productive to any great sexual interest. Those early women, suddenly hanged, were considerably less befouled than later victims who were permitted to view the noose: a device to heighten their terror and enhance my own sexual excitement.

By reading about prison hangings, I learned how hangmen used a rubber belt similar to a G-string to inhibit in a modest way the woman's defecation at execution. Using the idea of the rubber belt, I'd yank the victim's panties up into the crack of the buttocks before pulling her up. This practice kept the mess to a minimum, which was my preference at that time.

Initially the killings were done by ruse and solely by hanging. The entire scene was playfully carried out, every young thing being paid to pose as a capering Cattle Kate. The first few that were hanged provided very little visual stimulation. It was something of a disappointment, because I'd read in numerous sources where English hangmen of the eighteenth century could make a female condemned dance

a lively jig, a frisk or strut in the air. Later hangmen had females kicking like can-can dancers.

My Kates were not as thrilling as I'd expected. The best of them looked spastic. They'd shake, quiver and twitch, but there was no satisfying "kick and spin." I was doing something incorrectly. The problem turned out to be the rope. I was using a soft quarter-inch braided nylon, identical to the type used at modern executions by hanging of females. It was a fine killing loop, intended for use without a drop, and designed to close the woman's major blood vessels in her neck.

There were a surprising number of informative sources concerning the fine points of execution by hanging. I picked up on the technical aspects reported in these source materials from over the course of 500 years. By the end of my career, I was skilled enough to kill a whore instantly or keep her alive on the rope for an hour. The killing became an art form, and I became a Master.

The Kates would die with a visible final shudder and then go limp. I came to recognize the extinguishment of life and would waste no time moving the car forward so that the victim was suspended only a foot or so off the ground. I'd undress her from top to bottom. First the clothing, then the jewelry.

Then I'd take out my penis and after lubricating it with saliva, I'd slide it into the upper portion of the victim's buttocks. I'd ejaculate almost instantly. The Kates were dirty down between their legs, but the cleft of the buttocks was clean, and provided a perfectly suitable substitute so far as I was concerned.

I was positive at that time that whores were diseased and any contact with the pussy was potentially lethal. Over the years the sexuality came to the forefront in the form of sadism, but that was much later.

Fascinating Conversations

There were always interesting new problems. I learned that some women love to scream. A raven-haired Yankee girl who had agreed to suck my dick for twenty dollars took one look at the noose and began to shriek her lungs out. I was really taken aback by her reaction, because every other woman had groveled and begged.

I didn't want bloodstains in the car, so I cranked up the ignition and drove straight to the rockpit, tied the line with cinder block to her ankles, and tossed her in the water. She went down blowing bubbles, her mouth open.

Like everything else done routinely, killing whores eventually became boring. Then one day quite by accident I discovered the sexual exhilaration to be had from wrestling an unwilling whore toward the noose.

The pudgy blonde Kate had managed to get her head out of the pillow slip hood. She caught it on the rearview mirror and wiggled it up and off her head. She was a snowbird waitress from Minnesota who was very willing to play at sex with the hunky college boy.

I looked up from tying the rope to the bumper and saw her eyes as wide a saucers, looking up at the rope. I went around to her side and opened the door, and she screamed, "What are you *doing*?!!"

I told her very reasonably, "You're to be hanged for a whore."

She screamed, "You're crazy!" Then she levered herself away from me, her head against the driver's door, and scissored her feet at me, kicking. I grabbed her ankles and yanked her toward me. Her skirt slid up and I saw she had a hole in her underpants. Pubic hair was poking through.

I dragged her out of the car, then wrestled her over to the noose and she was sobbing and babbling and saying, "Oh God, please, no! Oh, for the love of God, please don't hurt me!"

The blonde provided a taste of something new and sexually extraordinary for me. I found that I enjoyed the way she begged. I loved the hopeless desperation in her eyes.

The eyes of the victims were everything: saucerian beneath a clear plastic bag, bugged out as the rope lifted them from the ground, desolate as the thin blade slipped into living flesh and angled up into the beating heart...

The average female is easy to kill. Every one I attended to personally believed my primary motivation was sexual. The professional whores were best at understanding the nature of their peril. I could say to them, "You are going to die," and most of them would nod and calmly accept it, at least on the surface. These females gave me my finest challenge because I could always count on at least one serious escape attempt.

The challenge was important to me. The whore was usually interested in the methodology planned for her death. Once I had her secure we were then able to speak freely. There were some really marvelous discussions. She'd ask, "What are you going to do to me?"

I'd reply, "I'm going to kill you."

She'd say, "No, I mean *how* are you going to do it?"

"It doesn't matter to me. Do you have a preference?"

It was at that point that many of them would start crying. Not all, but many. Then they'd all complain, "But I don't want to die!"

I'd just tell them as nicely as possible, "It's required that you die." And they'd go, "But why?" and I'd say, "Because you are a whore." That response would put the casual trollop into a panic, but the pros were never confused by my reasoning.

Fascinating conversations were always available, and every woman was different. One mentally acute young hooker upon learning of my interest in killing whores explained to me ever so reasonably that she was not a whore but a prostitute, and there was a difference.

I listened to her rationalizations with polite interest, slid the folded newspaper under her bottom, and pushed the seat forward until her knees were jammed under the dashboard. I asked her, "Are you comfortable?"

"Yes, I'm OK. Listen, I'm not a whore, really. I'm not. You don't understand..."

As it turned out, "I'm not a whore" were that whore's last words.

The Main Rule

Perhaps the most basic rule for a successful career in serial murder is that the corpse must be promptly disposed of. The use of remotely located rockpits solved that problem for me. The nude Kate would be wrapped in a plastic shower curtain and driven to the nearby rockpit, removed from the car, rolled out of her plastic shroud and dumped into the water with a cement block tied to her ankles. The entire process took less than one hour.

There were three separate rockpits with three separate stolen cars at the bottom. I found this necessary since I worked different areas at various times, and I'd want a disposal pit in close proximity to my execution site. I would search the clothing and personal property for cash, and then all else went to the dump, except the identity papers, which were burned.

The rockpits were deep and clear. I'd wear my SCUBA tank and meet the Kate at the bottom, untie the line to the cement block, swim her over to the car and tie her to the hulk. Each one was secured to the front or rear bumper of the sunken car by separate poly-pro lines at each ankle and a third line tied around the waist.

One problem I initially encountered was a grotesque swelling. The Kate would fill with gas and give the appearance of being hugely pregnant. Attached to the front grillwork of the car by her ankles she'd look like a big balloon. I was always very careful to secure the Kates well, so they would not surface or break free. Once I began to slit the Kate's belly, a cut from the top of the pubic hairline to the breastbone, gas formation was lessened, due to the fish, crabs and turtles feeding on the viscera.

A gut-slit Kate left outside the car would usually be skeletonized within two or three weeks, depending on the season. Kates placed inside the cars and secured to the steering wheel or left wearing a seat belt took a little longer.

Once the Kate was reduced to a pile of bones I would collect them, put them in a burlap bag and swim the bag to another part of the pit for burial underwater. A hole of a few feet could be scooped out on the sand bottom, the bones put into the hole and covered over. This disposal was virtually undetectable. On a good weekend I might take a half-dozen Kates to the rockpits, but sometimes I might go several months without hunting.

Over the years some of the cars may have been found and hauled out for scrap, but I never left a Kate in a car, so I'm sure the purpose of the vehicles at the bottom of the rockpits was never understood, just written off as stolen cars.

BLONDE ON A STICK

A full moon was kissing the eastern horizon the evening I saw them standing beneath the winking neon marquee of a Tastee Freeze with their thumbs waving at the sparse traffic.

I pulled over; they piled in, grinning and giggling. Townie trash heading for the bright lights of Orlando, the Happy Trails Dance Hall, and a night of fun only twenty miles down the two-lane blacktop. Forty-five minutes later they were bound, gagged and tucked away in my trunk, facing an uncertain future as they listened to the hum of rubber on concrete… well, at least one of them was.

The capture had been an exercise in simplicity. The first deserted stretch of highway found me pulling off the road onto the shoulder. I put the heap in neutral and pulled the gun. A snub-nosed black belly. I pointed it between the teats of the sassy brunette riding shotgun beside me: delighted at the shiver of fear that took her, the involuntary widening of the mascaraed shiny brown eyes. She froze like a doe caught in a poacher's jacklight. The blonde in the back seat squeaked out a question: "What are you doing?"

"It's a stick-up," I said, "You cooperate, you live. You give me any trouble, I'll stick this gun down your throat and pull the trigger. Now hand over your purse."

The blonde couldn't hand over the purse fast enough. It came sailing right over the seat. She leaned back and licked her lips and sighed.

"Now turn around and put your hands behind your back."

She did as she was told. I silently admired the lovely heart-shaped rump she'd packed into her designer jeans like so much sausage in a skin; I reached over the seat and snapped a pair of steel wristcuffs on her. Heard the sharp intake of her breath. I felt her eyes on me and gauged her rising panic.

"Why?" the blonde ventured.

"Lay face down on the seat and shut up, cunt," I answered.

She did.

I turned my attention to the brunette. Her cervine eyes were brimming. "What are you going to do to us?" she asked so breathlessly I knew she lived in fear of my answer. I rattled a pair of cuffs in my right hand; in my left was the small pistol.

Her eyes lowered to the instrument of death; her arms went behind her back, and she put her wrists together in a gesture of submission. An apt pupil. The wristcuffs snicked into place. I locked them and tossed the key out the window into the dark.

"You're going to kill us, aren't you?" the brunette asked.

I dropped my hand to her bosom, surveyed the contours of the warm flesh beneath her blouse, studied the quick rhythms of her heartbeat, and gently squeezed a sweetly scented breast. I went up against her ear with my lips, licked the lobe and toyed with the small gold stud.

"Yes," I stated without rancor, "I'm going to kill you."

A sob floated up from the throat of the blonde.

"Shut up, bitch."

She seemed to increase her weeping.

"You don't have to kill me," the brunette ventured as if it were a great revelation. "I'll do whatever you want... and I'll never tell anyone." She sounded utterly sincere. I ran my hand up her skirt and she parted her legs in eager submission. I found her encased in nylon pantyhose, her cunnus arid, her posturing sexuality a sham. I pushed at the covered portals with my fingers. She humped and grunted, "Oh! It's so good!"

I spit in her face and got out of the car, went around to the trunk and opened it. I returned to my little vamp and opened the door for her. She stared at me with an uncertain desperation. I pointed the pistol at her cleavage. She opened her mouth to scream, but it died in her lying throat as I reached forward and jammed the fuzzy Spaulding tennis ball into her mouth, tying it in place with a strip of bed-sheet.

A length of clothesline secured her ankles, and I yanked her forward, draped her over my shoulder and dropped her into the trunk. I fired a single shot into the roadside gravel and turned my attentions toward the blonde, who'd popped up off the seat the instant the gun went off.

I opened the rear door of the sedan. In the dim coach light I could see tears glistening through her makeup. I stared at the dark, wet stain at her crotch. The wetness slowly began to creep down the inside of her thighs.

"Where's Betsy?" the blonde demanded.

"In the trunk with a bullet hole behind her ear. Same place you're going unless you do what I say."

The blonde made a contemptuous face and cleared her nostrils with an equine snort; snot rushed out over her lips. She made a gagging noise deep in her throat. I cocked the pistol and pointed it at her.

"If I do what you want will you let me go?" There was a thread of hope in her question. I severed it deftly.

"No. But if you treat me real nice I won't cut off your nipples before I slit your throat."

She stared at me in mute apprehension. She began to tremble, the wetness glistening at her crotch and spreading downward almost to her knees. Then she leaned forward and vomited onto the back seat.

I seized her long blonde hair and dragged her toward me. She knelt in the grass wheezing and coughing and spitting. I gave her a minute to collect herself, then took out my throbbing erection.

She glanced at it and turned her head away. The long curved blade of my skinning knife opened her blouse, and parted the straps of her sensible white cotton brassiere. I put the blade against a soft conical pink nipple, and watched it harden into a bud at the touch of the cold steel. I pressed the blade against her breast. She trembled uncontrollably. I listened to the soft spluttering; a pungent barnyard aroma swirled up from the scat of her jeans.

"I'm so scared." It was a statement, an explanation, a plea. "Please. Please don't hurt me." Her eyes caught my own. I looked into her hopelessness, her defeat.

"Suck it."

She closed her eyes and opened her mouth. I slid my cock in and pushed it down her throat, clamped her head to my crotch with my hand and came at once. The blonde pitched forward and began to vomit some more.

I stood over her gagging form, leaned over and caressed her cheek. "You were real good, honey. Never had such wonderful head. You wanna do it again?"

She began to cry in earnest, as if her poor heart would burst with sadness. "Please. Please don't hurt me. I just want to go home. I did what you wanted."

As she whined my penis stiffened again. I jerked her head up and let her look at the twitching, bulbous stalk. She closed her eyes and opened her mouth.

"Just lick the head of it for a while, honey."

She lapped obediently while I held her fast, my right hand holding the knife to her throat. I came in her face this time, simultaneously cutting her jugular.

Twenty minutes later the blonde was neatly wrapped in black Hefty garbage bags and lying next to Betsy in the trunk. We were going to have us a burying.

Three hours from Orlando I turned off a State highway onto a dirt track that meandered through slash pine and old water oak. I caught the crimson shine of possum eyes patrolling the undergrowth for fresh carrion. They must have sensed my approach.

I parked the sedan beneath an ancient oak and cut the ignition, sat and listened to the cooling of the engine, while I watched the moonlight cast shadows across the little glade. Uncapped a bottle of Wild Turkey and took a long pull. I savored the idea of the cute brunette in the trunk sucking on a tennis ball.

I fished through her purse. Checked her ID: Betsy Brown, high school junior, sixteen. A 130 pound bag of blood and shit. A second ID gave the name of Loretta Devereaux, age 22. Betsy's ticket to party. I could hear her soft snuffling through the fabric of the back seat. Fate is cruel. Everyone knows that.

I emerged from the car, walked to the rear and turned the key in the trunk. As I lifted it, the rank odor of sweat-sodden female billowed out, causing me to take a step back. I shined my powerful 6-cell flashlight into her wide, apprehensive eyes. She blinked owlishly; her nostrils flared, taking in the sweet, cool night air. Her white linen gag was soaked with saliva, smeared with pink lipstick; her cheeks bulged unnaturally. She could not speak except with her eyes, and those eyes made a plea for mercy.

I reached for her, took a handful of hair and jerked her out of the trunk, flinging her onto the ground. She rolled, skirt around her waist, white buttocks flashing beneath the sheer taupe pantyhose. She lay on her face breathing heavily.

I approached her, kicked her smartly in the ribs, and listened to the suppressed scream behind the gag. It hardened my cock. I unbuckled my pants and drew them off. Knelt behind the shivering bitch and flipped her skirt forward over her head, rolled down the pantyhose then slickened her cunt and anus with a handful of spit.

I rubbed the head of my turgid penis along the crack of her behind. She made no effort to resist until she felt the push against her anus. She bowed her back in outrage and tried to roll away, clenching and knotting her buttocks against me.

I arose and returned to the trunk of my car. Flung the plastic-wrapped corpse of the blonde out onto the earth and removed it from the bags. I could feel Betsy's eyes following me. She lay still as a rock in the shadows. I took two steel concrete reinforcing rods from the trunk, and pushed them into the earth. Then I severed the blonde's head, carried it to a steel spike and mashed her head down upon it. There was a curious squish as the rod went up into her brain, and goo began to drip on the ground.

I returned to Betsy. "I want some ass, whore, or your head will be on the other stick." Betsy made love like a dream.

I woke up with the dawn, my head on my lover's belly. Betsy was already awake, unmoving but watching with rapt fascination as a dozen possums fed on the carrion blonde. They'd eaten a hole in her belly and were busy gutting her with sharp teeth.

I yawned, stood up and stretched, sauntered over to where the blonde's head viewed the morning through glazed eyes. I took out my dick and pissed in her ashen face; watched the possums trundle off into the high grass leaving their meal unfinished. I moved to the car and fetched a shovel from the trunk. I called to Betsy, "You've got to bury her ass, she's beginning to stink."

I marked out a grave with the blade of my shovel. "Six feet long, four feet wide, and say a good six feet deep. That ought to do it. Don't you think so?" I looked to Betsy. She nodded dully.

I walked over to her and unlocked her cuffs with a second key from my keyring. Her wrists were raw and bloody. She immediately reached for the gag. I slapped her face hard, spinning her around, knocking her flat on the moist earth of early morning. I glowered down at her. A mockingbird trilled in the brush. There was a busy drone of flies around the blonde.

I told her, "You dig that grave, girl. Dig it deep. Deep enough for two. If you even give me the idea you want to try something cute, I'll tie you up and start cutting until you're in little bite-sized pieces for the critters. Understand?"

She nodded solemnly. I answered her unspoken question. "If you're a good girl, we'll make love again." She got to her feet, leaving a large urine-soaked spot on the sand. She went to the shovel and began to work. I removed the cuffs from the dead blonde. Flies covered the stump of her neck, the opening in her belly. There was the sharp metallic smell of blood over the rotten stench of opened guts.

By noon the grave was finished. Betsy's hands were blistered and raw, and her blood streaked the shaft of the shovel. She handed the shovel out to me. I rolled the blonde's corpse to the edge of the grave and kicked it in. Flies hovered in a black cloud. I jerked the head off the iron spike and pitched it toward the grave. It bounced once and dropped in. Two points.

I went to the car and brought back the two purses. Dropped the blonde's into the grave. "Lay her out decent," I told Betsy. I watched as Betsy arranged the blonde on her back, carefully folding her hands across her bosom, arranging the head at the correct angle, setting the purse beside it. I knelt at the edge of the pit and masturbated as Betsy went about her work.

When she was done I said, "Now you, Betsy dear."

She hesitated. Ground water was beginning to seep into the grave.

I leaped into the hole and smashed the heel of my hand into Betsy's nose, crushing it. Blood fountained into my face, over my hands. She dropped to her knees, choking on her own spew of blood.

My blade cut away her skirt; it fell. I ran it along her crotch, slicing nylon and cuntflesh. I mounted her as she blew bloody spray into my face through her nose.

The knife went to her throat; cleaved through to her spine. Her vagina contracted in a death spasm and I sprayed her with seed. I licked the blood from her cheeks before I dismounted.

"I love you, Betsy."

My whispered endearment drew no response other than the incessant drone of the feeding flies.

Murder Demons

Torture for the sake of torture did not interest me. It was, in those days, important for me to feel good about what I was doing.

Whores were agents of evil, and as a good Catholic young man I had no difficulty with what one might consider philosophical gray areas. There was good and evil; a well-defined line ran between the two. Whores were evil.

Whores were to be killed. Once that decision was made, the problem became how to do it successfully. A great deal of practical study went into the matter. The whore had to be selected, transported, killed and disposed of. The best way to kill them was to hang them. It was convenient, quick, effective, silent and tidy except for the excrements.

The alternative method was usually the use of a plastic bag. The bag was tied over the whore's head and she died by suffocation. This method was convenient, silent and effective, but it was far slower than hanging and much messier. I got to the point where I'd push such women out of the car after tying on the plastic bag. It was less unpleasant for me that way.

There were variations on the kills. I'm speaking only in generalities here at the moment, so that you can understand that there was a plan and purpose and this was never a situation where some sex-crazed madman was snatching girls from the public streets every time the moon turned full.

Returning to this thing about torture… My experience was that whores see events in terms of sexuality. Please consider the speed involved in a kill. A transient road whore is agreeable to suck cock; she has no qualms when driven to a remote area.

I'd pull the gun and handcuff her, get out of the car. I'd go around to her side and get her out. She might say, "What are you doing?" or "I'm not into kinky stuff."

I'd take her back by the trunk, open it, take out the noosed rope, put the noose over her head, pitch the other end up over a limb, tie it to the trailer hitch, get back in the car, start it up, put it in drive and the whore would be pulled up. We are

talking three minutes on an average; five at the very most, between cuffing and the suspension. The victim doesn't realize what's happening until she's actually dangling, it's that fast.

Many kills were completely impersonal. The victim had revealed herself to be a whore and my responsibility, as I saw it, was to kill her. The killing was usually done quickly without any sexual molestation, rape or brutality. I knew how to set the noose so that the victim would be rendered almost instantly unconscious. I'd read the journals of the 19th century hangmen and knew exactly the point to apply pressure to cut off oxygen to the victim's brain. Some killings were almost peaceful. The whore would shiver, convulse, kick a bit and then be still.

As you might expect, this sort of kill was fairly boring. There was no stalking, no challenging ruse, no fun. The real enjoyment was in the hunt. The kill was satisfying, but the clean-up was work.

There is a post-kill depression that must be overcome. The initial impulse is to throw the corpse in a ditch, a canal, a hasty hole, to be rid of it at once. The average killer cannot deal with the actual harsh reality of the act. He has no sense of responsible purpose, no long-term commitment to what he's doing. A lust killer murders for sex, and once he's fulfilled his lust, he dumps the corpse and flees from the scene, and from himself as well. He looks back on the event and feels guilt rather than triumph.

There came a time when I decided to make the game more interesting. I did this by introducing the concept that it would be better if the whore understood she was to be hanged and concurred in my decision to destroy her and what she stood for. I felt that if she understood what the ultimate good purpose was, that our experience would be a fulfilling one of shared intimacy.

I'd read a number of accounts where the hangmen had sex with condemned females; the women were agreeable to the intimacy and acquiescent on the scaffold. I wondered how that might be: fuck the whore, then hang her, with the whore knowing she would die at the conclusion of the sex. It was a remarkable concept, and certainly not unique to the world, so I decided to try it. Let me tell you here about one very special experience....

The whores were mostly sad, stupid, moralless young women who, when confronted with the finality of their situation, simply fell apart emotionally. They'd listen for a few minutes and then begin a downhill slide punctuated by tears, slimy snot and pissy pants. The nicer I'd be, the more I'd try to make them understand, the faster they'd dissolve into great bawling sobs. But there were some exceptions.

The very finest of these exceptions was a wonderfully attractive young call-girl from Omaha who had just come down to Miami to try her hand at the snowbird trade. I was introduced to her by a friend who'd suggested we go visit her and get our dicks sucked. We went to her trick pad and my buddy went with her and got sucked off. When I went with her, I declined the blow job; instead I made an appointment with her for an all-night sex fest. She was agreeable, even enthusiastic. We set a date.

I was absolutely smitten by this sexy whore. She was lively, intelligent, and had a sensuous figure. I was enchanted. I wanted our assignation to be special. I went

right out and bought her a brand new rope. I knew she'd look exquisite swinging at the end of it. I took great care in selecting it.

As the date approached, I called her to confirm our evening together. I instructed her on what to wear. I wanted to see her in pink and black. She had long blonde hair fixed in ringlets that would look so nice against a black evening dress. Black heels and stockings with a garter belt. Pink bra and panty. A frilly brief. She assured me she'd look her best for me.

Never before had I been so taken with a whore. I was furious. She was seducing me and I was helpless before her daunting sexuality. She would have to suffer for that. Yes, *suffer*. I drove out to Davie and purchased an excellent horsewhip. I'd put her to the lash before hanging her! She'd pay for her seduction!

The following days I spent clearing an area in the center of a melaleuca copse. I hacked out an area the size of a large room with a narrow entrance trail. I assembled the gallows beam, nailing it up between two trees. On a second tree, I stripped off the small branches, hammered in a piton and hooked a pulley to it. The tree formed a living whipping post.

I dug her grave. Deep. Down to limestone bedrock. I hauled in two twenty-gallon buckets of water from a canal. I carefully surveyed the scene and then went back to town and purchased a step-ladder. It was just what was needed. I arranged the noosed rope over the gallows beam. Brought in a pair of Coleman lanterns and extra fuel. Towels. Knives. Buckets. Accessories. Everything was perfect for the whore.

I picked her up at her Dade County trick pad. She looked stunning. I bought her prime rib at the Forge. She ate a hearty last meal. Baked Alaska and brandy. I wondered if she'd be able to keep it down. Sometimes whores would puke. It was hard to predict and always messy. We drove north on route 27 through the night.

I told her how beautiful she was, how much I'd been looking forward to our romance to come. She yawned, burped, leaned against the car door and seemed to doze. She was bored. She'd heard it all before, many times. A beautiful bored whore. I knew I'd soon have her complete attention. She'd see me through new eyes. She'd be alert to every nuance of my speech. I watched her light up a cigarette and stare into the night. Her last night.

I soon had the car parked at the end of a limerock road at the edge of a trackless swamp. She looked puzzled. I cut the engine, pulled out a small pistol and put it to her face. She gasped. I got her cuffed. She was mine. All mine. Forever. It had taken less than a minute. Her initial thoughts were of sex. A bondage scene, she thought. She told me she didn't do kinky stuff. I was agreeable.

Drew her toward me for a kiss. She pulled away. She didn't want to kiss me. She demanded I remove the cuffs. Demanded! I just said no. She glared. Such a pretty fit of pique. All full of roast beef and ice cream and booze.

I needed to soften her hard look so I said, "Flies love a cunt but prefer a dirty shit hole. Are you aware of that?"

She just stared at me. Blinked. The hardness was replaced by wariness. "What do you mean?" she asked cautiously. I explained it to her. She said, "Please take me home." The first "please" of the evening. She was learning manners. I wondered if she'd say, "please kill me" before the sun set the eastern horizon on fire. I

shook my head, took out my penis, and instructed her to suck on it. Then I opened a switchblade and told her that if I felt her teeth on my cock I'd slit her throat. Quickly. Expertly.

She nodded. Kept her eyes on the knife. "Please don't cut me. I'll do whatever you want." I told her to think of my dick as a straw, and to suck my balls dry. She slid over, put her face in my lap and began to lick my penis. She got it up and took it in her mouth. I pressed the blade to her neck, and held it in place with my left hand. With my right, I explored underneath her skirt, squeezed the panty-covered labial lips. She bobbed her head up and down professionally, her tongue laved my shaft.

I slipped a finger under the elastic of her panty; her crease was dry. I ran a finger up her vagina. She made no response but to suck more fervently. My finger drifted to her anus, and pushed into its center. She tightened her sphincter. I pushed my finger all the way up into her and felt soft turd. Put my thumb in her vagina. I could feel the thin wall of muscle separating the two vaults. Warm drool ran down over my balls. I could hear the smack of her lips, the slurp of hot saliva. My crotch was wet with her spit. I fingered her anus, thumbed her cunt. Time passed.

She came up off my cock with an apology. There was a ring of frothy white saliva encircling her mouth, a clown's greasepaint. I told her to get back on the job. She said she'd had enough, she'd done what I wanted. There was an edge to her voice.

I took my finger out of her butt, my thumb out of her twat. I reached over and rubbed my finger under her nose. She drew back, eyes large and snapping with annoyance. Then she saw me put my finger in my mouth. I began to lick it. She watched, enthralled, the spit wet on her chin, the corners of her mouth glistening. "Flies truly love it," I told her.

She made a noise deep in her throat, swallowing. I licked my finger again and asked her if she wanted to throw up. "Take me home," she said, halfheartedly looking away, sensing there would be no going home for her ever.

"Gimme a little kiss," I ordered. She turned toward me and shook her head furiously, eyes downcast, almost demure.

I pulled up my trousers and let myself out of the car, went around to her side and opened the door, grabbed her by the hair, and jerked her out of the car. I flung her into the weeds and put the beam of the flashlight on her. She rolled to a sitting position, skirt bunched around her waist, black garter straps against the soft white flesh between her stocking tops and panty. Eyes rivaling those of a jacklighted doe - all wide, wet, startled, full of uncertainty.

I pulled her to her feet by her hair, turned a beam of light toward a narrow path leading into the copse of trees. I gave her a push. She stood fast before the dark entrance. I came up behind her, put my arms around her and drew her to me. I licked her neck, her ear, the line of her jaw, pressed my hard cock into her rump. "I'm going to stick it in you. Your cunt. Your ass. I'll fuck you nice." I felt her tense. She took a step forward. I took one back. She pivoted and swung a kick toward my balls that missed and made her stumble. I laughed. Took out the knife. She screamed. I stepped toward her. Tripped her, rolled her face down in the leaves, pressed the blade to her cheek. "Shut up!" I snarled. She went silent.

Beneath me, the well-fueled engine of her body huffed and puffed. I could hear her panting, feel her breathing hard beneath my own body. She was damp with her exertions. Mosquitoes hummed around us. Frogs sang a chorus in the swamp nearby. I smelled her perfume, the moist earth, the rotting vegetation around us. A jet whined far above, the whore whined below.

She sobbed, instinctively understanding the price of failure. "Please. Please. Please," she murmured. I put the point of the knife to the corner of her eye. Told her I'd poke it out if she screamed, kicked, or misbehaved. Whispering, I asked her if she understood. She sobbed, nodded a little. I ran my hand up her leg, squeezed her buttocks. She lay still, unresponsive.

I stood up. Brought her to her feet by her hair. Returned her to the car. I sat with her. The night was still young. She asked to blow her nose. I let her snort snot into my handkerchief. She wanted a cigarette. I lit one for her, stuck it in her mouth. She sucked on in greedily. I watched her, she watched me. Death watch. I let her spit the cigarette butt into the dash ashtray. She leaned back against the door. Great crescents of dark sweat stained her evening dress, her perfume mingled with the sour acrid stink coming from under her arms, leaves and seeds ornamented her bodice, her knees were pushing through her nylons.

She sucked in her bottom lip, closed here eyes, laid her greatest fear before me like a gift. "I don't want to die," she muttered, a statement as true as the moon, the stars, the eternal abyss, the gray mosquito feasting on her cheek.

"You'll live to see the sunrise," I promised. "Why me?" she asked the night. "Oh, God, help me," she prayed, her voice catching in her throat. She lifted her eyes and asked, "What do you want from me?"

I opened myself to her instincts and intuitions, let her touch the truth naked in my eyes. She saw her own fleeting mortality, the transient nature of her earthly existence; murder demons, capering.

She lowered her head and began to cry, hopeless sobs that left me untouched. I'd seen it before, understood the way of the whore. The cascading tears, the streaming wet cheeks, forerunners to the viscous nasal snot that would leave her face and bosom beslimed. The ultimate gambit.

I rudely seized her nose with my left hand and forced a jumbo Kotex napkin into her mouth with my right. I tied it in place with a nylon stocking. Her eyes were wide and blinking. Her throat working furiously. She suddenly blew her nose. Tendrils of mucus whipped out, clung to her cheeks, soiled her dress. She squirmed with fear and alarm. Her clever words silenced, her verbal ploys stifled, all her plans in disarray. There was a stench of sweat. Her flanks were sodden with it. Her tresses were becoming lank and greasy. There were twigs and leaves in her hair. I pulled her to me and wiped her nose, her chin, her mouth. I tasted her tears. Kissed her eyes, promised her that I would treasure her memory for a lifetime, that we would become one in flesh and in spirit. The whore began to weep anew, but with a refreshing sincerity.

My experience is that women have a predisposition toward deceit. Whores lie. They are creatures of expediency and calculated illusion. A commercial menstrual rag will stanch the incontinent flow of lies from a whore's mouth as well as the bloody slops from her cunt. Great truths are better communicated tacitly, with a

look, a gesture, a smile.

I'd promised the whore a sunrise, then turned her world upside down. She looked comic and vulnerable hanging by her ankles. Her head was in an empty 20-gallon bucket, her shoulders hard against the metal rim. She was so quiet I thought she might be unconscious. The night had subsided, and a gray light filled the tiny glade. The sun would soon be up.

I picked my way over to her and shined my flashlight beam into her face. Her eyes were wet and alive, blinking against the sudden glare. Mosquitoes rose from the bucket in a swarm to settle on her clothes. Her exposed flesh was a galaxy of tiny red welts. The flying insects of the night had fed well. The day shift would fare even better.

FLIES IN HER EYES

> I know what you want to hear about: Pussy. It's true, there's plenty of hot, wet hole to be had if a guy wants it. Show a road whore the singular deadly dark eye of a 9mm semiautomatic pistol and I'll show you a young gal who can set world speed records for wriggling out of her pants. So sure, you can have it if you want it, and risk fifty different varieties of disease that can make your cock rot off. I tell you, you're much better off to leave that dirty cunt crack alone. I learned that; you will too.

The serial killer researchers always want to hear about the trolling at twilight for victims; the sex freaks want to hear about the special thrill of finding a little minx with a smooth-shaved pussy; the sadists want to hear how the bimbo begs, and how you threaten her: does she want a stiff dick up her ass or eight inches of cold steel in her navel?

I know all you folks have your special interests, but this time we're going to hear about the practical side of serial murder.

Successful serial killing requires skill. More than fifty whores died at Pond Apple Swamp. Each died with her wrists chained behind her, peering out at the fading world through a cheap plastic bag.

Pushing them out into the weeds merely prevented them from peeing on the seat covers and stinking up the car; that was a sensible panacea for the problem of their filthiness.

Go out and bag one of these road sluts yourself, you'll see what I mean. You see, when you get down to basics, there's nothing particularly sexy about it. Popular novelists make murder sound erotic, like it was the ultimate sexual thrill, but the reality of it is something else altogether. It's *nasty*.

I spotted her at first light. She'd emerged from a semi that had cranked up and headed south toward Miami. I'd watched her study a road map and wander over to stand at the junction of State Road 84. She'd waved her thumb at a few cars rolling east. I pulled out of the Everglades Cafe and in a moment the pickup was made.

She was a semi-hippie, a Hoosier townie girl who didn't fit in back home with her love beads, her long hair, and her braless boobs. She was heading into Ft. Lauderdale, and said she'd be hanging out at the beach. Maybe get a waitress job.

She had these nice teats jiggling around under her peasant blouse, so I said to her, "I'll give you twenty dollars if you'll let me feel your boobies while you give me a blow job."

She took the pass right in stride. Told me OK without a glimmer of erotic interest, and that was that. No hassle or negotiation. Just "OK." She was smelly from the road. Probably hadn't had a bath since she departed Indiana. The long hair was lank and greasy. There were crescent-shaped stains of dried sweat under her arms. Her jeans needed a wash, and her hiking shoes were caked with mud. She dozed as we rolled east.

I pulled off State Road 84 when I got to Pond Apple Swamp, a pestilential tract of real estate populated by mosquitoes and water moccasins. There was a tiny sand track next to an oil pipeline right of way. I pulled the car in there, and we were concealed from the road by a screen of Brazilian pepper bushes. The girl yawned and stretched herself in the seat of the car. I fished a twenty out of my wallet and handed it to her. She accepted it without comment and put it into her purse. When she looked at me again she saw a 9mm pistol leveled at her gut.

"Do as I say and you won't be hurt," I said.

She nodded. Uncertain.

"Turn your back to me and put your hands behind you."

She did as she was told. Twisted around in her seat. I handcuffed her, quickly pulled a plastic bag over her head, tied it in place with a nylon stocking, reached across to the door latch, opened the door, and shoved her out into the weeds.

I let her thrash around for five minutes or so while I went through her purse. Retrieved my cash and hers as well. They always have a little money tucked away. For an emergency.

It was a pleasing kill, no problems at all. I got out of the car and found the young would-be penis-sucker face-down in the grass. There were already flies crawling across her denim-clad rump, whizzing around seeking out the source of the stink.

I uncuffed her wrists and rolled her over on her back. Her brown eyes were open wide and empty, slightly bugged. Some bloody snot was smeared around her nose; her tongue was sticking out a bit and there was considerable drool all over her chin. I'd seen them vomit into the bag, but this whore wasn't too bad at all.

I returned to the car and put her knapsack and purse in the trunk, locked up the vehicle and resigned myself to tote the bitch into the swamp.

So there I was, looking down at the bug-eyed corpse. Her aroma was not about to improve, so I leaned down, draped her over my shoulder, and hauled her away into the vastness of the trackless mire that was Pond Apple Swamp.

I knew every inch of the Pond Apple. It was a good quarter mile to where I wanted to go, and what little trail there was at all was usually underwater. I slogged along, keeping an eye cocked for snakes. I had me a little camp back in there, a place to take my girlies, where we could be assured of absolute privacy.

I'd been out to Colorado working the major mountain passes in the front range. Hippie chicks heading for the Haight, starry-eyed wannabe starlets angling for a spot in Hollywood, hookers shooting for Las Vegas – their bones litter nameless mineshafts on the road west. Down they went by the ones, twos and threes.

Killed me plenty on the road west of Denver, and while I was out there I learned about pitons. These are devices used for rock climbing. A piton is basically just a circular metal ring at the end of a spike. I bought me a bunch and hauled them to Florida and hammered them into the trunk of a huge old strangler fig tree deep in the swamp.

There was a little island out there, dry ground most of the year. Probably an old Indian mound. It was a long haul through water and muck with a hundred and thirty pounds of dead meat over my shoulder, around which hundreds of flies were swirling, drawn by the stink of the whore. I managed to get her there safely, and plopped her down on one of the raised roots of the fig.

Two weeks earlier I'd had the good luck to bag a pair of fourteen year old runaways from a state training school for delinquent girls. Cute little things who promised to suck my peter dry in exchange for a lid of grass. The only thing I let them lick was the inside of the plastic bag I'd tied over their heads. I'd hauled them back to the camp and left them upright, their wrists wired to the pitons pounded into the old tree. I strung them up naked, except for the cheap peace sign neck-laces. It amused me to see those satanic symbols dangling between their little boobies.

That had been two weeks earlier. Now there was nothing left but a pair of with-ered forearms that were wired up high enough to be out of reach of the carrion eaters. The rest of the bones were scattered about the small island. The peace necklaces were at the base of the tree next to the ivory white skulls. It had only been two weeks and the girls were completely skeletonized.

I was delighted. I walked around collecting the scattered bones and put them in a pile. I couldn't leave them heaped up on the island to await a chance discovery. That wouldn't do at all.

I pulled the peasant blouse over the head of the Hoosier girl and noticed that she did indeed have a fine pair of teats. I removed her shoes and socks, unfastened her jeans and pulled them down. The white nylon underpants were full. I'd come to notice that early morning kills were usually far dirtier than afternoon and evening kills.

I stood over the half-naked corpse and stroked my cock. I ejaculated almost instantly. A few minutes later I pissed on the whore, directing my stream over her breasts and belly to wash off my semen. That took the edge off my emotions.

I zipped up and occupied myself with wiring the whore's wrists together with

heavy-gauge leader wire. I ran a length of poly-pro line under the wrists, put the cord through the dead-eye of the piton and hauled the whore to her feet, then let her down a notch so that she sagged languidly with her arms stretched above her head. Nice figure. She was pretty enough, even with her head in a plastic bag.

The day would be hot and humid, a fine day for decomposition. I studied the dead face behind the clear plastic. The eyeballs were already turning milky but the whore retained the marvelous look of wide-eyed discovery I'd seen so often when using the plastic bag on them. Her head was slightly tilted. The area around the mouth was drooly, the lips moist, the gray tongue just sticking out enough to press against the plastic. Nice.

I slid the knife blade beneath the knotted nylon and cut it, removing the bag from her head. Flies descended immediately on her face and crawled across the eyeballs, buzzing with delight. A juicy morsel.

By high noon I had tidied up the island area. The bones of the two delinquent bimbos were neatly packed in two separate plastic garbage bags, awaiting a trip to the quicksand pits further back in the swamp.

Corpses are generally found because they stink beyond belief. I always had a remote place to take a girl, somewhere she could rot undisturbed.

I eyed the whore. Her guts were beginning to swell. A good sign. The gases had forced everything in her intestines out the rear door, and her underpants were loaded with fermenting feces. Purplish blood was spiraling down the insides of her ivory thighs. The lining of her uterus was commencing to collapse and run out her vagina. Already her lips, nostrils and eyes were covered with what appeared to be white grains of rice. She was beginning to stiffen, but that would pass too. Everything would be fine.

The Pond Apple Swamp quicksand pits descend into the limestone caverns beneath the land itself. From time to time these pits boil up as springs. Be so incautious as to step in one of these shallow springs and you will vanish into the bowels of the earth without a trace.

Watching my step with infinite care, I emptied out the two bags of alabaster bones and then one by one, pitched them out into the bubbling spring. They'd sink, sit on the sandy bottom for a minute or so, and then just slip into the eternal sands, as though they'd never existed.

By three in the afternoon, I'd returned to my whore. She needed me to help her prepare to meet her new friends. I removed the gold posts from her pierced ears, and the rings from her fingers. They'd want her naked and unadorned. I helped her out of her soiled panties, being careful to avoid her filth.

The brown mat of public hair was entirely ordinary, and matted with filth and blood. I took out my penis and urinated on her crotch. It washed her off a little, but she was still a mess. Hopeless and disgusting as only her kind can be.

I watched as her backside seemed to vanish beneath the living blanket of black and green blowflies, going about their business competing with the ants for a fulfilling meal. What they seemed to need was better access to the yummy parts. I drew my long-bladed skinning knife from my belt sheath, and pushed it into her just beneath the breastbone. Then I drew it downward to her pubic area, opening a neat incision. Gas hissed from her belly.

I gagged at the stench of her fetid guts, but the flies seemed to burst into joyous song, increasing their industrious drone and buzzing tenfold. They seemed to be up to the task ahead.

I turned my attention to the rope holding the whore up, loosening it and letting her sag until she was on her knees. Her viscera flopped out of her belly and rested on her thighs. The sightless eyes seemed to stare at her belly through the curtain of white worms, her head hung forward between the upraised arms. Appropriate. On her knees. Doing a whore's penance.

I punched the thin blade through her eyeball into her brain. Fluids from the burst eyeball ran over her cheek and dripped down between her swinging bosoms into her lap full of grayish guts. Good.

I inserted the blade into the second eye. The flies buzzed furiously, raising up only to return with renewed vigor. Flies in her eyes, ants up her nose. Satan's helpers carrying away his own little by little, in microscopic pieces.

The shadows were beginning to lengthen. The heat and humidity remained oppressive; the whore was rotting wonderfully. With nightfall the creatures of the swamp would come to her, feed on her flesh, rip out her innards and drag them through the stagnant waters, adding to their stench.

Already I could hear them splashing, drawn to the blood scent. They would devour her, gnaw her bones. The swamp beasties have to eat just like anyone else, don't they? They were accustomed to being well fed at my little island haven. Waste not want not. And thus we are an integral part of the food chain.

I turned away from the rotting pile of meat, and kept an eye cocked for deadly snakes. It was tedious slogging back to the roadway, but the slut needed her privacy. I left her to rot in peace, to become one with nature.

I know what you're going to say! You'll say that this story is disgusting, and that I'm an evil fiend for committing it to paper. You who relish the latest episode of Friday the Thirteenth, and countless other occasions of mindless sex and violence. You love to be shocked. You're fascinated by depravity.

Yes, you! The very ones who memorize the slaughters of a Ted Bundy or a Henry Lee Lucas, and then dance and caper in an orgy of self-righteousness when these dark folk heroes are executed by the State. You revel in violence: murder, war, execution, every manner of social disaster. Your TV and film industries thrive on it. You're begging for a close-up look at murder – the real thing. And you dare to criticize *me?*

Your Most Depraved Client,

The Butcher of Blind Creek

BLOODY INSTRUCTIONS

Malignant Intelligence

I recognized at once the smirking famous face, and my heart skipped a beat as Ted Bundy fixed his gaze on me with a sudden grin of recognition as if he were meeting an old friend.

The year was 1986; the venue, Florida State Prison. We were in the visiting area used by inmates who are condemned or in maximum security. Ted came striding over and said, "I know you!" He was personable and self-assured, confident in his demeanor, but I could see the madness blazing and snapping behind his eyes. And now that malignant intelligence focused on me as it had once focused upon the helpless victims he had left dead in the broad wake of his journeys across America.

Tender Victims

"I know your face from the detective magazines," he challenged. "You're Schaefer, aren't you?"

Cautiously I admitted that I was indeed, and what of it anyway?

"We've got to talk," he said. It was a command, and also an opportunity not to be missed by one interested in going into the dark shadows world of human existence. I agreed that we should get together, and found myself looking forward to talking to the famous fiend in private. Ted arranged it with a friendly medical orderly, and he and I were soon put in for medical call-outs at the same time.

We were not supposed to take anything with us when we went to a medical call-out, but when I left the cell I stuck the news clipping from the May 13, 1973 *Palm Beach Post* down into my pocket. When the guard searched me and asked me about it, I merely told him it was an item of legal material concerning my case, and with a quick look he let it go.

I was taken down the hallway and locked in a holding cage next to Ted. For several hours we were left in the cramped little cells side by side. It was there I first encountered the evil personified by this human monster known as Ted Bundy. I found myself recoiling with revulsion, yet curiously fascinated.

While we waited to see the doctor I took out the newspaper clipping and slid it through the bars. He read it with apparent interest and questioned me about it.

One of the first things that he noticed about the accusations was that I was alleged to have killed two girls in Pompano Beach in the eight and nine year old range. Ted told me that he had never been able to grab a kid that young, that he really was not attracted to kids of that age at all. I mentioned that he was convicted of killing a girl of age 12, but he defended this act on the grounds that he did not know when he grabbed her that she was so young. He claimed that she was matured beyond what anyone would have expected a 12 year old to be. The girl had

well-developed breasts and looked older than she was, and that is what had caused him to make the grab.

That did not stop him from being curious about what it was like to snatch and murder a pair of prepubescent kids. I told Ted that I had been reading a story in a magazine about the life of Albert Fish. I read how Fish had developed a taste for human flesh and I wanted to give it a try. Fish had claimed that young girls made the best eating, so I grabbed a pair that looked tasty.

You should have seen his face when I told him that! He wanted to know if I had cooked them, and I told him that I had taken the pair to a remote area and slaughtered them, and then roasted them over an open fire on a spit. He couldn't get over it, the very idea had him squirming on the bench. He wanted to hear all about it and of course, I provided him with all the details that he could ever want – and more.

Murder Frenzy

Ted was really not into the outer limits of sexual depravity. He was a ghoul, and what he did was to be expected of a person who was into ghoulism. His personal technique was more on the order of spotting an opportunity, making his capture, and then taking his victim to a quiet place for the kill. The kills were made in a variety of ways, but that too was a matter of convenience. His more common modes were ligature strangulation or beating to death with an object such as a tire iron or a club.

This was usually done in a frenzy, for as he was getting into the act it seemed to him that a power or force was coming over him that made him go wild and savage. After the killing he took his pleasure with the corpse in a more leisurely manner, and depending on the situation, he might save the corpse for future use or he might simply dump it after he was sexually sated.

I found all this very interesting because once Ted opened up, he really spun out the tales and you could see that he was transporting himself back into time and reliving his acts. I watched him recite his murderous deeds with a smirk on his face and an erection bulging in his trousers. Ted loved his evil acts.

Showing him the *Post* story really got his undivided attention. By making Ted think I had more experience, it was as if he was trying to show me that he did in fact out-perform me. I would listen to him talk for a while, then I would toss out some new depravity and he would consider that before trying to top it.

Ted was, of course, fascinated by my tales of murder as well. I told him that if one was intent to make a lifestyle of murder that he should achieve maximum pleasure from the acts while he was able to do so, since sooner or later there would be some slip-up and the fun and games would come to an end.

Ted wanted to know whether I had ever confided to any mental health workers that I was a ghoul, and what their reactions were. He was actually embarrassed about his affinity for corpses, and if I were not careful he would retreat back into himself. Of course, I told him that I had confided my own love of corpses to my legions of shrinks over the years, but that they were a non-judgmental lot and

there was never any problem. They were bound by the rules of doctor/patient confidentiality, and that prohibited them from revealing my secrets. I told him that the shrinks were mostly curious about it, rather than being critical.

Then there was the discussion about the messiness of murder and the general reactions of the victims while they were being killed. We went around a bit about that and I gave Ted a number of good pointers on how to keep the messiness to a minimum. The one particular incident that put him off the most was the murder of Denise Naslund. He had captured her while she was on her way to the ladies' toilet at a state park and when he was finished with her murder, there was urine and manure all over his car.

I explained to him that it was to due to his impetuous and frenzied actions that he was having all these problems. That his actions were too hot-blooded and filled with passion, and that he should have taken a more reasoning approach to the problem of the victims making a mess all over the place. He asked how that was possible under the circumstances… and I explained it to him in considerable detail.

My approach was always one of cool reason. My captures were done with deliberation and there was a certain excitement leading up to the killing, a give and take of conversation that provided a certain amusement as well as excitement. I explained to him that it was a far more worthwhile adventure if one would linger over the victim and enjoy the anticipation of the acts to come. He couldn't quite understand it, since he was in such a big hurry to render the woman dead so he could get on with the grisly sexual activities that were to follow. I concluded that Ted was not a sadist but rather a serious ghoul.

The conversations were always fascinating and I always came away learning something new. I doubt that Ted gave this sort of information to other inmates because none of the other ones, except for Bernard Giles, had such horrifying allegations squarely laid at their doorstep. I feel sure that Ted most likely confided to someone else at some time that he was a ghoul, but I have never seen any confirmation of these suspicions in print.

One of the popular misconceptions about Ted is that he was a rapist/killer. That is untrue. Ted always killed the women first and then raped them after they were dead. Ghouls, just like everyone else, have their individual sexual preferences. Bundy was attracted to anal sex and used his victims that way first. Once again I relied on my extensive experience to help give Ted some pointers in the ghouling game. It has always been my experience that women killed in the evening seem to defecate far less than women killed in the early part of the day. This maxim seems to hold true time and time again, and it does eliminate one of the foremost problems that confront the ghoulish killer, and that is filth. Yes, there is a school of ghouls that do not shy away from excrement, but these ghouls are of low station and generally to be avoided.

Ted returned to his personal graveyards, the areas where he kept his corpses. He was not particularly interested in burying the corpses, but usually left them out in the weather to rot, or at times would wrap them up in some sort of protective cover to keep away the carrion feeders and the maggot causing insects. Ted knew a thing or three about maggots from direct experience, and could match me when it came

to details of corpse decomposition which I had learned from texts for persons interested in mortuary science and embalming.

The two women that Ted killed at the state park in Washington, the ones that he told me were the Jessup/Place copycat crimes, were done in the high summer and therefore the rate of decomposition was much faster than victims killed in the cooler seasons. Ted tried to solve the problem of early decomposition by carrying the corpses to a higher elevation so that they would be preserved a longer time at the cooler temperatures. Ted used these corpses sexually for as long as he could stand it.

Experiments in Terror

My own preference was in the preliminaries and the increasing terror generated by the woman's awareness that she was in the hands of a homicidal maniac. I was entranced by the varied ploys that the captive women would use in order to save their lives. Of course not a single one of them managed to save her life with a ruse, but it always made it better when they would make the effort. Most of them would try something, and I made it a game to see how long it would be before the victim would request to be killed.

This entertainment varied from one victim to another and it might take the form of a physical or a psychological torture. If and when the lady decided to say that she'd had enough, I was quite willing to put her out of her misery... if she asked nicely.

You'd be surprised at how quickly this sense of resignation could be brought about. I picked it up from my studies of the mass executions in Poland and Russia during WWII. I had always wondered how all of those people could be lined up and shot without a fight. They seemed resigned to it. That fascinated me, so of course I had to conduct my own experiments – and I did.

This sort of experiment is perfect for a person of sadistic tendencies, since we sadists do not consider our victims to be genuinely human. Ted never thought of the women he killed as persons but only as objects. I did the same and found it an excellent way to avoid any human feeling for them. I simply called them all my "Kates" and let it go at that. I guess one would consider that a *sociopathic* quality but what the hell, we all have our faults and I am no different than anyone else in that respect.

Ted, of course, was missing out on a lot of fun by simply taking his women out and bashing in their skulls so he could be about the business of taking down their pants without protest. I found it far more rewarding to have the woman beg me for the love of God to allow her take down her own pants and give the pussy to me. It was not that the ladies found me so attractive, it was more on the order of their finding the alternatives far less attractive.

The Kate would be wondering what she had gotten herself into and by and large she was thinking that she was in the hands of a sex beast when that was not the situation at all. She was, in actuality, in the hands of a homicidal maniac who had no qualms about telling her exactly what the score was, and what she could expect

in the hours to come. The Kates didn't want to believe that they were going to die. A human enough reaction I suppose, but that would abruptly change when I produced a shovel from the back of the car. I would politely open the door for them and invite them for a little walk in the woods. The average Kate might not believe up to that point that she was being carried off to be killed, but at the sight of the shovel, or perhaps the look of deadly intent on my face, the Kate would become desperately alarmed about going into the forest or the swamp with me.

There was no overt threat necessary; the threat was always implied and it was much more interesting to watch the brain wheels spinning around and coming to their own conclusions about what was happening and what, if anything, could be done to prevent the murder from occurring. It is at times such as these that women can become very clever talkers. I assured Ted that with more than 170 victims to my credit, I had heard all the tales that any female could invent to prevent herself from becoming a murder statistic.

There is a challenge in encouraging the lady to come along of her own accord, and I found that was best accomplished by offering her a choice. One perfectly effective choice might be this: I would take her breast out of her blouse and out of her brassiere if she were wearing one, and holding it firmly in my hand I would flick on a butane lighter and invite her to come with me quietly and of her own free will or I would burn off her nipples. I would convince her of my intentions by lightly playing the flame over her naked bosom and allow her the freedom to make her choice.

I assure you that for the most part the ladies decided that they would prefer to see what fate awaited them in the woods. I say "for the most part" because there were indeed some who did make a fuss, and some who attempted a ruse or even a physical attack. The ladies who did such foolhardy things did find themselves dying much more onerously than their cooperative sisters.

The Maggot Problem

Ted appreciated the differences in our respective styles, but couldn't understand my aversion for the women after they turned putrid and began to rot in earnest. He didn't seem to mind the maggots, but I did. They were forever a problem to be dealt with.

Leaving the victim clothed after the killing helps to keep down the maggot problem. And a plastic bag secured over the victim's head is excellent for keeping flies out of the facial orifices.

Consider: Maggots are caused by flies and flies are attracted to stink. It is axiomatic that any time one keeps a victim for more than three hours, the lady is going to have to pee. In these situations usually the victim is bound and helpless with her wrists secured behind her back. The anxiety of the situation will cause her to want to relieve herself, and if the fear factor is enhanced then incontinence often occurs. The stink of urine will bring the flies at once.

Yes, there is the option of simply taking down the lady's pants and letting her pee, but that option is rarely chosen. Many times the victim would tell me that she

had to "go to the toilet." They were always very coy about it.

The proper reaction is to simply ask the victim what she expects you to do about it. Remember now that these women expect rape at the least, and any messing around with their clothes can cause more of a reaction that a direct move to murder them. The female victim seems to be a lot more confident when she has her clothing on and it has not been set in disarray or messed with.

I have had such victims ask me if I would unbind them for the purpose of allowing them to go off into the bushes alone for a pee… or whatever. Incredible as that may sound, it has occurred. Of course, they'd get nowhere with that request.

Playing Doubles

Ted was, of course, a tyro when he nabbed Ott and Naslund; when I nabbed Jessup and Place I had been in the ghoul game for almost 10 years, so I knew what to expect from these juicy young creatures at the end. By then I was into doing double murders and an occasional triple when the opportunity arose, whereas Ted at the same point of time was only able to handle singles. He was playing at copycat and doing a poor job of it at that.

Doing doubles is far more difficult than doing singles, but on the other hand it also puts one in a position to have twice as much fun. There can be some lively discussions about which of the victims will get to be killed first. When you have a pair of lively teenaged bimbolinas bound hand and foot and ready for a session with the skinning knife, neither one of the little devils wants to be the one to go first. And they don't mind telling you quickly why their best friend should be the one to die.

Giving the victim false hope is always fun. For instance, say you have the Jessup and Place girls and you decide that one will live and one will die. But which will be the lucky one? Ask them and they will tell you in great graphic detail why each is the best of the litter for you. Sex? You cannot imagine how companionable such a little teenaged vixen can be until you have one at your complete mercy. My, how they do ask for the privilege of doing whatever might please your amorous interests. Anything at all they are agreeable to.

Take the Place girl, Susan. She was a heroin addict and was without any means of legitimate income. How do you think the girl earned the money to support her narcotics habit? Yes, with her sex; so she was indeed quite knowledgeable and skilled for a young lady of age 17. The other bimbo, Crystal as she liked to call herself, was a veteran of the beachfront hippie pads and skilled in her own right as well. I ask you, what does a fella do when confronted by so much agreeable young flesh? One does the best that one can and asks questions that would make a Tangiers whore blush. But the young bimbos, their asses on the line so to speak, were quick enough to answer each and every question and assure me that if they had never tried it that they would be quick to learn.

I have found that professional prostitutes are the finest victims when it come to a ghoulish murder because they understand at least to some degree what is going on and will even, if one is lucky, get into the spirit of the act and do their part to

make it a stunningly fine event. There have been several hookers that I have murdered that have simply told me straightaway that they have suspected that their lives would end in just such a way.

Hookers are interesting in that way, unusually keen at understanding why they must die. I would compare it to the cow that is suddenly confronted by the hunting leopard and stands there rigid with fear, allowing itself to be brought down. Skilled hookers are often like that.

This is not to infer that each and every whore is the same, they are not. The killer must demonstrate mastery over his victim and convince the victim that the death act is in her own best interest and the best interest of society. This is not as hard as it might sound if one maintains self-discipline and personal control. Ted would simply fly apart and go on this murder rampage and before he knew it there would be blood and brains and gore all over the entire area. All quite unnecessary when one sits down and carefully lays out a plan and then puts it into effect.

Private Graveyards

Corpse disposal is an essential consideration for successful long-term serial murder. The police only become involved when they have a corpse. With a quick kill the risk of discovery is minimalized, especially if it is also a silent kill.

During the late sixties I incorporated into my victim base women who sought out or offered narcotics. There were fewer remote areas to be safely used as killing places, but by that time I'd learned that my car made a superior death chamber. The routine was to "arrest" the doper, put her in handcuffs, wrap a length of cord around her ankles, push a Kotex into her mouth, and tie it firmly with an Ace bandage. This was followed by a plastic bag pulled down over the head and tied in place with a scarf. The victim would be dead within five to ten minutes. This method also worked well when two or three were to be killed at one time.

My rockpit disposal method was initiated as a response to several bodies being discovered after being dumped in remote areas. I found this annoying and vaguely threatening. The Kates from the hanging shed were quickly out of sight beneath the rockpit water, and once secured to the bottom would not come up. Their bones could be further concealed by underwater burial, but this was not always convenient.

I'd average maybe 50 miles a day traveling one place to another, and occasionally had to pass up a tempting kill because there was no appropriate disposal site. I never acted in a spontaneous manner, and since I didn't want to miss these opportunities, I constructed a series of corpse pits adjacent to my killing sites.

These holding pits were merely dirt holes 3 feet deep with a plywood lid that could be covered with dirt, foliage, and other camouflage.

I'd pick up my whore, make the kill, put her in the holding pit, and go about my business. The kill itself never took more than 20 minutes. Later I'd return to the pit and pick up the whore for a proper burial.

South Florida had a high water table at that time, and a whore buried in a shallow grave would swell and come to the surface. Carrion animals would dig her up

to feed on the decaying flesh, and the smell could invite discovery. Victims need to be buried deep. As a rule of thumb, mine were never buried at less than five feet. My private graveyards are now under the chic subdivisions and parking lots of South Florida, and they will never be found.

Murder for Fun

I am sure Ted, upon hearing these tales, was disappointed that he had not taken more time to smell the fear of these pretty blossoms as he sent them to their doom across America. At least the ladies who fell into my hands enjoyed an interesting death and, after all, that is something. I was never one to go about bashing in pretty heads, and found that to be brash and impetuous to the extreme... but then Ted paid for his lack of self-discipline in the end, didn't he?

There is no doubt in my mind that Ted Bundy was insane beyond cure. During the years 1986 and 1987 I fed his illness. I stoked his sense of depravity and encouraged him to reveal his true nature. He did so with a flair, maintaining an attitude that even if I did have more victims, he was the Best because he had a much more developed sense of depravity. It was true I could not top him in reality, but I could always beat him with my lively imagination. I was curiously privileged to hear the litany of his madness come to life, because he believed from what he read about me that I was a fellow traveler along those dark and sinister paths leading to physical and spiritual destruction.

Recreational murder. It's increasing here in America as the morality of our society sinks deeper and deeper into a morass. But you don't want to hear a treatise on the state of our society. You want to know more about the killing, don't you?

That's OK, everybody seems to want to know about that part. The killing fascinates people and while they say that it is awful, those same souls are running to their films and magazines and books to vicariously relish the thrills that persons like Ted are bold enough to consummate as an act of will.

What would you like to hear about most? If you're not afraid, write and ask me your questions, because with more than 175 victims, I am an expert in the ways of death... and what comes after death as well. Yes, the ghouling. That part. It truly makes no difference to me here in this hellpit of the Florida prison system for two life terms.

So until I hear from you, be careful. For there is an underground of murder out there, and who can say... perhaps you have already been chosen as one of its victims.

Ted, after all, is dead. Or is he? Seems I'm always hearing that some killer has gone on a rampage somewhere and is slaughtering victims much like Ted did. And so the madness continues...

THE MURDER CHANNEL

I do not agree with the proposition that the writer of a story is into the things that he or she writes.

There is me personally and then there is me the artist with words, and when we are discussing one thing we cannot leap over a line and get into another area. To say I am a sadist because I write sadistic stories makes no sense whatsoever. It's as nutty as saying I write murder stories, therefore I want to kill people. John D. MacDonald wrote some very raw murder scenes, but I don't recall anyone daring to infer that he had a mental problem; Evan Hunter does some pretty grisly stuff too, but nobody has locked him up for it.

I make an easy target because I am a prisoner and I've been accused of being a serial killer. People say it must all be true because this guy writes about murder like he was there watching it go down... or he was doing it himself.

The part I really don't like is the attempt to tie me into child murders. Accuse me of killing mature females all you like, but sex murder of eight and nine year old kids is beyond the pale for me. Anybody accusing me of killing someone under the age of sixteen, I'll take a polygraph any time. I've had endless problems due to these accusations.

I am in the business of writing for the entertainment of my fans – people who prefer bizarre topics and who have trouble finding writers who cater to their preferences. I have always been concerned with writing realism in my murder stories. You want to know what kind of fiction this is? It's a new genre, a sub-genre of crime-horror-fantasy. I call it Schaeferism. Who can say for sure where it is going to lead? The whole idea is to explore new trails in the area of literature.

It bothers me that when I say that I'm writing fiction, I am disbelieved. I could understand that – *IF* it weren't for the fact that I have been studying fiction writing for a long time, since 1963 officially. It's not a question of this guy being accused of murder and then saying, gee, I'm a fiction writer, but it turns out he'd never written or studied anything. I've been studying the art in depth since high school; I studied creative writing in college and beyond. And after all that, I get accused of murder and the cops steal my stuff and then come along and try to mold these crimes to fit my stories.

Then suppose I'd stopped writing. Wouldn't the cops say, he never really was a writer, he was a diarist; and after we took his diaries away and locked him up, he never wrote another word. How would that look? It so happens that I went to prison and used my skills to entertain myself and polish the style I was already developing before I went to prison.

There is no real proof to back up the allegations that I committed any crime, so what the State's Attorney did was create a monster with no credibility and the thing took off from there into the fictional 34 victims. The facts of the case show what happened, and to this day there is not one shred of evidence that I committed any murders anywhere.

My problem has been that nobody believes I am innocent. No matter what I say or do, that remains a constant. Since I am disbelieved, my feeling is that I might as well use the accusations to my artistic advantage. I recognize that my life is wrecked and that it will be impossible for me to ever have a normal social relationship. Since I'm shot down in flames socially, I don't really give a fuck what people think of me personally, so long as they will just leave me alone. I am accused of all this bizarre shit every time a bone is found in Florida. Why deny it? I'd much rather say, yes! I killed 175 women and here's why!

I specialize in fiction. "Bloody Instructions" is based on the fact of Ted Bundy approaching me, and captures the gist of our conversations in prison. I have turned those encounters into fiction, but the fiction is convincing because I draw the details from reality.

If I am writing fact, then I will simply tell you that the work is factual and leave it at that. For example, "Jesse in Flames" is something that I lived personally, and should be read as a non-fiction selection. I knew all the people involved in the crime, including one of the victims who was a cop when I lived down in that same area of the state. I have personally seen quite a few men, and a few women too, walk down that corridor to the death chamber, and I have always carefully studied their demeanor. In a way, I am fortunate to have been able to be up at Florida State Prison for those 23 executions and to be able to plug my emotions into the atmosphere surrounding them, as it will be a valuable thing to incorporate into my future stories.

The movies would have the public believe that all these executions are done in the same way, and that the persons to be executed more or less cooperate with their own killing. Not so. Some of them are resigned to their fate and go along quietly, but others put up quite a struggle. Tafero was one of the few who handled it in a brave manner and did not have to be dragged to the Chair.

I have experimented with a lot of different styles. When Roy Hazelwood of the FBI said I am a sadist because the stuff I write is sadistic, I took that as a challenge. I have never had a sex partner accuse me of being sadistic with her. In my opinion, none of the stories I'd written in the past had been about classic sexual sadism. I can write to order, just as I have done in the past with my private fetish customers, and to prove it I wrote "Blonde on a Stick," which I'd like to dedicate to Roy Hazelwood. Now he can say that I do write sadistic stories and cite "Blonde on a Stick" as the prototypical example. I molded this story to fit the accusation levied against me.

"Blonde on a Stick" is not a real event which has been fictionalized. It's only make-believe. Where did it come from? Out of my anger – anger at being called a sadist, at being locked up in solitary, at being treated like a piece of dogshit by "correctional officers." I sort of "zone out" when I write this stuff, and from that source I produced the story. Now I cannot tell you if that zone is within me or from some cosmic murder channel I can plug into at will, but that is how I am able to write so realistically.

"False Confessions" is another completely imaginary story, written in the flat style of a reminiscence. It is merely a matter of style, and of making up things to fit in with the topic being addressed, which is the why and wherefore of serial

murder. "Flies in Her Eyes" explores serial murder and ghoulism – reaching for new levels of horror and degradation.

Where I live, here at Florida State Prison, people are electrocuted. That's a polite euphemism for killing human beings. The people who work at this human slaughterhouse are by necessity mentally and emotionally predisposed toward cruelty, violence and murder. Many are sadists. They all enjoy being a part of the killing in some form. Each individual plays a small part in the killing act on behalf of the State.

In prison I can talk to genuinely evil people — the real life boogeymen who do unspeakable acts. I've chatted up authentic ghouls and serial killers, homicidal sex maniacs who come as they kill. How many writers have had the chance to talk to Ted Bundy — as a fellow convict, a peer? I took down the spoken confession of Henry Lee Lucas' sidekick, Ottis Toole, the Devil's Child — the man who told me how he raped, murdered, beheaded, barbecued and *ate* Adam Walsh. I enjoy hearing the weird things people experience. It sparks my creativity and puts the sting in my stories about real-life murder fiends, deadly and twisted in ways we'd all rather not consider.

I could even tell you where I got the basic factual data to fashion into fiction scenarios: One title I recall was Kogan's *Theory and Practice of Hell*. Another one was *The Roots of Evil*. I also used *The History of Torture*. The Ghoul stories are, of course, distinctly different in that they deal in a melange of insanity and perversion. Krafft-Ebbing was the major source on sexual perversions of this nature. And of course Flannery O'Connor. In 1964 I read "A Good Man Is Hard to Find" and "Good Country People" and saw the Herschell Gordon Lewis movie *Bloodfeast*. Flannery's Misfit and Fuad Ramses were the little kernels that gave rise to my homicidal maniac, The Ghoul.

During the late sixties there were quite a few adult book shops that sold fetish novels. The top money was in S/M, B/D and unusual fetishes. This was attractive to me because reading such material, I could say to myself, "You can cook up something better than this." I used factual accounts of real events and fictionalized them. By the seventies this sort of porn format was in decline and being replaced by historical treatments of fetish topics, with titles like "The History of the Hang/Shit Fetish." These works presented the topic as an academic matter using psychological text case studies and profuse illustrations and photos. The purpose was to beat the "redeeming social value" rule.

Take sex, for example, bestiality: there are places in other societies where the family dog is used to clean the shitty behinds of kids. A girl grows up with a dog licking her ass. In the USA we frown on that, but if one does a study of the cultural idiosyncrasies of societies where girls grow up with a dog's tongue lapping between their legs and does it in a way that's academically sound, it beats the obscenity problem.

I was a full time university student, full time hunting/fishing guide, part time hack writer with ideas to break into the fetish trade. It was fun to do when I had time, but after 1971 I never had time for writing. Once I saw my efforts were not income generative I chunked the whole mess of manuscripts, magazines, photos and all into the boxes and stuck them in a closet and forgot about the whole thing.

None of that was criminal in nature. It was not seizable under the terms of the warrant issued. But they seized it. They read it. Five weeks after the stuff was seized, they come up with this "Greatest Crime" crap.

I've never tried to say I was a hotshot new talent. My basic bitch has been that I had a *right* to write whatever I pleased in my own home; that the police had no *right* to seize it absent a warrant stating they wanted my literary work; that the State had no *right* to use it in a murder trial absent some nexus between the item entered into evidence and the crime charged; and that newspapers and magazines had no *right* to quote from my writing and to say that I write fiendish stories, and therefore I am a ghoulish, corpse-loving fiend. When the Ghoul digs up a corpse to make love to it and its toes fall off, prosecutors all over the State immediately eye the author as a villain.

"Powerline Road," "Expecting Dinner," and "Into the Mind of the Ghoul" were written with intent to offend. Vomit bags should be issued with this book. But I can't be faulted on the detail. The Ghoul character is perfectly insane; the condition of the bodies is perfectly accurate and if the reader isn't shocked and chilled by the mindless horror that defies understanding, then I need to turn in my pen. Those tales cut along the edge of reveling in murder and perversion.

I'm not going to say: Oh, that stuff is just twaddle and nasty and you can't print it. I'm not a phony. I wrote serious fucking maniac stories. I was concerned with making the stuff gross and nasty and crazy. I worked hard at it. It's valid prose. And it's non-criminal.

A disturbed personality is always going to find something to lash along its madness. With "Into the Mind of the Ghoul" we have the first stirrings of the maniac's tortured mind. Then in "Powerline Road" the fantasy slips into reality. The Ghoul is patently crazy in his actions but his reflections are fairly lucid.

You will never know the long hours I put into the Ghoul stories. The ironic part is that what the police stole from me might be termed working drafts. "Murder Plan" is skeletal, a bare structure on which to flesh out a yarn. It annoyed me that this was published when it was not anywhere near where I wanted it to be.

"Powerline Road" and "Expecting Dinner" were much further along, but dealt with the implementation of the insane compulsions manifested through sex and violence. It's the old case of the intellect presenting the problem to the will and the will says, let's run with it or let's drop it. But the Ghoul is all full of short circuits in his psyche. He goes directly from ghouling around to luncheon on the corpse's money. Instead of losing his lunch, he *buys* his lunch. Because, of course, he is *out* to lunch!

If I didn't have the emotional capacity to chuckle at all this I'd have been totally a basket case by now. I just roll with it. *Mass murderer!* You bet. Best in the business... and let me tell you how it's done.

My stories have been well researched for realism: I have watched people die from gunshot and stabbings and various other means when I worked Emergency Room Security at Broward Medical Center. I've seen people hanged (suicides), smashed in car wrecks, having heart attacks, blasted by shotgun.

The research about how people rot was taken from mortician texts and homicide investigation texts. The mortuary science texts are particularly good, because

they go into the chemistry of putrefaction. You get an hour-by-hour discourse on how a corpse decays into a puddle of slime. I used that textbook material for the part about the girl in the canal and the disinterment of the girl in the hole. The toes rotting off. Classic touch.

If you want to be a good horror writer you need to have a command of these things. You can't just sit down one day and write a convincing horror tale without doing some exhaustive research, and I'm sure Stephen King will tell you the same thing. Squash the baby, flatten the cat, hang the whore and watch her rot.

The Ghoul is a negative character — the reader is supposed to hate him and fear him. He represents the blackest depths of the human heart that is twisted beyond comprehension or redemption. There is a queer chilling power that runs through "Expecting Dinner." I'm not talking great writing. I'm talking raw fiendishness — here's a sexual psychopathic monster that will scare the wits out of you. The prose is actually drab; the emotion, the madness, the perversion ooze through it like a bloody slime. The purpose is to wallow in the insanity of the character, his homicidal delusions and sexual dysfunction. The Ghoul is ponderously sick throughout his entire being, and the prose reflects that drab, morbid hopelessness.

The Ghoul stories raise gooseflesh — not because of the clever prose, but because of attention to the horrible little details. Don't you love the way I have the maniac feeling *sorry* for his victims? What a twisted fucker he is! Ted Bundy in the Chi-O house with his club evokes *terror*, but my character evokes *horror* via his base depravity, incomprehensible vileness.

The melange of perverted psyches I used to shape my Ghoul character, while based on the Misfit, are a cross-breeding of various types. I relied heavily on three especially Ghoulish true cases: Sergeant Bertrand in Paris, Ed Gein and Bela Kiss. These three were corpse-fuckers. Fish was also a corpse-eater. The confusion and remorse I based on the Heirens case. He was the original Catch-Me Killer, who would sneak in and steal women's clothes. It was an escalation of perversions that ended up with Heirens becoming a serial killer. Bela Kiss had over 20 women in his drums. Pickled in alcohol. Bundy visited the rotting corpses of the women he killed. He liked to tart them up with fresh makeup and nail polish. That's *ghoulism*. Gives you the involuntary shivers — if you can let yourself think about it.

The fascination with hanging is perversion more than crime, but well documented in older psychological case books. Mainly it was that the person was "imprinted" sexually by the spectacle of public hangings, and the vision became a masturbation fantasy. Then he got "locked into" the fantasy and it blocked regular sex. There's no limit to the weirdness you run into in these books on abnormal sex imprintings, so I dumped all this in a pot, and stirred up a real ding-dong of a homicidal maniac.

Insanity is hard to capture on paper. There has to be a *throb* as the mind jumps off the trolley of rationality into the abyss of madness. In many of my stories I weave murder into sex as a social perversion. I do murder as an expression of insanity, rage, and power. But I don't do murder as a mystery in the classical sense. There is no "whodunit" aspect, rather the focus is on the "whydoit." I dwell on the rapacious destruction of beauty, a feature of murder that angers people. I gnaw away at areas where other writers are too timid to venture.

Murder, as I write it, is not a rational act. In "Cut Bait," the theme is homicidal insanity; it's a horror story. It's not supposed to make sense, but it does make your skin crawl. I'm not going to tell you if it's a true story or not. I'd prefer to see you sweat.

I focus on realism, so my Ghoul looks like a regular fella. I stole this concept right out of the Bible. It says the Devil can appear as an Angel of Light. That is to say, he can fool you because you cannot recognize him. In my stories, you never can recognize the monster until he nails you. "Spring Break" is the perfect example. It's a horror story, only the monster does not come up out of the Intracoastal waterway to grab the girl. He's a human monster — the sort of monster Vincent Price portrayed in *Conqueror Worm* and other Poe classics, and Hitchcock dealt with in *Psycho*. Normal people cannot understand a Norman Bates. He's, well… psycho.

My character is scary because he is ordinary, but he is living in a dimension of insanity that causes the reader to gasp in revulsion. Squashing a kid with a truck is gross, but it happens every day in real life. A homicidal sex pervert sticking his toes up a dead girl's squishy cunt is riding a line of madness that teeters on sick humor. It's frightening but it can be funny as well.

"It's downbeat, it's crawling out from under a wet rock and leaving a slimy trail… it's… the Ghoul!"

That work was done 20+ years ago, and since then I've progressed as a writer into other areas. I'm still good for a few more rounds with the Ghoul, though: *Trick Baby Meets the Ghoul, The Ghoul and the Hitchhiker, Slice of Life/Slice of Death, Lavender Lips, Bagged by the Ghoul.* ("Her mouth was open. A lavender hue was on her lips, pink flecks of lipstick clung to the visible gray tongue. I wondered if I would catch some weird disease if I kissed the pretty corpse. I decided to find out and removed the transparent plastic Kleen Cleaners bag from her head.")

If you read it superficially you get a turn-off because of the nastiness. But if you sit down and really read it, there is the underlying vibrancy of insanity. You'd like to dismiss these stories, call them jack-off fantasies for perverts. Then upon reflection, you think this could be real! That's what is really scary.

But I really cannot see where anyone would even remotely consider this stuff indicative of a criminal mentality. It's not even worth a XXX rating as it's written. I anyone had read the stories, and asked me, "Hey, what's all this mean, Jellybean?" — which nobody did, not even my defense lawyer — I could have readily explained it all.

I once got thirty days in the Hole for submitting a story to a magazine. The editor was so upset he wrote to the prison demanding I be punished. I was too! Talk about *hot stuff!* It was a biker's testimonial. Red hot smoking gospel from the mouth of a Scooter Tramp turned to Jesus. I wrote it as he told it. Dope, murder, sex perversion. All of it. I wrote my story true and for that I got the Box. Compliments of an editor who didn't like it. Everybody likes murder tales, but nobody likes the maggots up the nose part. Well, I'd like to let the folks know that murder ain't nice.

I've had prison officials scream in my face that I'm a sick pervert for sending out my stories. Bad for the self-esteem. But inside, deep down in the artist's soul of me, the applause was ringing and the announcer was saying "Let's have a hand for the master fictionalist who put an adult state official into a screaming fit over a story!"

Killer Fiction creates a small wound in the area of the brain where social awareness is housed. It's a social indictment in the guise of entertainment. Anyone who says, "This is the most disgusting thing I've ever read" is paying me a compliment. I like superlatives, like most disgusting. What people hate about my stuff is the confrontation with their own mortality. These stories are designed to make you throw up and leave you looking over your shoulder for a long while. As for those timid souls who read my work and hate it: *Good!* My intent is to get a valid emotional response.

The "Starke Stories" slam the system that degrades people in the name of corrections. People think prisons are country clubs. These stories just give a hint of what it's really like. I portray the sick, perverted individuals who staff them and populate them. "Early Release" is just a beginning.

"Nigger Jack" rolls into forbidden territory, but it's very accurate. The validity of the execution scene goes to the basic truth of the event. Do women really bleed when they are electrocuted? Do their guts really burst? (Yes.) Now we are dealing with a fact that people would rather not be confronted with. The cracker mentality, the casual racism — I'm a real authority on prison racism — these are important to the realism. But the main focus is on the sexual overtones that accompany female executions in prisons for men.

I do not write these stories to degrade the reader. Gratuitous grossness is not intended, but I do strive to offend your social consciousness to the point where you say, "I refuse to allow these executions to be done in my name — I am The People!"

"My Ticket" is a satire on how I ribbed Bundy; "Death House Screams" is about the 1979 Spenkelink execution, and how the State violated Spink's body by packing him. "Brutality" is a matter of opinion, and the FSP Administration does try to make executions suitable for mixed company.

I am not deluded. I've never said, Gee, I'm the new Papa Hemingway, I'm a budding Norman Mailer, Elmore Leonard, whatever. I'm not. I'm just G.J. Schaefer, Storyteller, Dabbler in the Art of Prose, and I enjoy lifting up the rocks scattered over the meadow of our society and watching the creepy-crawlers in human skins scuttle hither and thither. I don't have to live with anyone but myself — and I like myself just fine. I'm a recalcitrant bastard and I'm crazier than a shithouse rat — but not so one would notice.

I make decisions. They aren't always right decisions, but nobody runs around calling me wishy-washy. More like manipulative: An ex-cop survives in prison by being the slyest, motherfuckingest, most expert manipulator he can be. Bet yer ass I'm a manipulator, and mean, and stubborn... but also above-averagely honest, loyal to a fault and true to my convictions. And I work like a *fiend.*

I have this ability – a gift or a curse or whatever – and I'm in a dilemma as to whether to run from it or continue to explore it. I enjoy writing and the controversy of being way out there where nobody else dares to go. It appeals to my innate sense of adventure. Now how do I get these critics off my back? Stop writing? Or continue to write and polish my skills?

I am inclined to quit writing this sort of stuff. I'm thinking about writing about the saints. I was always enthralled by pictures of those kiddies about to be gobbled up by lions and tigers and then, later, nubile young Christians dangling from crosses or about to undergo all manner of horrible torture for the sake of their faith. It almost seemed as if it might be fun to be a martyr.

KILLER FACT

Letters from GJ Schaefer to Sondra London

1989

3/15/89. I live by the Laws of the Criminal Underworld, and what is called the Convict Code. I wipe my ass on the Florida Statutes, the U.S. Code. I have become, as a matter of necessity and survival, a master criminal.

… I am *not* of your society anymore. I am of the criminal underworld. My word is my bond. Your society does not understand that anymore… If you betray my trust I can, *if* I choose, have you and your kid dead at the bottom of the Chattahoochee river within 30 days. Such matters take longer when I can't get near a phone.

… My sister was raped. The rapist was dealt with. A man threatened my stepmother. He spent 4 days bound & gagged in a closet and his house was robbed of every thing in it. I don't fuck around. Mess with my family and you get hurt.

3/21/89. I am, at this time, enmeshed in a world of boundless evil. I am, factually, a captain in the Dixie Mafia; (I joke about it but it's not really a funny matter) … I have, factually, the power to have you killed. I have, in the past, used these powers.

Now. If you betray me or the people I am associated with to the police or if you fail to keep your word with respect to our Project — and I've explained it to you so you know, we've agreed — you shall be put to death in accordance with the traditions of the Underworld. If you are interested in the exact formalities of how such matters are concluded I'll be glad to explain to you. So. I warned you at the onset you would have an adventure and now you've been warned of the penalty for betrayal: Death. You know what betrayal is so I do not need to explain that. Conduct your affairs with Honor. Understood? Questions? I would not have you die due to a lack of understanding.

… True Story: About 1983 my dad had to come up with $12,500 or lose his house. A certain Crime Boss sent a person to him one day with a check for $12,500 to pay off the debt and he was told verbally. This is a gift. It need not be paid back. My dad was *shocked* to his soul. He kept after me, I got to pay the money back. People don't give away $12,500 to an old man!!! Oh, but they do, Dad. In my world. My mom receives a check every month for several hundred dollars to supplement her retirement. Compliments of the Syndicate. She's the mother of a sub-chief. Her life should be eased a bit where possible. Not ostentatiously. Extra money in the pocket. Tribute from the Underworld. I am loyal, after all. See?

3/22/89. Personality Disorders. Believe it or not it's as easy as pie to avoid the draft. Just slip on a pair of panties, wear a garter belt & nylons and voila! Instant

1-Y classification. Really, you only need to *tell* the people at Army induction center you are 'queer' & that's sufficient. I was drafted. I got down to the point to be sworn in and in my best thespian manner asked if it was gonna be OK to be in the Army if I'm queer? There's maybe a hundred guys there, all macho posturing and I come out with I'm a queer. Fastest dismissal you ever did see. Oh, they interrogate you a bit but the key is to be sincere. They are looking for the phony faggot, limp wrist type; so you just play the straight man… '*Of course* I want to be in the Army, I just wondered if there was any rules against wearing panties.' Believe me, they throw you right out the door.

I played the role to a tee. I never hid my 'perversion.' Wore my nylons right to class… I'm laughing up my sleeve & wearing a garter girdle and never consider Vietnam as an impediment to my academic career. Same with the photos. Bondage ritual! Oh my *God!* Major League freak action. I never hid them. I was very open about it. It was simply a case of doing the necessary to get what I wanted: My University Education…

If I'm a pervert because I wore garter belt & nylons to class then I'm a pervert. I just don't happen to give a rat fuck whether I'm regarded as a pervert or not…

I did not have *sex problems*. A problem means you are unhappy, discontented. My sexual orientation is 100% heterosexual… My Felice *requires* domination by a man because she was taught sex was *sinful*. She has very low self-esteem in the area of sex due to *guilt*. She needs to feel helpless before a man's force… *she* has a *ex problem*. I understand it and am helping her cure it… I certainly do not regard myself as deviant. I'm sure Boy George laughs all he way to the bank, as does Alice Cooper. I'm as valid an entertainer as either of them…

Jessica Zurriaga: I invented her years ago. Ran ads under her name. Made a buck. I wrote as a woman. Had about 500 'slaves' & submissives answer. You train the slave to wash out your panties and return them with $10. I had a lady handling the mail for me. The slave sends the lingerie. The lady wears it, gets it nice & nasty, mails it to the slave for cleaning. I'd write the letters… You can get a pretty good extra income from closet slaves who don't want to meet you. I used to purchase my photos… Tell the slave. Send $5.00 to see my naked tits. Money rolled in… Time & postage. Shit, I've *got* time! [Smiley Face]

… True story: So I'm Mistress Zurriaga writing the freaks. The prison censors pick up on it. Confiscate my mail. Give it to the psychologist. They stick me in s*ex education!* I go see the shrink; I say, 'I run a fucking slave empire!' The guy is entranced, he cannot believe I'm pulling it off. I convinced him. No more s*ex education* class. I became the joke of the prison but I'm laughing because guys *pay* to wash the shitty panties of my bitch. Big Pervert. Sure, but I'm raking in the coin. Ain't I? …

Dear Felice,
   Your letter of March 13 is in hand and I'm in Atlanta, in Georgia; here in the 4th floor suite which is a nice change from my stuffy office. As you might expect I'm very bored with the celebrity lifestyle. The secretaries are really quite whorish wearing mini skirts, shamelessly displaying themselves in hope of catching the eye of the new media Star. I really prefer a woman who enjoys the quiet home

life like yourself. Having lunch with Paul Newman was pleasant. Do you ever see his films?

Oh, I do not mind your questions about the whores. How can you please me unless you know their techniques? You are well aware I do not tolerate female foolishness. You confessed to me already you are guilty of oral sodomy. A man licked your cunt. You *allowed* him to do it. Didn't you? Did you ask him to be kind and spare you such a degrading act? No! You laid on your back with your legs spread and your hole open and *enjoyed* it. I tolerate no lies from a woman. I'll take the strap to you for a lie. So what you are, Felice, is a man's fuck-slut. This is not to say you are a bad girl but unfortunately you did engage in sexual perversions, serious crimes that would put you in prison in some States. I know young girls make mistakes in life and I don't hold that sin of sex perversion against you and you know very well that few men would ever accept a woman who's committed willful sodomy; so you ought to be on your knees thanking God I can overlook it. Isn't that right, little Bitch? I'm always truthful about it.

You do have some favorable points. You are willing to try to please me. I know you will please me well because if you do not you shall receive a good strapping. Yes, I've given the strap a lot of thought and while you DO have a good heart and your obedience level is high, there is a little thread of insolence that needs to be removed. I'm very good at detecting such insolence in a woman. When I tell you to suck on my penis the *only* thing I want to hear on your lips are spit bubbles bursting as you mouth my pole. Yes, I'm quite observant of female insolence, you already know that.

I've spent a lot of time on you. Certainly more than you deserve. I've done that to train you to be perfect. I have no doubt you shall be perfect. The day is approaching when you shall be called to my side and from the minute you arrive I expect instant, unquestioned, perfect obedience. I assure you that in public you will receive every courtesy due your status and in the bedroom you shall, under pain of the lash, perform better than a whorehouse fuck-bitch. The leather across your fat ass will put a stop on those thoughts of *sin*. Feli will fuck like a whore or be whipped soundly. I have spoken on the matter. Do you dare to question me?

I'm very pleased we are in agreement in this area. I want my Bitch trained quickly and completely in obedience. It's a man's right, and a woman's duty to submit to obedience. I certainly do not expect to have to use the strap but, if we need it it'll be there for you! A successful woman is well disciplined by her man. I know you agree on that!! [Smiley face]

Tomorrow I'm going to examine a set of cunt rings. If I like them I'll get you the set. You wear them like earrings only on your cunny lips. Very nice. 22K gold. Here's a little sketch how it looks. You hook the rings on the labia. A ribbon is drawn through the rings and tied closed. 3 rings on each labia. A tidy little bow at the top on a symbolic chastity belt. The rings will look very chic when the cunt is shaved. Have you ever worn cunt rings before? Many whores wear them. Very decorative with crotchless panties. A bit expensive. Almost $900 for the set but worth it if you are excellent on the bed. How do you like my idea?

Now, my groveling little slut, I have a meeting to attend. I'll be lunching with Sondra London from Hollywood, the TV actress. If you are a good girl and ask nicely I'll tell you about it in the next mail. You are as lazy & useless as ever and I can't believe a girl with a 38" butt doesn't wear a girdle. It's very sluttish, you need discipline and you shall receive it.

Prepare yourself for a life of Service & Obedience because I will see you soon. Faithfully & Loyally Your Love, Gerry

3/24/89. I *am* a Syndicate man, not Mafia of course, but my Boss has associations to the Mafia people... Legal Beagles, *good ones*, sit next to the seat of Power in prisons... I took the proverbial "offer one can't refuse" and was never sorry about it for a minute... When I put on my O/C subchief's hat I *am* "Don El Tigre" (my handle in the life, a tribute to my rapacious attitudes) and I can scare the living shit out of you... To survive I needed to become a criminal and because I am a person with values, I've become a very well respected criminal, a feared criminal, a sincere criminal and that has opened doors enabling me to wreck Stone... I live by the code of the Underworld, better understand that now.

I'm enclosing 2 letters to sex perverts in my trick book. One is written as a Bondage Mistress, the other as a working hooker. Mistress Helga is a *real* person, Mistress Felice is *me*. [Smiley Face] ... Once again, I'm writing these to show you that I have the skill to deal creatively with sexual deviants of both genders and I am *not* in any manner sexually dysfunctional or unable to talk about sexual topics. My only sex problem is a lack of pussy. "Sex killers" are usually unable to carry on routine heterosexual relationships. I not only carry on routine ones but every imaginable sort of deviant ones as well.

Hi Nickie Dear,

I'm down here in Atlanta for a few weeks. I was asked to give a small class on Slave Management & Training to prostitutes associated with COYOTE. Quite a few hookers are going into the area because it's sort of 'safe sex'; so I was invited down as a 'Consultant' to speak on the topic. The money is good, the parties are fun, but I prefer my own slaves... have you been thinking of my cunt? I do hope so! I've been waiting to hear how you want to begin your servitude. Yesterday I was demonstrating one of your favorite topics: Enema Bondage. The slaves were a real disappointment. No sexual discipline at all. None. I used the Chinese Enema style. The slave being hooded and hanged by his heels. There were three of them hanging there hoisted aloft by a pair of dykes. I gave the ladies the enema preparation instructions verbally so the slaves could worry, and to speed things up I used a full strength caustic enema, very warm water and detergent. The first slave, a young man about 20, climaxed the moment he felt the bulb against his anus; the second slave, maybe 25, he took about an inch of nozzle and squirted jizz all over the place; the third slave (35 to 40) took the entire nozzle but his erection was throbbing so I demonstrated a new technique of fast withdrawal of the nozzle and the slave came. I can tell you, Nickie, those were the sorriest enema slaves I ever did see. The hookers were all delighted since they get paid when the man climaxes. My own feelings on it was that the men were cheated of full orgasm since the climax should coincide with the expulsion of the enema. It's the same problem I see when prostitutes administer the lash. I've watched several slaves whipped down here. Within 5 to 10 strokes the man is pumping cum. Properly performed the ritual calls for 39 strokes of the lash plus: the 40th stroke laid on precisely to induce orgasm.

The only woman down here who seems to know her business is Mistress Helga. I went out to her place in Chamblee and saw her use an 11-foot bull's pizzle whip

on a slave. Hung him up by his wrists naked. Stripped herself down her garter belt & black silk stockings, shook out the whip and let fly. The first snap made him shit like a cow, the second snap put him into orgasm, the third snap knocked him out cold. I was very impressed even though Helga was just showing off. I'm not *that* skilled with the bull's pizzle whip. I do best with the whip we call the 'cat' but most of the whipping is with the big leather strap called a Red Hannah. Do you have a preference? I'm going to have to put you to the strap eventually. Are you ready for it?

Tomorrow I'm being fitted for a new costume: Georgia State Prison Execution Matron. Wait until you see me in this outfit. Black tight skirt & blouse with silver piping. Black patent leather boots and belt and, best of all, a black cowl with a mask!! When a murderess is put in the electric chair these uniformed matrons strap her in and hook her up. My slaves will *love* this fantastic uniform. What uniform do you prefer for our initial meeting?

You can write to me at the business office. I check for mail every day. Depending on what you prefer maybe I'll work you in on my way back north. My cunt needs your tongue.

Mistress Felice

Dearest Hank,

I flew down to Florida for the Slims and the Lipton. You'd have absolutely gone crazy seeing me in my little tennis skirt without panties. I was kept very busy but I did watch Steffi Graf and Chris Evert in the final match. I had a good time and made a lot of money. Now I'm in Atlanta working some business conventions. It's the next best thing to a money tree.

I'm such an awful bitch to you but surely you understand that a girl needs to make her money when she's young? I'll be working Atlanta... Then I have a job in Wharton, NJ. Is that close to you? If so, maybe we can spend some time together? What I had in mind was just some fun. Fix you up in drag and we can shop and eat out and 'be girls together' since I know you'd really like that. Wouldn't you? I think you'd be able to pass for female if I were there to watch out for you and guide you along. I wouldn't charge you unless you want to have sex. That's fair isn't it? Wouldn't it be funny if we were together and you got an erection while wearing a dress? We'd need to tape down your cock to be on the safe side. You'd have to use the women's restrooms. How do you feel about that? You'd be OK. There are stalls to go into. Nicely private. Just remember to sit down to pee!

... Would you like to smell my panties after I've been sitting in them all day? Are you SERIOUS about wanting to be my sex slave? I'm really thinking I could go for it.

Write me your best effort on how you'd make love to my cunt. Convince me you really can make me squeal with pleasure. I also want some photos of you in drag so I can see what I need to do to help feminize you, and some photos of you nude with cock erect. Best effort. If I like what I hear and see I'll stop by after my job in Wharton.

Please assure me you are not troubled by my being a prostitute. Men only want me for 1 thing — I'm used to that. How can you love me slut that I am?

Write soon! Your Favorite Hooker, Felice

3/29/89. Along with all the other unpleasant things you're learning you're gonna need to learn about children being sold and child porn and prostitution. The first three photos are of little girls available for purchase. Age 8 to 14 is the preferred age, but 14 is a bit long in the tooth. The recruits are, of course, scrawny. These are raw material of the trade and these 3 photos show callow hopefuls. The procuress is off to the right. Low rent area.

The second photo shows girls in a working stable. (1983) On the reverse is their names and note Eric (Cross, Mervyn) and Tanie (Arbaquez) and the query about the 'new found lost souls.' It's an inquiry as to whether or not to put them to work. The one called 'Venus' is a regular, I've seen her in action. You'll note these girls are fed. I'll be sending more such items, including the entire working string of children, older girls who do sex work, individual whores.

3/30/89. Some years ago a lady journalist contacted me with the 'let me tell your side' proposition. I gave her a rather long initial interview and then later on I found out that she made a transcription of the interview and took it to a certain police chief. She now lives in Washington State. She's a free lance writer, you might even recognize her name. One of her rewards for this trick she pulled on me was that her police chief pal got his judge pal to fix her up with a false commit-ment order to a penitentiary for women. The old Florida Women's Prison before the one at Broward... I'm telling you this story so you know I've had some *bad* experiences with 'journalists' using the *same* approach you've made: 'I'll tell it Fair.'

4/7/89. Now, as for *business*, and this is for your information *only*, as I see it there are two ways to write the book: Should I prevail in Court, the book tells the tale of a cop victimized by corrupt officials. Should I ultimately lose in Court then the book takes a different slant. I've not yet worked out with *exactitude* how it will go but my general theme would be the rendition of the 34 murders known and x-number unknown. I would capitalize on my famous billing given freely by Mr. Stone. I would earn money, which would be my way of insulting the Establish-ment. I'd have no problem giving you "34 victims."

My preference is for *truth* but since I'm the victim of a lie and my life is very unpleasant *if* it is to remain that way until 2016, I'm gonna at least die famous — or infamous — as the case may be. Famous for coming back from the pit of hell that is FSP and turning the table over on Stone/Schwarz, or infamous as the per-son Ted Bundy sought to emulate as a killer of women. Unlike Ted, I will plead *guilty* to all 34 *after* the book is written. [Smiley Face] Truth will have nothing to do with it whatsoever. If I have to be a mass murderer I'm gonna be the #1 just like Stoney Baby said in 1973.

4/12/89. The enclosed prospective letter: Fantasy 34-L-#1, shows you I'm en-tirely sincere in my revenge against Stone and the "State." The procedure would be to verify police or official interest in clearing up an old case. This case just so happens to be one in which I am already a suspect so it's a good one to start on. Once you establish official interest — as opposed to them saying 'those women

turned up alive in New York in 1968' — the next step would be to obtain some newspaper accounts of the case. Working off those clippings I could easily fill in the blanks with a good sex/murder tale about how "I" killed them. Do it up as a "How To" Non-fiction Guide to Serial Murder by the Best in the Business.

...If my Habeas is rejected I want to be able to make literary headlines: "International Sex Killer Reveals All." *All*. The 'special pleasures' of corpse fucking, how to make a girlie scream and scream and scream — into her gag — like when you light their pubic hair on fire with a butane lighter; [Smiley Face] to warm up the pussy on a cold fish type who don't want to fuck; the way they get while they watch you dig their grave. All that nice unwholesome stuff...

So let's start on this Nancy case... and be forewarned, I *don't* intend to stop at 34. 34 are *known*. Remember, I had a *boat*. An ocean-going boat; and I know how to gut a girl so she doesn't float to the surface...

> Fantasy 34 Letter #1
> Dear Sir,
> I am a Media Writer in Atlanta, GA.
> During a recent interview with a certain person I was told about the murders of two young women which may have occurred about 25 years ago in your area.
> According to my Source he forced the two women into his car, drove them away, sexually abused them and killed them. He said he doubts anyone has ever found them so they may be listed as Missing Persons. This may have occurred around 1963-64. The area was Ocala National Forest near a town called Altamonte Springs, he says.
> It was a long time ago, but he claims one of the women said her name was Nancy. What I found interesting was that the person is willing to plead guilty to the two murders but has kept quiet because he fears the electric chair.
> My purpose in writing this letter is to verify if possible that such a potential crime did take place around your area many years ago and, if so, could the person who did the crime plead guilty in exchange for a sentence less than death?
> If such a possibility exists I will pass the information on to the lawyer representing the Source. Please respond promptly in writing and please do not ask me to become further involved or give a statement as it would be contrary to my privilege as a Journalist.
>   Sincerely, S.L.
>   P.S. Would there be a reward for the person who obtained the information leading to the conviction of the alleged killer?

4/12/89. If truth is *not* to prevail then I'm going to turn over the applecart in another way. I'll make their fantasies become realities. I'll sit down and write up the deaths of 34 women and you can put the May 13, 1973 headlines on the dust jacket. Let's see anyone argue with *that* as a gambit. I'll spend my life in prison but I'll live as best I'm able... I'm a realist. I'm practical, and I'm dangerous because *I DON'T GIVE A FUCK*... I'll plead guilty to every murder they come up with. That'll be my revenge... Fuck em. When I gut a slut she doesn't come to the surface like Jack Murphy's do. People *already* believe I'm a mass murderer. All I need to do is say: "Yeah, I am, and here's how it went down..." Either way you get a big fat profitable story to tell. [Smiley Face]

If I'm gonna do life for 2 murders I may as well do life for 42. Life is life. I really don't care.

4/16/89. There is a part of me that does *not* want this experience perpetuated in a negative sense as a book about "How to Commit Mass Murder" (by the One who Does it Best) but I also realize I am stuck with a certain persona bestowed on me by Stone and pals and I *can* claim that I was believed to be the #1 Serial Killer, and present the "6 Dead 28 May Be" story as my license to exploit the situation financially. I'm angry enough inside to do that... but I'm also astute enough to see that it can be proven in Court that I am framed... so I'm willing to wait. But if the State insists on running with the lie then I'm excused from any adherence to the Truth. I mean, we are *not* gonna play with separate rule books and if the book they choose is the Book of Lies then I'll feel perfectly comfortable with the rules of the game and I'll give them a "true account" of such mindless bloody horror that the reader will shrivel up with revulsion. So you say I killed Peggy & Wendy? OK. Fine. Now let's talk about *how* they died. It's like Stone telling people I murdered Place & Jessup by hanging them from that tree limb. Total fucking bullshit. His fantasy, if you please. But I'll rub his nose in it — maybe — write up a nice story about chopping the head off the one girl while the other was tied up and watching. I'll come up with something real horrible, bet that.

4/19/89. People are forever thinking I can't carry on a solid heterosexual relationship with women. Murder is the antithesis of fucking. Certainly I'm a sex maniac, just ask Elton Schwarz's wife if I'm not. What I don't understand is why everyone keeps trying to make a correlation between my sexual activities and murder. With Ted, murder was a part of his foreplay. It qualifies as 'rough sex,' I'd say, and he lacked sensitivity concerning the girl's feelings but in his case the sex was conducted after the murder. Ted must have had a certain amount of tender feeling for his lovers since he admittedly returned to them time and time again to tidy them up and spend quiet time with them while they rotted before his eyes. I admit his sexual tastes were bizarre; far more so than mine. By comparison, my lovers were generally content and are even asking for my attentions to this day.

So while I am complimented to be known as the greatest sex maniac of all time — move over, Don Juan — I am annoyed by all this murder talk. Peggy & Wendy just happened along at a time I was curious about Mr. Fish's craving for the flesh of young girls. Fish was one of those fellas who'd say, 'Try it. You'll like it!' and along comes two little Grace Budd types — young and tender — and solicit a ride. I assure you those girls were *not* molested sexually. I found the both of them very satisfactory, particularly with sautéed onions and peppers. Should it be in the cards, I'd be glad to do up a nice cookbook. It's mostly a Mulligan Stew affair when one is on the road, although I was particularly fond of flank steaking them. I always had campers drift over to try my fare. Passed it off as wild game for the most part. Once a girl gets over 25 she's a bit tough and stringy. Hippie girl hikers, lean and mean not tender like Peggy & Wendy, but one cannot constantly grab kids off the street in the same area, so I had to be on the road a lot. Me and my big black frying pan. You learn that it's largely a matter of catch as catch can in such situations.

As you might expect the girl usually perceives the situation as a sort of sex perversion/rape in the making. Put a gun to her head and she is agreeable enough to be tied and led into the woods without a problem. By the time she's hanging by her heels from the killing tree, it's far to late for any resistance. Contrary to popular thought, hanging a girl by her heels does not cause her to lose consciousness. I've carried on entirely normal conversations with upside-down girls. Naturally they are curious as to what I'm up to. They never for a moment consider they are to be butchered for meat.

The slaughter is anti-climatic. A razor-sharp knife drawn quickly across the throat; cleave through the vertebrae and the head is severed. 3 seconds; 10 seconds at most. Set the head down on the ground and you can watch the eyes blink. I've chatted up the heads. They can hear fine, and answer by blinking the eyes. The heads stay alert several minutes, quite interesting really but not sexy.

The trick to this is to regard the girl as an animal. A dear lamb even. No reason to be cruel to her; after all the motive is culinary, not sadistic or sexual. Look at her in terms of a piece of meat, but not in the usual connotation that implies. Nobody gets unduly annoyed when Lykes Bros. butcher meat. As a society we are conditioned to eat beef but some other societies are keen to enjoy a nice human stew. It's a matter of taste, really, but I would no more have sex with such a girl than I would with a sow. The "murder" is detached from the realm of "sex." I suppose there are weirdos who might find it "sexy" to have some nude girl suspended upside down from a limb but if one is confronted with the situation one sees it in a different light.

The Place/Jessup scene was such a perverted mess I'm truly offended to be accused of it. Butchering is skillfully done, almost an art and if one is working on a pair of sows it's double the chore. I was always a good provider in the meat department; ask Teresa. I even enjoyed cooking the special cuts I brought home... Now, such cruel accusations to endure.

Well — is it a salable product? Nice touch of horror about the eyes, huh?

Needs work, sure, but I think I could manage to put something together there.

Those magazine stories have really caused me untold problems. I don't suppose you could ever understand how something like this can upset a person. You notice that no police or dee-fense lawyers are pointing out the impossibility of my having murdered Briscolina/Farmer on the 25th of October 72 when I was in South Dakota. It's enough to make a man bitter, angry, and vengeful... but if I'm gonna get stuck with it forever I'm gonna do it up *right!* [Smiley face]

4/24/89. OK. As things stand at the moment. we're in a transitional period. If the "Powers that be" do not let me go then we can present the stories as true stories. You can write a forward to the effect that I'm convicted of 2; suspected of 32 others and due to the SOS law I can't write about the 2 (but *you* can [Smiley face]) but here are the other 32... which is why I told you to check the 1963-73 Ft. Lauderdale papers for unsolved murders... and why I sent you the laws governing public records. You get the police reports, I'll taper the stories to the reports. Research takes time but it'd be worth it $-wise if I'm not gonna get out. Of course if I am vindicated you still get a good tale because it shows the danger of writing

realistic prose and then becoming the focus of a murder investigation. The stories are still good fiction, only I don't say they are based on fact.

4/27/89. Now: I see from the material you are amassing that lists exist of 'victims.' As you go along and see a victim by name or jurisdiction pop it into your data bank. Then write a letter to the police agency and get a copy of the crime report: Missing Person or Murder. Your slant should be that you are doing a book and want possible GJS victims. Send a copy of the "Greatest Crime of the Century" cover along so they know you are onto the Biggie. The purpose is dual: 1) We want an *accurate* portrayal of the initial accusations by Stone. The *enormity* of it all. Murders all over the fucking *world*.

With the cops your slant should be that you are accurately exposing the fiend so need some proper detail. Any links. (And of course you will try to get the fiend to incriminate himself when confronted with his dastardly deeds) For instance: Leigh Hainline: You do a short history of L.H., run her photo(s), link to me, give a nice *accurate* picture of who she was and what she was. Each victim gets this treatment. Mary Briscolina: You go into all that and at the end you say: One problem here gentle reader, GJS was in S.D. when this victim disappeared. *Fact.* But let everyone have their say. Of course if I don't get out I'll be glad to confirm that Mary Alice was a lovely girl, she sucked cock like a wet dream; so nicely in fact that I let her decide whether she or Elsie Lina should be strangled first. She let Elsie go first; then made a good act of contrition (cocksucking is a sin for Catholic girls) and then took her medicine like a little dick-eating fuck slut — wiggling and squirming and peeing all over the front seat of my car while I was trying to knot a stocking around her neck… [Smiley face] Either way we *win*. The second part is we just forget the fact that I was 2,000 miles away at the time. Nobody will care. Believe me. The People *want* a ghoul. But one safely locked away. Like Ted.

Anyway — you need to get busy on that too. [Smiley face] Such research takes time, but cops are real helpful if they think you are gonna bust the fiend/killer. Once you get your own list, based on the material you have already, then I'll give you areas I traveled in and approximate times so you can write and ask about corpses discovered around that time in those areas. The 'Buzz Number' was 34. I'd like to be able to match that. Crowder had one, a Jane Doe, he tried to pin on me: Loop Road Jane Doe. You can get the paper on that one. She was bones, but that leaves a lot of latitude in making up a nice 'confession.' There was also a corpse down on Singer Island. A young girl. Palm Beach County. Just over the line from Martin County.

You can get the paper on Singer Island Girl from your pals, I suppose.

You'll want to run a few pages of "Photos of Mutilated Women" from my personal collection. Mark them: Known Schaefer Victims. Then pick up some old murder/suicide victim pictures from the M.E.'s office. Unsolved cases. Caption: *Another Schaefer Victim? Authorities Believe…* That should get the flames crackling. And then you could extract a sentence or two from The Ghoul to heighten the puke reflex. Nothing too obscene. Routine 'flies in her mouth' stuff. Big caption: *Schaefer says, "Green River Strangler is an amateur."* We'll surely think of something. [Smiley face]

5/10/89. *What to call me:* "Accused Serial Killer" is OK. Where you are off base is in that you are thinking in terms of a formal legal accusation. Pull out your Giant Dictionary and run *accused* down. I believe you'll find that *accused* will fit, as *ghoulish* can be twisted to fit... Stone accuses me of 9 or 10 in the newspaper. That's your ticket to "Accused Serial Killer." What do you think now, partner?

6/2/89. *Spring Break:* I re-wrote the whole thing... The police will run to the unsolved murder case book and look for a parallel; which is what I want. I want people to be unsure. Is it really fiction or is it The Ghoul wearing a mask of a fictionalist? The way it is now nobody will be sure. The way it was, the reader said, good story! Set it down and forgot about it. See what I mean?

... I had a variety of different characters I invented and wrote as. Jessica Zurriaga was a dominatrix and ran the whole gamut of S/M & B/D fetish. I had two prison women characters. One was a matron character. One was a girl on death row. This was nickel-dime stuff to pass time. What I learned was that the trick is to pin down the mark/fetishist... decide which fetish they are into and send a nice letter with your photo in the corner... "and by the way buy my book *Jessica and the Cringing Slave Boy* for $20." Or whatever...

Another example: Panty fetish is common. Run the ad for panty fetish people. Letters come. You send the letter that tells them how you model panties for a catalog company and "I'll model just for you — *IF* you subscribe to DDK." You can get lingerie model photos for 5¢-10¢ each in quantity. I used to get Dad to send me B&W panty model photos cost him 10¢ each. I sold them to niggers for $1.00 - $2.00 *each*...

Eventually we can get a load of fetish stories by GJS to sell the freaks. No problem. I have a real squirmy imagination. Whatever conveys a sense of the forbidden does well.

6/8/89. First I've heard about being the Sex Beast. Gee, I hope he put my address in there so I can get some cute groupies. That's a good idea about a grant to study the Sex Beast. What's a prototype serial killer? Are the 20 victims listed? Who can they be? Milk Joel Norris for whatever information you can get, then we'll sue him for his gold teeth for libel. [Smiley Face] Sue him, his publisher, everybody. Great Publicity for K/F! [Smiley Face]

Sounds like a good book title: *The Sex Beast.* The title alone would sell! But do try to find out who my 20+ victims are in Oakland Park. "Killer Fact." Sure. I'll confess. Find me out from him who I'm supposed to have killed!! Well... I'm a real celeb. The Sex Beast. I like it better than the Butcher of Blind Creek. Hey, if anyone should get a grant to study the Sex Beast it should be you... *"I Slept With The Sex Beast of Oakland Park... and Lived to Tell the Tale!"* Sounds like something out of Playgirl... or Ann Rule's genre. [Smiley Face] Your Very Own Sex Beast, [Monster Face] John [Smiley Face]

6/14/89. Don't get me wrong. I *like* being the Sex Beast. It's a hoot. Really, the funniest handle of all. I'm a Sex Beast yet I've never been accused of a sex crime. It's so bizarre I can only laugh. But a side of me does not find it amusing at all.

Part of me is *VERY PISSED OFF*. Naturally so. Wouldn't you be?

Here are some hints on my past experiences working the mail order freak trade:

1. Always require the freak to pay postage.

2. Photos: Freaks *adore* photos. Get some black & white film and *play*. Matron Miller must be stern... a secret slut revealing herself only a teeny bit at a time. An obedient freak should be rewarded with a photo. Obedient as in sending $.

3. Invite questions. This reveals the freak's hidden desires. Remember, *fetish* and *guilt* go hand in hand.

4. Personal touch. The kissed letter. The little handwritten note under the machine script.

5. The pitch for cash... send me a little something.

I got over a thousand letters on one ad I wrote: *Imprisoned Stripper*. I wrote as Jerri and was doing about $100 (1975) a week without benefit of a machine to print the letters. My fingers were raw from writing. That wasn't even freak trade. The nice thing is it's all *tax free*... Figure with a little effort you can get 100 freaks at $50 a month each. Only way to start is to run some ads and see what the mail person delivers. [Smiley Face] I'll answer 'em. You print and send them out.

6/20/89. FBI-H wants to talk to me because I'm a TOP Serial Killer in his data bank. He wants to discuss Sexual Sadism with me because his theory is that I am a sexual sadist *and* a SK (Serial Killer). Now *this* is between *you and me*. I'm not the great SK and I'm not the great sadist. FBI-H doesn't know that yet.

The *purpose* in seeing FBI-H is to collect data for MQ... film, tape, etc. = $ for SL. If the project is done right. Big $. That's OK. But to me personally the important thing is to get to the heart of the truth of the entire fucking mess because it's gotten entirely out of hand.

Consider: I'm in a book as a prototype SK with over 20 victims near O.P. and a nice fearsome title, the Sex Beast. Now it's time to clear up the waters. The way that's done is to make a list; let FBI-H make a list. I'll even help him. No shit. I *do* want to know just how fucking bad and beastly I am. Unlike Ted I will not hedge. I will confess all. But before I get to that point I need to know who is dead and who is missing. Real people. I want a big fucking box full of pictures of real victims I supposedly killed 1963-1973. For FBI-H that will be an easy task. He puts out a request on the NCIC network to all police depts. homicide and missing persons bureaus, serial killer units, etc. for data on their 1963-73 unsolved cases. Particularly road whore killings. OK. We will go over each and every case and I will give a detailed confession to each crime. *Then* we go on the Box to see if it's a True Confession or just more Actual Fantasy. The Box will show either Truth or Deception. The True Confessions go in one pile, the False in another. *Then* I'll plead guilty in Court to *all* cases that come up as True Confession *if* the plea is to a reduced charge of a non-capital murder based on SK illness, *and* I receive admittance to a *hospital* for study as a SK prototype. All sentences will run concurrent and for a specified time. Not an open-ended Life. My theory is this: If I am a real SK then I need treatment and study, not torture dungeons.

You (MQ) have a virgin S/K, the Greatest S/K of Them All, never before studied by anyone. The H-person must give some quid pro quo to discuss sexual sa-

dism with the Master Sex Beast. It *starts* with the list and M.Q. access and help with a nice grant from Uncle Sammy so she can pay the cable company and Georgia Power while recording for science *The Confessions of the Sex Beast* (on sale at all better bookshops). [Smiley Face]

1990

7/20/90. Interesting story about Newton. I can't wait to see what sort of lies he printed about me in his book. The Joel Norris lies were pretty good. Encyclopedias are supposed to be real *factual* so Newton's lies will be even better, ultimately, than those of Norris. It seems to me that to become a SK all one needs are the *unbiased* allegations of police and prosecutors — guys that never lie! When they read "False Confessions" I'll be right up there with Lucas. We already know Lucas lies. I have a far better imagination so I'll be able to lie better and more convincingly in print.

7/30/90. Newton seemed sane and fair minded in his response. I'm wondering who started that Sex Beast crap? … I like to take negatives and turn them positive. *Sex Beast* might be a great title for the True Story [Smiley face].

7/31/90. People might go for something real bizarre like: *Ask the Serial Killer…* or they may jump for *Ask the Executioner…* something along the outer limits. Any ideas? I overtly gravitate toward that which is most offensive to the greatest audience. I enjoy shocking the reader. Rubbing his nose in the shit and gore.

8/8/90. The Newton quote is excellent. [Smiley face] … Enclosed is one KBS (Killer Bull Shit) = (Killer Best Selections) letter. I figured I'd send one to him and see if he's a *true* freak — as in he'll pay for freak material. Maybe lure him in to spend some money. You decide.

8/31/90. I am sending herein an idea for you to make up into a flyer. Here is what I came up with as an initial first rough draft.

> Killer Best Selections:
> Media Queen presents, for a limited time only, the most shocking opportunity ever to be awarded to true crime story fans. Yes, the opportunity to correspond personally with G.J. Schaefer, the internationally controversial author of *Killer Fiction*, and an entire host of homicidal social horror crime classics.
> G.J. Schaefer, who prosecutors claim is responsible for the sadistic murders of 34 nubile young women, is known to students as the Sex Beast Killer and, police aver, is a rare and deadly sex ghoul who has ravaged the cooling corpses of murdered lovelies on three continents over a period of more than ten years.
> G.J. Schaefer, the personal confidant of notorious sex killer, Ted Bundy… Depravities carried out on the rotten corpses of Ted's many victims that were revealed to Bundy's trusted prison pal, G.J. Schaefer.

G.J. Schaefer, the cellmate of arch-fiend, Ottis Toole… the Devil's Child told it all to G.J. Schaefer.

G.J. Schaefer, prison law clerk for the condemned of death row… Disgusting procedures that violate the bodies of trembling females warranted for a ghastly death by burning… from G.J. Schaefer.

G.J. Schaefer, one of the most frightening authors in America today, will write to *you personally*…

For more information about how you can participate in this unique program write today to SL, MQ, and ask for details of KBS!

9/11/90. I came up with some new ideas for KBS promo and blurb flyers… Below is a wacky promo that I did up and which you can expand upon or reduce as you see fit…

Killer Accusations:

G.J. Schaefer, the subject of more than 1,000 phone inquiries to Fla. police departments concerning dead and missing women since 1973!

G.J. Schaefer, investigated by law enforcement agencies in 15 states, for links between his horrifying writings and missing and murdered women nationwide.

G.J. Schaefer, fully credited with more than twenty six murders within the city of Oakland Park.

G.J. Schaefer, fully credited with thirty-four serial murders of women across Florida and around the nation.

G.J. Schaefer, fully credited with the beheading murder and slaughter of college coeds in Morgantown, W.V.

G.J. Schaefer, depraved cultist and confidant of cannibal murder fiend, Ottis Toole, the Devil's Child, and confessed killer of little Adam Walsh.

G.J. Schaefer, associate of sex ghoul Ted Bundy, and the single person who propelled Bundy into his life of female slaughter.

G.J. Schaefer, The Sex Beast of Oakland Park!

G.J. Schaefer, The Hangman of Europe.

G.J. Schaefer, The Maniac of Morocco.

G.J. Schaefer, The Butcher of Blind Creek.

G.J. Schaefer, Body Snatcher, Necrophile and Corpse-loving Fiend.

G.J. Schaefer, The alleged Greatest Serial Killer in United States History.

Killer Factualities:

G.J. Schaefer, convicted of the machete murder of a Broward County narcotics informant.

G.J. Schaefer, convicted of beheading Lt. Gene Sedberry's personal drug snitch.

G.J. Schaefer, convicted of executing a pair of undercover narcs in 1973.

G.J. Schaefer, convicted of hanging two Fort Lauderdale whores.

G.J. Schaefer, found with the photographs of more than one hundred of his slaughtered victims in his possession.

G.J. Schaefer, law clerk to more than three hundred condemned men and women on Florida's infamous death row.

G.J. Schaefer, punished for a plot to murder a circuit court judge.

G.J. Schaefer, punished for plotting to have a state prosecutor murdered.

G.J. Schaefer, punished for scheming to have a Florida sheriff murdered.

G.J. Schaefer, author of the most controversial book ever to emerge from a prison dungeon on the topic of murder, death and madness.

Reader Warning:

Killer Fiction was penned by G.J. Schaefer, widely regarded in international police circles as the most depraved, sadistic sex killer of the twentieth century. Wanted for questioning by police in 15 states and numerous foreign countries spanning three continents, G.J. Schaefer, ends his 18-year reign of silence with *Killer Fiction,* perhaps the most horrifying book ever written on the topic of sex murder... You will shudder with horror... You will vomit with fear... Your blood will run cold... G.J. Schaefer, regarded by the Florida police as the number one criminal in the entire history of the state, now drags you down into the black depths of homicidal insanity to wallow in the steaming blood of slaughtered young women who scream on the blade of the knife and kick at the end of the hangman's rope and die in a frenzy of homicidal blood lust...

Experience the reality of sex murder: Listen to the horrified squeals... Visualize the spraying blood... Smell the acrid stench of whoreblood... Young harlots made to dig their own graves in the swamp and the brutal acts of horror that they endure before the release of death.

G.J. Schaefer writes murder as it has never been written before: Rubs your nose in the stink of it; lets you watch the flies crawl across the vacant eyes of the victims; shocks you to your core as maggots feed at the sex sodden orifices of young beauties face down in the muck...

Read *Killer Fiction!* You will never view murder dispassionately again!

OK... It's hype, but it is all based on the accusations that I have endured over the past 18 years, so why not work it all into a personal mystique? After all, it's only fiction!!

1991

1/18/91. To add an enigmatic dimension ponder this thought that you are *not* amongst the 34. In light of what has been said about me by Stone and pals have you wondered *why* you are alive while others almost certainly are *not*? I also know you've wondered how close you came to being on Stone's list... and how many of those on the list were your surrogates. All I've told you is that 'Stone wouldn't lie.' I have told you several times that the TS will be a story beyond your strangest fantasies. Now let me say something else to encourage you to stick around instead of suiciding... You came down here and asked me if I was a real SK. OK. Fine. You got an enigmatic answer. Not a simple answer. Have you considered that *IF* you were married to me that you'd have husband/wife confidence in law and could never be compelled to testify against me *or* be prosecuted as an accessory even if I were to show you a basket of severed heads? Let's turn *that* option over in your head. I'm said to be *The Greatest* SK of this century. Either Stone is a liar from the onset or he knows more than he's telling.

You have said that what I write is socially valuable. Suppose I told you that KF/BKF is all *true* and that I can back it up with burial pits, that the metal rings where whores were hanged alive in the swamp can still be found (probably) and that Stone was correct to say #1 SK billing belongs to me? You are a silly bitch to even

contemplate suicide when you have the top story of the century in your pocket. I have told you that either way the habeas goes that you'll get the story...

I am not suicidal or compelled to talk as T.B., HLL/OT and others are. I can wait to see what unfolds since the TS is still unfolding. I am also not crazy enough to direct any cop to any crime site, however I *am* crazy enough to prove to my *wife* that I am not full of bullshit. The wife who cannot be compelled to testify as to what she saw. Example: What if I showed you a collection of skulls? Or heads in formaldehyde buried in a trunk? Could you write it from the point of view of the whore who is about to contribute her own head to the collection? The whore would have every opportunity to admire the collection, see the empty lab jar, be *told* she'd be a very valued addition to the collection. Could you capture the spirit of the event? Blondes and brunettes, Cathies & Sandies. Suppose I could show you something like that, something that no living woman ever saw, would you think me a SK?...

I've had absolutely genuine experiences with Evil. I'll tell you an absolutely confidential story here... There were some young women who were about to die. They were already naked for the slaughter. Frightened out of their wits naturally, I fed on their fear — rather the evil entity did — and as I walked over to this one to kill her she said to me: Jesus loves you and so do I. It was as if a sheet of glass came down between us. She was as close to dying as 5 seconds and everything stopped. Frozen frame. I recall taking several steps back. I recall it absolutely. Then another woman, she was about to be killed to; she said, "No, nobody could love him, not even God could love him." I walked over to where she was laying on her back and looked down into her eyes and saw her hate. I killed her. It was bloody and efficient. Then I killed the rest. The one who'd called out the name of Jesus died quickly, mercifully. That was the *only* time in the career of the greatest SK of them all that he ever faltered after the woman was naked for slaughter.

You know that I am a creative person. I read *The History of Torture,* the works of Schmidt and Berry on how women were properly hanged, the Sansones on beheading and much more. I was an *artist* with a noose, a master with the headsman's blade; I've crucified women, watched the flies work on living cunt-flesh, seen gagged women strangle to death on their own vomitus. I've *skinned* women. I *loved* killing whores...

I can prove to you what I was if I get out but far more importantly is what I have become spiritually. The TS will shock you to your core. It's pure evil, demons, and manifestations of violent horror through myself physically... *Killer Fiction* is *loaded* with malignant energy from The Murder Channel. It's almost as if I can plug into Bundy's energy force and get it down on paper...

So — I didn't want to get into all this deeply but you need to know that Stone really has *no idea* what I was up to... (I was *framed*, remember that)... This letter is private & confidential and for you personally and exclusively. No names, no locations, just KBS but you can bet I can back it up should I get out of here... I cannot give you any details without the testimonial protections that come with marriage...

1/19/91. There were quite a few contributing factors that led up to my 'going out of my mind' so to speak. Eventually we will explore them but I will tell you here and now that plenty of young women died because you couldn't help me resolve my various crisises in 1965. I tried to tell you about it but you couldn't deal with it. You bolted, abandoned me; that's when it started. I tried to handle it, I even tried to get it over to a shrink but there was nobody in my world who could give me a clue about what the problem's roots were. Finally I decided to just let it carry me along. I could come home soaked in blood and say I'd skinned out a deer or a hog. What I was skinning was whores. Once I went for a *whole year* and murdered every woman I had sex with. A *YEAR!!!* I even went after *groups* of women successfully. Bundy was a pure amateur compared to me. He was sex driven. I was *hate* driven. Big difference. He was guilt ridden, I was a killing machine. He strewed corpses across the country, I made a whore disappear forever. I was *extremely* conscientious about it. *You know* how dedicated I am to getting a thing *right*.

I could have a perfectly normal sex life with Teresa because I was *not* a sex killer. I was a destroyer of evil. A paladin. I was so skilled at hanging women that I could, sometimes, kill them so quickly that they wouldn't even pee while on the rope. That's a remarkable feat. I never at any time required more than 2 strokes to behead a woman. Never. I was absolutely skilled at it. I had a lot of practice. Bundy couldn't even get a hard-on unless he was strangling the shit out of some girl or bashing her brains in. A pervo-sex killer. *I'm* perfectly well-adjusted sexually. You *know* that. [Smiley-face] I laugh my ass off about all these SK experts who say SKs are all sexually maladjusted and cannot function with a normal woman. What crap. Hey, dead pussy is disgusting. Believe me. I'd go out and lift a few heads and come home and screw Teresa into the bed. I'd get a road whore (if she was a cutie) and have sex, then pay her, and then kill her! Then I'd rob her. [Smiley-face] You can believe it or call it KBS but here's my point: I'd *really* like to make some sense out of it.

As you say to me: The cops don't have anything on me. They don't even have corpses for most of the tally and the absolute truth is that I was framed on Jessup & Place. It's just so bizarre it makes me crazy. So you have that as a story twist. Incredible. What does it all mean? It certainly does mean that God was watching out for me. To what purpose? I don't know just yet. But it's something.

I let Satan get control of me. I hated Evil. I wanted to destroy Evil. I went and immersed myself in the battle but destroyed myself in the process. God saved me by allowing me to be framed by corrupt people. Their prosecution was built on a lie but my own acts were also unjustifiable. I was, for a long time, comfortable in the rightness of what I'd been doing. Now I can see I was dead fucking wrong and out of control as a rational human entity. I'm *truly* sorry about all those things today. I really am. I would never hurt anyone (not even Stone, Snake and pals) if I walked out of here tomorrow. I've been spiritually reprogrammed. (Bob Erler would understand me) My question right now is how to make my horrible experience a positive force for social good and spiritual advancement.

How can we do this? Obviously with extreme caution. I don't want to gloss over the essential depravity and ghastly pure evilness of what occurred but I do not

want to get my self in any more trouble by digging up body dumps and private graveyards. Maybe we could let KF serve as the foundation for the TS and then say in the TS that I admit all accusations made against me. I deny nothing. I see no reason to go beyond Killer Fiction in TS. Anyone who wants gore can go to KF. The TS should be as accurate as possible and deal with *how* I got to the place where I went off the rails of humanity… and *how* I got back from the abyss of madness… and that was because of a personal relationship with Jesus Christ…

1/20/91. I am the top SK and can prove it. I am *not* going to prove it to the cops to my detriment. I can and shall prove it to you personally and privately however I do *not* want to do a book that glorifies the acts. I want to make it a positive social statement… I will never show anyone but yourself the actual hanging trees, (Stone's limb is not from my tree) butchering sites and private graveyards. You *alone* will have the secrets of what really happened at the death sites.

You squirm over Denise Naslund being degraded. Let me tell you, Denise never knew what terror was all about. I can tell you about whores who screamed and screamed and screamed… clitorectomies, the way to skin a cunt pelt, creative things to do with cigarettes and nipples. Ted was an amateur. Denise was lucky she met him instead of me. But then I wasn't kidnapping girls from beaches and schoolyards. Even so, you can't publish what I did. People would not believe it.

The TS will be told by you or it won't be done. I do not require it be done. I am forgiven by Jesus for those acts. I am healed of those impulses to commit them. I have some trouble even coming to terms that I did do such things once upon a time. I'm aware that nobody other than yourself has a capacity to understand a *little* of what occurred. You were there when I was trying to overcome the rage. OK. I lost that fight, but later I won it over. What occurred was not your fault in any manner. Your abandonment of me then *did* trigger years of brutal slaughter but that's long past and now we have this opportunity to go into it in depth and try to make some sense of it. Don't we? It's a unique chance for us to examine it… turn the negative past into a positive future.

As you know I've always harped on Stone's list of 34. In 1973 I sat down and drew up a list of my own. As I recall, my list was just over 80. I wasn't exactly taking names. J/P was a F.U. because I was never there. That was borne out by the forensic evidence, there's nothing at all to put me at the crime scene. No getting around that, is there? Same with G/Wilcox in Ft. Pierce. You can prove I didn't do it by forensics. But I was very careful never to leave a pattern. I killed women in all ways from shooting, strangling, stabbing, beheading to odd ways such as drowning, smothering and crucifixion. One I whipped to death with a strap, another I beat to jelly with a baseball bat while she was hanging by her wrists.

I was the best. But then I like to do things well. I renounce what I did, what I was, and am absolutely sure I'd never do such an act again. I was truly possessed by murder demons or whatever it's called. I want to stress that this letter is *absolutely confidential*. If you can't handle it destroy it. I've carefully avoided making any specific claim here about any specific case so legally all you have is KBS.

1/21/91. It's actually very uncomfortable for me to try to go back into time and re-capture the emotions and feelings that accompanied those horrible acts. For me it's not a thing I take lightly. It's not fiction. I can deal with things fiction all right but dealing with fact is upsetting. I would never even *attempt* to deal with such matters with a stranger. There are enormous trust factors involved.

I was so skilled at my craft that no pattern has ever been attributed to me. I've never been connected to a crime scene anywhere. Even the FBI does not consider me to be a suspect in any unsolved crimes. When you consider this in terms of skill it's a remarkable feat. The SK experts try to tell you that SKs are sex killers. This is a generality based on their belief that murder is misdirected sexual energy, and for the most part this is a truth. However in my own situation, as you will recall, my rage came up when females *whored* so the murderous act came from moral outrage rather than sexual interest. I rarely killed a woman nude.

I set my projects up like military campaigns. There were two primary types: Road Whores, which were almost always "quick kills," and whores of long acquaintance. I put a minimum of 6 months between the initial contact and the kill proper. Some whores I tracked for several *years*. A woman I met in Ft.L. might die a year later in Indiana. It was easy. I was an *excellent* lover. A whore would recall the good sex and come to me at a call. I had a whole address book filled with prospects. I'd go on a campaign every summer. I've worked almost every State and all provinces of Canada. Quietly and efficiently. Most victims were buried deep and the area restored to a natural look. No grave mound or such. No shallow graves. No dumping the corpse in a ditch or a river or canal. I used many different ploys. I was completely dedicated to what I was doing. Absolutely focused on it from 1965 to 1972. I had many female friends, so there were normal sexual relationships. Sex is wonderful between people who are friends or lovers. I had periods when I chose not to have such relationships, but I never allowed myself to kill for sex or as an alternative to sex per se.

Many of my kills were much like the Tiffany Sessions case in Gainesville. Miss Sessions goes out to jog and never comes back. If Tiffany had whored in Lauderdale a year earlier and her partner rolled up in a car she'd likely get in if just for a chat. She'd be dead inside 15 minutes and buried within 2 hours, or driven maybe a hundred miles away from Gainesville for burial. It's really very easy to do when you work according to a plan. I am nothing if not *organized*. When I was hanging Kates I did so with *efficiency*. I had it worked out precisely what would be done. A reasonable, workable, excellent course of action and it was viable year after year. Caution not passion. This is not to say each kill was the same. They were not. I was interested in variety but it was not impromptu variety. My aim was to kill whores, not necessarily toy with them or torture them. But I did torture a few.

I am not going to burden you with specific cases because then you would be tempted to run to FBI-H ... You will be concerned about if I can prove I am the #1 SK. Probably not. Certainly I can prove many cases, give you skulls and bones, all that sort of thing. I'm not claiming a huge number, it would only come to perhaps 10 to 12 per year for 8 years. I had a list of around 80 I could recall. That's not really a *lot* balanced against Lucas/Toole but it beats Bundy and Green River and the others. I've killed as many as 3 at one time. I would say it runs between 80-

110. But over 8 years and 3 continents. I did very well in North Central Colorado. I worked the major passes and got whores headed for the West Coast. I also worked the trans-Canada highway; around Calgary area was good. But many of those kills were quick ones. I really do not remember the exact number, or every kill. Some were very memorable. One whore drowned in her own vomit while watching me disembowel her girlfriend. I'm not sure that counts as a valid kill. Did the pregnant ones count as two kills? It can get confusing.

I don't suppose the individuals are important to your study so we don't need to work with specific persons or locations, do we? You can think about what proofs you might require and maybe someday I can come up with them for *you*. I will not do anything suicidal for you such as take cops to bones, *never*. The SK business was a part of a former life. I'd never return to it. Have *no desire* to return to it.

Now we need to decide what to do with this situation. I will work *only* with you. No FBI-H. No shrink. You must swear confidentiality. I *will* (upon release from prison) do retrogressive hypnosis on a minimum of 5 cases (a shooting, hanging, strangling, beheading and skinning) but that depends on my release and the confidentiality involved. Perhaps this will be sufficient proof of SK status?

If you cannot be faithful to my trust in you then *do not* pursue this thing. I am probably at least one of the top SKs of this century. Certainly one of the most interesting and maybe the most articulate and introspective. I am no doubt the most *skillful* killer. Cool and calm at my avocation, and that is unusual. I felt *good* about killing whores and took a great deal of pleasure in my work. I regarded killing whores as a *mission* of personal importance. I'd work several jobs to get enough cash for a trip around the country each year; then I'd be on my mission and totally dedicated to my premeditated goals. Sometimes I'd have women specifically targeted in other States but I was *always* flexible. Never did one know me by my real name... I'd call her and say: "Hi, this is Joe from Atlanta. Remember, we met in Ft.L. last year?..." Like that. And the whore would/or would *not* meet me at some local spot and 4 hours later I'd be 150 miles away with her corpse in the trunk ready for burial. Her friends might say, "She went to meet some guy from Atlanta and never came back." I'd be in another State before anyone even officially missed her. I *never* had any problems on that score.

If you want to look for GS victims, look for women age 14-35 who *disappeared* between 1965-1972. I never *knowingly* killed anyone under 16 but some had no ID. I've hanged 16-year-old whores. I never knew the names of many road whores. Or I only knew false names. That's a problem right there. Any time you choose you can go down to the Lauderdale strip and find runaways who will talk play-for-pay. The little bitches look lost. Just go up and ask if they want to work for a lady who will give them a nice apt, cash percentage and dope connection. Days free for the beach, nights tricking with men sent by the lady. No street work. Most can't wait to go with you. I took them out and hanged them. Straight to the hanging tree. Dumbest cunts in the world. I had these two tied and noosed, about two minutes from suspension and she goes, 'What's going on? Are you going to hang us?' Too stupid to know she was being murdered. She was hot to ride the sheets, couldn't wait to meet the madam. 'What kind of dope can we get? How much money will we get?' She didn't even have a full pubic bush!

Where they came from I couldn't tell you. I can only tell you where they ended up. Runaways. 'Comb your hair so you look smart, honey. Lay on some lipstick. Open up that blouse and let me see your titties.' They were so gullible. The call girls were so much better. Confident. Sassy. Sleek. But in the end they were brought down off their sexual thrones. They'd wheedle, beg wonderfully, and die in the most horrible ways. I enjoyed working on professional sex kittens with the knife. It was a pro who was slashed with a whip, a pro who was beaten into jelly with a baseball bat, and the first woman to be skinned was "high class tail." I always got the phone numbers and addresses of their "best girlfriends." "Hello. Is this Meg? Suzie's friend? She asked me to call you. Can you meet me with $500 for bond money? Come alone. Be discreet. Suzie says you can be trusted." Usually the pal would zip right there and in a few hours she too would be in hell.

I'd have nice chats with the prosties. They'd do anything to survive. I'd know everything about their best girlfriends before they died. A classy prostie will pay well to live. They have stashes of cash where they live. I'd call the friend, send her to get the stash cash and deliver it to a certain place because Suzie 'got a deal on some righteous shit' and needs the money fast. I'd get Suzie, the cash and the friend. I had a wonderful time with professional harlots. They usually understood they were in mortal danger once they realized they'd fallen for the fake cop routine. You could almost hear the voice inside their heads go 'Uh-Oh!' Several of them said that they'd had dreams or premonitions that they'd die at the hands of a 'trick.' They were fun kills. Every one of them. We played games. Russian Roulette: You suck the gun, I'll spin the cylinder. Games about asphyxiation: Gag the girl, hold her nose; wear the plastic bag until the girl turns blue — breath holding contests, strangulation contests, new ways to wear your nylons. Piss on my seat covers, I'll piss on your face. OK, honey? And if they played well they died easy. If they were bitches about it they died very, very nastily… like hang her by her ankles, gagged, then piss up her nose. Yes, there were so many unpleasant ways to kill them. Most of them played nice and prayed for the best.

Speaking purely logistically, murdered professional whores may never have hit missing persons sheets because I'd contact the girlfriends and tell them I was referred by Suzie. They'd say, 'Hey, where is she? Everyone's been asking about her.' I'd say, 'Well, last Monday she was at the Beachside Hotel at Acapulco with a guy called Chuck. I don't know where she is today.' I would kill one friend and lay several false trails maximum. I don't imply here that I did this every day or even every month. I just did it regularly. When I wanted a superior murder experience I called a call-girl, they were a special treat for me particularly the ones who were intellectually acute as well as physically lovely. The call girls were a breed apart from the street hookers. The street hookers would collapse emotionally and succumb to terror and hysteria. The call girl would be snapping her intellect looking for the key to the exit of her dilemma. They'd try all the gambits in their tricksy minds. I'd let them talk. I appreciated it when they finally understood that it wasn't a sex thing but a death thing. They'd look at me and say, 'I'm going to die, aren't I?' I'd say, 'Yes.' You had to appreciate their expressions, the looks they gave me. I wasn't violent, brutal, threatening. I was calm. Utterly serene. They knew they had no power over me. Maybe the first time they'd met a man

who could not be controlled by their physical charms and mental acuity. Each one died differently. Some were acquiescent; a few kicked up a fuss, but they all died. I enjoyed each and every experience.

But this is all 20 years ago or more; so what purpose is served to relate it factually incident by incident? Exploring the emotional side of it might be worthwhile. I've mixed feelings about it. On the one side, I am annoyed that I was framed by Dean & Schwarz & Stone on the J-P case. They try to make me look like a jerk and make up all that bullshit when I am obviously cleared by the forensic evidence in both J-P and G-Wilcox. They try to make those cases look alike when in fact they are obviously dissimilar. That annoys me a lot. Of course that could be their strategy. They know I'm a top notch SK but also know they can never prove it because I do perfect clean up work so what they do is release lies and misinformation that makes me look like a bumbler. Same strategy with Dolan. Everything I said about Dolan is absolutely true. They try to say I killed Lee H. even though Dolan was a dealer, Lee was a snitch and Dolan was one of Lee's suppliers. I know this because *I* introduced Lee to Dolan. Dolan told me *twice* that he killed Lee *and* the Hallock woman. He tried to recruit me to kill N.K. Price and *two* others. That's fact, which I told Snake, who told cops. But the cops ignored Dolan. Just let people think that Lee & Hallock were mine. I don't need Dolan's kills to pad my score! That's insulting to me. My accomplishments were excellently planned and executed but they were *bad* deeds. I can see that now. I had a purity of purpose but was absolutely wrong in my implementation of my purpose: to stamp out Evil. That's an impossible task, and murder can never be the answer.

1/22/91. OK. My letters to you are *confidential*. Particularly the most recent stuff about the SK topic. You wanted to know if you were wasting time with me as a SK. That's a valid *economic* question. I'm assuring you that you have one of the top SK's of all time on your MQ roster and that I shall be able to prove it if I get out. What proof do you require? I cannot *prove* them *all*. I need to be sure I don't cut my own throat with this business. I was never one to strew corpses all over the landscape like some people we know. So you may *not* go around telling my secrets — *our* secrets — to my detriment. You have a pretty good realization of what offends me so just use your own good sense in that area. OK?

I'm concerned about what you will think and do when you find out that what you currently believe to be KBS is not. Right now you think it's all KBS because you cannot conceive that what I've told you can be true. I've committed horrors beyond your ability to comprehend. Get me into retrogressive hypnosis and you will be *stunned* by what I have to say. You see me as I am *now*, a person renewed in Christ; unconsumed by hate. Passive even. My goals are spiritual, eternal, unworldly. I need to *work* to plug into the Murder Channel. 25 years ago I'd hang a cunt and watch her kick out her life and never give it a second thought. You were there before the madness began and after it ended. I know some whores who died smelling shit and Chanel. Their own. Maybe it's too intimate to put into prose. I've told you and told you that you are onto a story beyond your wildest dreams. You think I'm KBS-ing you. Ha!

I loved you in 1965. I love you still. It's not sexual. I love you unreservedly. I

don't care who you screw. I'm far more concerned about whether you can handle this TS stuff — especially when we get to the part where *you personally* were involved. We shall address all that down the road. I do wonder if you'll *betray me* as you did then; not sexually, but in some other manner — perhaps because of what I did to your female sisters... Still I think the story has merit if we do it together. [Smiley-face]

1/24/91. We can cover every case. Some will be in more detail than others. Once I've exhausted their list then we can go to work on my list. The problem I have is not so much in giving you the proofs you'd want but at what place do I draw a bright line?

Example: I could take you to various locations and show you where corpses were set out to rot as described in BKF. I could show you the pits where the cars are that were feeding stations for crabs. But do I show you bones? Skulls? You can say to me now — and you do — John, you are full of KBS. The MQ could right now get laughed out of Court if she tried to sell the reality of BKF to a jury. All that changes the minute I give you a corpse or a head. I can show you where victims were hanged, where they rotted in the open air or where they rotted underwater but as long as I don't show you where the bones are so to speak you are OK legally. But does failure to show bones constitute failure to prove the allegations in the TS? We'd need to resolve that. I cannot prove quite a few of the kills, some 25 years old. I cannot even give you an exact figure, but I'd say between 80-11. Since I went after transients, runaways, hitch-hikers and hookers the police reports would probably have issued at the place where they originally lived, not Fla.

Ted couldn't remember all his kills. He had only a percentage of mine and they were less removed in time too. Mine are 1965-1972. I've killed as many as 3 at one time and cannot tell you today what their names were or where they came from. I *can* show you where they died. Maybe some personal relics such as rotten clothing, shoes, such as that. This is not a simple problem. Proof. [Frowny face]

1/27/91. What I tell you is absolutely confidential. I will not be giving you any specific detail in letters. It's KBS. The day I show you proof it's not KBS then we have a very different sort of situation. Right? There is the matter of my family to consider as well. Remember that.

My battle has been to overcome the problem of SK-ism. I believe I have accomplished this through Jesus Christ. It's also helpful that I was able to have had these experiences so there is no mystery or area that needs to be explored. I am heterosexual but a female cannot get my interest via sexual allure. I am indifferent to this form of female control over men because I know that females are all the same sexually. Their shapes vary but once you peel them down what you see is a cunt. The quest for cunt is instinctive so then it becomes a matter of self-control over a natural urge. Once a person realizes what's going on it's controllable.

Killing whores is the same. It's very pleasant but after a while it becomes predictable and there is no more mystery involved. The interest becomes the individual as opposed to the *act* of killing. Since I've experienced every sort of killing that interested me I've no desire at all to go back and repeat something that could

only be repetitive. There are no great passions remaining. Both the sex and the killing was fascinating but ultimately unfulfilling. Time for something new and I believe that is to be found in things spiritual rather than things physical. I am even of a mind to consider that this entire killing thing got started because I viewed whores as a serious threat to my soul. I now that's too simplistic but I believe it was a large contributing factor. I believed what the priests had to say about women, sex and hellfire. Remember I made *daily mass for about 4 years straight* (1960-1964) so I was under a certain Catholic mind control thing... Well, we'll have to explore all that; maybe under hypnosis. It'll make a wonderful book if we can decide on how to present it in a dignified manner.

2/27/91. Sure, I could write Murder Demons. But you wouldn't like it, you wouldn't believe it, and it would never make it to the PG audience you are angling for. You ask me to write a torture scene, yet you constantly criticize me for mentioning excrements as if I toss it in there gratuitously. You want torture: If I wrote you about killing a certain hooker with an emergency road flare... they look like a stick of dynamite. Grease it up and use it on a whore like a dildo. Flares are fairly long. Run it up to her cervix, nice strokes. Run it up her poop chute. Easy strokes. Pull it out and there'll be a big dab of shit at the end. Ask her, 'You want that nasty stuff up your cunt?' Shakes her head. So you pull up the little tab and it bursts into magnesium fire. Give her a red hot fuck. Push that fire up her snatch. It will burn through her cervix and go into her womb, then through her womb and into her guts. Convulsions like you can't imagine and that whore will literally *pump* shit out of her ass. Stick that flare all the way up in her and her cunt will *smoke*. Damnedest thing you could ever see. I'd say shock kills them more than anything else. Yes, I can give you some first rate torture. But you'd never use it because it's too nasty. You can't even handle tame stuff like "Freak Trade." So why would you tell me to write it real and true when you must realize you can't publish it?

3/1/91. Now for something confidential... We have been dealing in fiction. You mentioned about the *eyes*. I have given you a very brief glimpse of something that no woman alive today has ever seen. You understood the message viscerally. You were able to snap down on a message that should erase any doubt you ever had about whether or not I am for real. I was able to communicate an absolute truth to you with a single look... You now know *one* secret. *Silence of the Lambs* is a reality. Oh, not the exact same scenario as the film; not the silly motive Harris offers his readers. You have access to the real thing!

Consider the nameless, pricey prostitute who is handcuffed, her ankles tied, and after much time she says, dreading the answer, 'Are you going to kill me?' She is answered with the eyes. She sees the eyes, the whetstone, the razor sharp skinning blade. How does she handle that reality? Badly, of course. Like a cow in a slaughter chute.

The novelization of the reality would be no problem but you would not be able to deal with those realities. You request a 'torture scene' but a graphic torture scene that was grounded in reality you could never bring yourself to publish. Your own pre-conceived notions of what murder is all about is based on TV and novels

and these mediums are all sanitized. Every time I deal in a reality in my fiction that has to do with an excrement you scream *taboo* yet one of the very initial fear reactions women have is to pee in their clothes. They start shivering as if freezing to death and while they're shaking they're peeing all over everything. They issue a stencxh of sweat that is very distinct, an absolute smell of fear. The bowels don't go until the onset of pure terror, usually. the girl will succumb to terror and go into a state of hysteria and lose control of herself completely even to the point of drooling. It's unbelievably disgusting; not 'sexy.' they are prone to vomit. But all this is taboo in current prose. Right? So how can I write about what you request? Obviously I cannot. It's not a question of not being able to write such a novel, it's a problem of overcoming the social and cultural taboos that accompany real sex murder when it's reduced to popular prose. No?

I have told you that you are privy to a more sensational story than you can ever realize. You are not going to get it in a rush or without establishing serious trust over a long period of time… You got a personal one-on-one revelation that communicated to you that you've a unique opportunity to do a major work on someone once called "The Greatest Killer of Women in the USA in this Century." Not #2, but #1. The Greatest. And the most proficient. I'd like you to do Toole before you take a crack at me, for the experience. Nobody else will get the GJS story. I know you're impatient but that's just too bad. I won't be rushed, forced, intimidated or relax my caution. You'll get it all, in time. Trust is the keynote.

3/9/91. I was pleased to hear you liked the *Murder Demons* scenario I sent to you. It was a basic first rough draft. I think it's probably hard for the reader to catch the insanity of such acts of butchery, the violence is progressive. The scenario in MD is an advanced case of insanity. A bright, luscious, sassy sex kitten is far more interesting than some dirty road whore because she *knows* at a certain point that she has encountered the living nightmare that she instinctively understands she will not survive. A change occurs at that realization; physically the woman emits a stinking greasy sweat almost as if to fend off the predator by making herself hugely unattractive via smell. It's not the smell of exertions, or sexual trysting, but a rank odor and very distinctive. Unpleasant. A smell of terror. There are many small things such as this one can recount if one knows the dynamics of reducing a confident sex pot call-girl to a whimpering lump of ravaged flesh that begs for death. I guess I could do MD as a novel. Could give it a try…

I think it will be explosive publicitywise if Stone comes out and says something about the proof of my being a necrophiliac / cultist is in my stories. The KF stories are low key compared to what is coming in *Murder Demons* … if I can pull it off.

3/10/91. I've been sharing things with you at our visits that are very private. It's a question of trust. We are making good progress and I want to let you know here in a general way, avoiding specifics, that *most* of what you have in the past thought was KBS is not. You cannot in your most bizarre imagination conceive what went on out in those swamps… it was pre-meditated, cold-blooded, wanton savagery that I'm not sure can be replicated on paper. It's a bit like the ACA reporter who said OT is in a separate category. I'm like that. There were no 'patterns' to lock

onto. I'm a 'category of one' and so far off the end of the bell curve that I'm honestly concerned that if I told you what really happened you'd be too freaked to continue our relationship which has come back in a very healthy way. I keep saying, 'You have no idea of what you're on to with me,' and it's true. It was very much a matter of Murder Demons and Jilani, for all her insanity, made that very clear and *she* was not the only one…

I was so glad to hear Nolte's girlfriend freaked out after reading KF. Yes, they are fiction, but yes, they are *real*. The astute reader will be able to discern that they have a rare look into the face of death and madness… My problem has been, how do I get where I want to go in reality without SL betraying me to the cops? That's been a hard question but one we can solve, I think, via the use of fiction as a medium. MD as a novel in the voice of The Ghoul. I won't give you any real people, places, etc. that a cop could use as a fact and you would have to agree to always stress that the book is a work of fiction, albeit written by a man said to be the Greatest Killer of Women this century. The important thing is that *you* understand that what you have is reality. The proof will not be the disinterred heads of nameless sluts. The proof will be the prose. The outline scenario I sent of MD is only a hasty few hours 1st R.D. I was thinking that your response would be an angry one, that the great truths would fly over your head and you'd snap at me about the excrement… (you can torture her but she can't shit…) never aware of the factual reality that captive whores smell of sweat and urine always after a few hours and that ultimately the victim defecates! Kill her quickly and the BM is simply a response to contracting muscles, kill her slowly and her bowels get loose and eventually she can't hold her mess and she'll spew a volcano of crap, a shit puree that is all slimy and hugely disgusting and it gets all over everything. The victim becomes stunned and subdued when she unloads in her clothes. It's a curious thing. Most women will pee from sudden fright when the capture occurs so wet pants is a reality but the captive eventually floods her clothes after some hours. She gushes piss. It's like a marker on the road to her doom, and predictable.

MD will, of necessity, be repetitive if you want reality. The SKs business involves a certain repetition but a creative SK, a student of murder, is somewhat more interesting…

Another thing: I think it's very necessary to stress fiction and frameup to avoid the sorts of problems you mentioned about Bret Ellis. I don't want those problems and neither do you. They can be avoided by using care. Does Thomas Harris get such threats? We need to take care to minimize such things. This very thing is one important consideration I evaluate when considering my future approach when I go back to Court. If I yell frameup (which I can do with clear conscience because it's true) then a lot of that hate gets defused. The very moment Stone screams "KF proves he did it!" which he will do, then you have a national soapbox to go after Ellis & Harris & all the others. It becomes a Rushdie situation in a sense. And *you* will be handling it. Huge publicity. You can see it in your mind's eye, can't you? All this is coming toward you (us) in time. You get concerned because your own 'sense of music' has shut down and it upsets you. But you don't see it in terms of your spiritual self (music is spiritual) narrowing and focusing on what your inner self senses coming toward you on several serious levels: Murder Frame-up, Liter-

ary Freedoms, and Real Murder Demons. You've had a fit over the reality of whorehouse hang-shit which is harmless fetish. But in MD you will have to deal with almost 10 years of the most horrifying murders that you could *never* imagine, a secret life that *nobody* has ever learned of.

I personally did recruitment of hookers. I had them sign contracts to work in Fla. or other places. All very formal. Work conditions. Housing. Dope perks. All part of the hunt! C'mon, we'll drive out and meet The Boss. They went to slaughter, sometimes 2 and 3 at one time. I'd hang them. Behead them. Drown them. Shoot them. Gut them. Skin them. Crucify them on real crosses. And much more... Stone introduced my machete into evidence. Hey, I had a *real beheading axe*. I had a *real beheading block* where *real whores* knelt and perished in the ancient death rituals. They brought in my mooring lines... I had beautiful, stretched and oiled *hanging ropes* that stretched carefully selected beauty's necks. Stone's show was a farce. Even so, I sure couldn't drop stuff like this on you until we had established certain trusts. You'd yell KBS. Ha! You simply don't know the depth of what went down. You can't handle it except in small increments. It's too horrible and too much. We'll just have to take it a little at a time. Explore it. Together. I guess that's enough for today.

3/11/91. Today I got the enclosed denial of the habeas from the Bar. Note the denial was Dec. 12, 1990. I'm wondering why nobody — like my lawyers — never told me. Most urgent that Notice of Appeal be filed. Last chance is 11th Circuit...

3/12/91. As for myself. You will *not* be disappointed when we get to the TS. I need to get the legal part settled before I can get into the TS. Keep in mind that what I *do* I do well and extravagantly. I like to be the *best* at what I try. Why I could write a book about my travels and adventures in the outlands of human existence and what I met there and what the *voices* told me. Oh yes, there were voices. Voices with perfect clarity. Some of my most intense experiences were certainly spiritual... but not religious. I want an end to the legal part so I can freely explore, with you, the other realms.

4/9/91. What crimes am I supposed to confess? Sykes? Farmer? Briscolina? What do you think Murder Demons is? Fiction? You want 'confessions' but you don't recognize them when I anoint you with them and we've just gotten started. SL is not gonna get some cheap exploitation of the SK experience. No sanitized Ann Rule or Darcy O'Brien mainstream SK-fluff. The TS will put the reader on site. Murder is nasty. Disgusting. I'm not gonna participate in any "Murder Can Be Fun" stories. We're still kicking around how to deal with factual nastiness such as pissy jeans and shitty panties. Haven't even touched on the ones having their periods, the ones who vomit while gagged, a girl who's been sitting in her own shit offering sex as she watches her rope being noosed. Sex, the slut's answer to everything. It's not nice, none of it. To write it in a way that could be construed as attractive violates something. You never get a clear picture of Ted kneeling over the Chi-O girl gnawing on her buttock, her anus plugged with a Clairol bottle. It's

all fuzzy and amorphous. My girls deserve better. They were too filthy to consider fucking. Nobody ever mentions that about murder. A sex killer I was not. I am unique. I guarantee it. But when I do a MD novelization of the reality it has to be a reflection of the actual horrifying acts not some watered own mainstream pablum. No?? Can I do it? Certainly I can. I will too. In proper time.

4/17/91. I've been thinking through a piece about how I got into S/M with CW at an early age. She was a pure maso and trained my teen self to be her sado partner. Classic pattern. Masos (called 'Bottoms' in the freak life) call the scenarios and require a partner who has good *control* to interact with. (Sados are called 'Toppers') By the time I was 17 I was a skilled 'topper' — thanks to CW. [Smiley face] There was a real conflict because I'm not a true topper — as SL knows. I'm a natural romantic so Sado went against my emotional grain however I *did* freak with CW regularly. So what I had, at age 18, was a blend of "normal" relations and a good knowledge of S/M as a topper.

SK-ing was simply carrying the topper role beyond the parameters of the scene. Easy to do emotionally if you are a veteran topper. "Legion of Decency" touches on that weird life I had in addition to the normal life. It's mental and emotional discipline involved. S&M is like a stage act. It's all ritual and fantasy. Fun, really, if you are secure in the roles. Being introduced into the games at age 16 probably got me twisted to some degree but not hopelessly so. By the time "Gatorbait" occurred I was a skilled topper, not a slave to emotions that would go out of control during a sexual encounter. There were other factors as well but CW was a princess wherein S/M was concerned. Pure Maso. So you have Gatorbait reality and LOD reality, both fictionalized. I was thinking of something on the line of pre-Gatorbait, maybe one of CW's scenes. No murder. No *severe* violence. She wasn't a pain freak. No blood. She was hot for *mastery* in sex. Force her, 'rape' her, slap her around, rip off her clothes, light bondage stuff only. If she felt threatened then she'd fuck like a rabbit. She had no choice. Fuck or die. I came to understand it once I began to research and write S/M, B/D, etc. I mull it over but there are a lot of raw nerves still exposed. It's not easy to address it.

4/19/91. Had ES/RS not framed me I'd be perfectly content to fly right into the role of "The Great SK" for you. RS already dubbed me the Greatest SK in U.S. History so all I need to do is accept the position. But I cannot in good conscience do that just yet. My private graveyards are private, not public. The SK experience is a personal one, not a public one. All they could do was accuse me of known murders, that I did not do and when I screamed about it loud enough they had to admit I wasn't really connected to those cases in any criminal way. Time has even proven me innocent in a number of the cases; others were convicted, missing persons did come back alive. I can take a certain pride in the fact that I am The Greatest SK because I've never been connected to a crime scene anywhere. The J-P crime scene is an insult to an organized SK. It annoys me to be accused of leaving such a *mess* strewn about because GJS never left a mess anywhere. Not from the very first one to the last one.

I'm no Henry Lee Lucas with a death wish or a partner or living witnesses to point fingers at me. I never ran around leaving people dead in a roadside ditch... and I feel no obligation to a society that condones a murder FU. SL shall have it all in good time but I will not be rushed nor will I now "cooperate" with the police. Fuck the police. Fuck society. Anyone who wants the inside track can put down their cash and read the book. Yes, I told you I'd give you names, dates, places, but your current position is that if I give them to you that you will give them to the cops. So get real yourself. I'm not going to death row for you.

4/20/91. The problem with telling it is that it does become repetitious. I was never locked into a specific fantasy or ritual the way SKs are. The average SK is recognizable by the M.O. but my situation is an anomaly. I was a combo of a number of different factors. The early S/M stuff with CW gave me a taste for enjoying fantasies that I could incorporate into SK-ing but it wasn't necessarily predominate or impelling. True, the rope was the usual M.O. but that depended on the venue and mood. It's sort of complex and not precisely in keeping with what SK experts like JN and others write about it.

5/18/91. Sadistic old me: When I was with you in 1965 I'd never had a "straight" sexual relationship before so you were the first — and my preference — but after you and then L—, I was more drawn into FT type girls. I had a 'double' sex life. During the late 60s there was a large focus on obtaining the 'Big-O' — the most intense orgasm sensation. People in the sexual underground *know* that the supreme orgasm is achieved by ligature strangulation... sensations so transcendent that freaks are constantly dying from hanging themselves. FBI-H wrote a whole big thing about it — I think... I read what he sent way back when. Both genders can get off on this but more men get killed at it due to failure to understand how to manage the scene. Do it alone and you are gonna end up dead, eventually. I had four women over a period of almost four years who were stone freaks for this. Three of them would go 'all the way': Full suspension, death strap bondage and hood. The fourth lady could never bring herself to do full suspension on 'go all the way.' She went for upper body pinions, no hood, and slow, controlled strangulation. The first three were greedy for the 'O' but #4 was into 'the scene.' There must be perfect trust. The girl puts her life on the line and gets hooked on a sexual sensation that is so powerful people die trying to achieve it. You are not the type female who can understand the female submissive... believe it or not there are women running around who cannot enjoy sex unless they feel absolutely helpless. The one who wanted the slow strangulation was married with kids! Catholic. Sneak out in her car at night on some pretext and I'd meet her and using a cord and doweling post I'd give her a 5-minute orgasm... but had I made a wrong move or not been skilled at the art of it then she might have been quickly dead meat. But I'm excellent at mental/emotional compartmentalization. I like to be *the* best and I like to take things to extremes. I hate moderation. I could 'top' a woman so neatly that I could have made a career out of it. [Smiley face] I had the offer to do some from a FT madam. She told me I could pick my clients — all women — that

I was handsome, sexy and perfectly in control, a rarity in the trade. I showed her a trick: I used one hand — I had hands like steel talons in those days — pressed her neck and she collapsed to her knees; then, just using pressure, I made her cream her pants. She was *fascinated*. I told her I could do even better with a braided nylon rope... so we chatted and I got the job offer, referrals only, no House work. Of course I was fascinated by all that... and got *paid* for topping!... But I was in love with Teresa at the time, had a very nice normal hetero sex thing with her, plus at that time, there were three freak women I serviced and within a year of marrying Teresa I'd quit topping altogether. I quit writing to freaks. Quit fiction. I was very straight while Teresa was around. Turned over a new leaf. [Smiley face]

So what's to tell? I was *into* the sexual underground. The Freak Trade. [Smiley face] I did my thing, the girls did theirs and everyone was cool. It was the late 60s, there were no rules as far as the FT went. I was selective, very choosy... as usual. [Smiley face] I might add here that I do *not* suggest anyone get into the FT. Avoid it at all costs because it ends up bringing only misery and problems.

5/20/91. 1965: What I eventually had was a dual sex life... I had two fundamental sexual base experiences... I admit I really did *like* the sadismo. Pure power is what it is. Wonderfully illicit. And there is the power of knowledge about how *some* women are. I was taught to respect women — the Catholic thing — but there are women, plenty of them, who require total domination before they can enjoy erotic sensation. You can't imagine what it's like to really work a woman over; slap the piss out of her and take a belt to her; call her filthy names and when the scene is over she says: "That was good... but beat me harder next time with the belt." It's unreal.

But success is vested in understanding the woman doesn't want to be treated rottenly on a regular basis. She has a need for the abuse sexually, and as a topper one must have a perfect comprehension of the scenario and the need on each individual basis. The 'victim' must be able to say to *herself*: "I had no choice. He told me to orgasm or he'd kill me!" I was excellent at creating an air of menace. But when the job was done I'd treat the woman with kindness and respect. It was very weird. But always fascinating. By 1969 I'd learned to use the noose and, of course, did death strap scenes with a few special ladies. I'd never ever get into that scene again. I'd say I've mastered it anyway. I had it down pat.

8/7/91. I've repeatedly told you that I will *not* agree to anything wherein I am portrayed as a SK. You are to *STOP* referring to me as a SK. It's not true, and not remotely provable. You want me to say I'm an SK so you can make money from the lie. I went along with the KBS to help you sell books but there is a limit. I'm in U.S. Court, my case is before the 11th Circuit and you want me to go on ACA and be touted as a SK. Are you *insane*? No, I think it's just greed.

I've given you the opportunity to have the F.U. I do sincerely believe you will sadly regret promoting that true story as something I've made up. You were given the chance to go with the truth but you encourage me to participate in a lie. I wrote you months ago: No more KBS. You seem to be unable to separate the fact from the fiction... which is a damned shame.

By even mentioning SK and my name in the same sentence you are not acting in my best interests or in the interest of truth. You are supposed to be my press rep. And you're using that position to generate suspicion of me as a SK instead of the victim of a FU. I find this particularly troubling since I told you long ago that *if* my challenge to the FU failed then I'd do a fine KBS for you. Somehow you've lost sight of what we planned and now, right in the middle of my federal appeal, want me to be a SK for you. Explain how this is in my best interest, will ya?

8/14/91. I've told you time and time again not to refer to me as a serial killer. You've left the zone of reality and gone into your personal fantasyland and that *sucks*. You never sent me that PP because you knew I'd never OK it for KF. You can just pull that bullshit right out or you and I are gonna have a problem.

The offending material is almost exclusively on page one so to make it easy on us both just delete that page: TSKWLM. It's a personal reminiscence that has no business in a work of fiction. It's out of kilter with what KF is all about. It's a fucking misrepresentation of the truth, unsubstantiatable opinion and an unacceptable intrusion into my personal life; a truly cheap violation of personal privacy both my own and that of my family. So you get it the fuck out of there, you hear? You've got your fucking nerve even mentioning my family in a book of fiction. You clearly lead the reader to believe that KF is not fiction but factual accounts of real crimes committed by me. Are you working up a new reputation as a cheat & a liar & a whore so you'll fit into the business world better?

Too fucking lazy and disinterested in fact to go read official records that would show I'm not in any actual way connected to two dozen dead or missing women. Nope. You sure don't want truth lousing up your tidy, malignant, pre-conceived notions that I did all Stone claimed and more. Where's the truth, Sondra? That was the entire base of the whole project: Let's get to the truth. What you are engaged in at the moment is spreading lies and strengthening misconceptions.

The alternative to getting back to what is honest and true is this: We fold up the MQ tent. You go your way, I go mine and no hard feelings either way. It also means all things GJS are halted now and forever. No more sales, no more printings, no more *nothing*. I'll have Gary drive up there and the two of you can carry all my drafts and other materials to the city incinerator and burn it. All of it. After that if you print anything or indulge in any actions that can be construed as an attack on myself or more importantly, my family, then we can have a war and I'll respond in a manner that will let you know that you don't fuck with my family.

You have become uncommunicative with me. This non-communication started around May. It's almost as if you've said to yourself: "Since he won't write me some juicy KBS I can push as SK-Fact what I'll do is market KF/BKF as fact thinly disguised as fiction," or "Since he won't agree to TSKWLM on ACA I'll just fix him by putting it in KF — fuck him!" You pulled this sneaky shit and never even wrote and asked me about it so, knowing you're not a goddamned idiot I figure what you're doing is pulling some smart-assed whore's trick.

You don't need me to caution you about what I'll do if you continue to publish blatant falsehoods about me as a SK or if you ever print any other negative or embarrassing items about my family.

Hey, *you* have a little family so you can appreciate my sensitivity and protectiveness.

I'm puzzled as why you want to pull all this rotten stuff on me. I've even told you that I'd give you a 'True Crime' book *after* you make an honest effort to check out he FU, *if* the habeas fails. I've promised you win-win but for some reason you want to dismiss the truth and run with the lie right now... It's like you're deliberately going out of your way to do things you *know* are going to annoy me... Oh, if you wanted to get my goat you sure enough did succeed. I've been in a snit all day... so *please, shape up!*

8/20/91. I've received your letter of August 15. You violated both the wording and spirit of our agreement when you inserted unauthorized material into KF. There is no doubt in my mind that you made that move in an effort to embarrass my family and attempt to ruin my habeas corpus litigation in U.S. Court. What you've done constitutes a personal betrayal and treachery of the meanest sort so I'm not surprised to see you want to discontinue our project... I will say here so that there is no misunderstanding later: Should I learn you are representing me to any one as a serial killer or sexual psychopath or maniac of any type then I shall make every effort available to me to destroy yourself and your daughter. I'm *not* referring to murder. I am referring to *ruin*. And if warranted, pain. Simply stated: If you continue to attack me then you'll get it back ten times over.

8/24/91. As I've said in my last message, if you call me a serial killer or continue to attack me or my family then, and only then, will I move against you and your family. You see, it's up to you. Your choice entirely. I'll find out if you do something against me, or them. So just don't do it and you and I won't have a problem. I'm not a sneak. The day I set out to come after you I'll tell you and I'll even tell you why...You really need to sit yourself down and think. I'm in the worst prison in the entire country. I have people in here who owe me favors and any of your police or lawyer pals will confirm that if someone wants to nail you they can do it. Drive up from Miami, do the evil deed, return the next day. There are professional criminals in here who can have this done easily. You can't protect against it. You know that I speak true.

Treacherous, two-faced, double-dealing whores are not my favorite people. Shit, you're as bad as Elton... who is so scared he went into Federal Court and lied under oath. I'll break him. I'll never quit. Never. He carries a gun; so does Teresa. I haven't even made my move on him yet and he carries a gun! Will he carry two when his face gets broken? Traffic dispute. Happens everyday down here. Don't be naive, OK? I can't get things done *fast* from solitary but I do manage.

10/22/91. I'd like you to avoid calling me an SK and do emphasize that it appears to be a FU... *If* I lose in Court — and I haven't lost yet — *then* you can market me as an SK and it won't matter. I'll tell you when. But either way you *win*. Don't you think so?

11/17/91. Now I know who the Sex Beast is. How about that! Nice job on the research, kid.

I can see where you're having money problems so I'm gonna give you a chance to make some cash… Go to ACA and get your fee… I'll cooperate… Let's quit bickering and go out and make money!

I love to terrorize you and drive you to drink but it's no fun when you are so down, so I'm gonna give you a break and, if you want to have a truce then we'll run with this new thing and later after it spins down I'll terrorize you some more. If you are a good girl I'll let you wear your official Serial Killer Death Head Ring on national TV… Chop-Chop! Write Soon, John

11/27/91. I am aware that you are more interested in my unusual experiences in the sexual underworld than you are in my being framed for murder. CW was a sexual disaster area who couldn't come unless she was literally slapped into insensibility, her clothing actually ripped off her back and her ass; all the while hearing what a dirty little wet assed bitch she was, a rotten little sex slut on her way to Hell, etc. etc. After a few years of that I knew my way around masochistic females. That's not my erotic tastes personally but I was interested in it academically. I have an inquisitive nature and I learned to give certain select females what they couldn't get elsewhere: An expert topper who was so cool they could feel the chill. A rare bird. Most partners are into the sadismo role and get off on it or go too far. I'm into control, the greater discipline. You can't appreciate any of this because you are not involved in it… It's like FBI-H studying people who die during autoerotic asphyxia. He sees a scene but does not comprehend what he's seeing. He doesn't know the R&R (ropes & rituals) so he guesses at it. Show me 50 photos of women who committed "suicide" by hanging and I could easily pick out those who died due to having an inexperienced partner swinging them. Yes, if a gal has an unskilled playmate she does die. There's a proper way to go about it. I know all about it. You see, most men are sexually greedy. Not me. I made topping an art form. I made a study of it and I had some women who dearly appreciated my skill. You don't know enough to know I was into it but writing about it in a letter doesn't get either of us anywhere. What I should do is write a primer on how to hang a freaky chick for her maximum pleasure. That'd sell, but you wouldn't publish it due to sexism, or something.

I won't mention that I've had to keep my foot in your ass to bounce you down the one true road; that you've had me so angry and frustrated that I've threatened to wring your neck, none of *that* goes public… I want out. You want a job and security. It's not at all incompatible and we can achieve these goals working together on this. Please abandon this kick you're on about threats and fear. I've told you and told you: do *not* portray me as a SK. Now is that hard to follow?

1992

1/15/92. (1) ACA: I can't really comment… reactions are coming in… they are 100% of the opinion that ACA trashed me… (2) Mike Newton: I had a letter from him. Answered it. I think he is qualified to run with the TS so I'm tentatively agreeable… I'm cognizant of the fact that people say ACA & SL fucked me over but I'm not the type to listen to what people say and act on it.

1/19/92. You particularly need to warn Raymond Null about any use of my work without MQ authorization or any implication that my fiction is fact and not fiction because if he should make that claim I'll have him in Court and make him prove it. I'll even handle the case myself and I'll make him go broke on the copying fees for the discovery and the interrogatories alone. I know over 100 expensive nasty legal tricks. Do warn him. I *love* to sue. Absolutely love it.

You should have ACA do a second episode. The initial airing seems to have focused on the accusations against me and the second airing might well focus on the physical evidence that counters those accusations and lends credence to my claim of being framed. Maybe get MN in there to announce he is going to investigate the case as a journalist/true crime writer. Stir up the controversy but angle it into the question as to whether what I claim could be true. The lawyer-wife romance, all that… Should ACA do a second episode then the value will go up on the books and story. Again, controversy.

1/28/92. I've always been a creative writer and such people are often regarded by the rank & file as being weird characters. You've been having the problem of assuming too much, such as my fiction rises from my life, such as KF/BKF is all or partially true. It's a common trap people who are not similarly skilled in creative writing fall into. What I write has nothing to do with me personally, it's fiction; although I've experimented with you and found that I can write virtually anything of a negative nature, tell you it's factual and you'll believe it in a flash. A good example is when you told me you didn't believe I was a SK and I told you I could convince you that I am via my writing and personality conveyed via the written word. I simply used your own notions and imagination against you. I changed your mind using my writing talent and you still don't even realize that it was an exercise in writing for me and has not a thing to do with actual reality. You ignore facts and twist suppositions and conjecture to fit the notion you want. You are willing to twist my fiction into your own speculative reality and the moment I say, "You're right, it's all fact," you'll simply accept that as gospel and never require any proof at all beyond the stories themselves. I just can't be a fiction writer, can I? You *need* a monster. Adios.

1/30/92. There is something maybe you don't understand. I'll explain it: I fight. Nobody is gonna steal my manuscripts and use them to make a buck or print that I'm a SK in 1992 without getting sued by me. That includes Null, Norris, Newton, you or anyone else. New Year, new policy. Now I do realize that I probably won't

win money but I can cost my adversary a hell of a pile of money in legal fees. Null is "on notice." He can be smart, like PK was smart, and *drop it*, or he can learn first hand what a vicious, single minded litigator I can be because I'll not only sue him, I'll have him arrested on a formal criminal complaint… and I'll make it stick — maybe. I'll try… hard.

… I've trained myself to learn how to fight a legal war instead of asking one of the dudes from the Satan's Disciples Nation to arrange something violent. I'm on the very worst FSP population wing with the baddest of the bad but I help the nigs with their legal shit and that gets me accepted. Quite a few of these dudes are with gangs and I've got some with good contacts to Yankee urban gangs such as The Vice Lords, the Latin Kings, El Ruken, and Satan's Disciples Nation.

2/17/92. I care a lot. That's why I've told you that if you even try to rip me off or tell people I'm a SK then I'm gonna be your serious enemy. I really don't want to be that so I've given you ample warnings. You just blabber on about "threats" and never see the truth and light and reality.

I've told you many times that I don't care if the TS is written or not. But if a TS is to be done then it will be done right, and anyone who thinks they can rip off my TS under "public record" is gonna be sued and sued and sued. Engrave it in blood upon your heart of hearts: I shall not tolerate any cheap ass TS bullshit story a la JN. And the only reason JN and his publisher isn't sued now is because *you* asked me to hold off on it. I'll have his fucking book taken off the market or die trying. And I'll cost him a ton of money. You think I can't? Or won't? You just watch me. Piss me off a little more.

Now let me give you the word here: If you want to do a TS about me then we'll come to some sort of contract agreement and do it. Me, you, MN. And if you don't want to do that then I'm gonna say to you here: Forget a GJS TS. And if you want to challenge me, fine. I'll rip your fucking heart out in legal actions.

2/19/92. Bottom line: We need a simple contract. Good communication. A schedule and a plan. You *do not* want me for an enemy. And you'd be in a good spot if you had the TS rights because there's more to come on the TS. For instance: If I lose in US Court I'm gonna have Schwarz, Teresa & Dean crippled. Arms and legs. But here's the interesting part. I'm gonna *admit* it was me who had it done. Make them charge me. Then tell *why* on the record, in Court. A bold stroke. But it's consistent with my determination to expose the FU. I'm not gonna tolerate their doing this to me.

I've said from the beginning that I wanted us both to benefit by our association. I see now where you are consumed by greed and want it all and seem to think I'm too pussy to make a move on you. I'm *not*. Don't try me. Are you listening? I can have a nice young vicious Negro fella knocking at Beau's door within 30 days. Dare me to do it? Think I'm kidding?

You'll also recall that I went on ACA so you could save your home. A gesture of personal concern and kindness for you and your kid. You assured me that ACA would be balanced and fair and talk KF & FU… ACA made me look like a SK who writes about his crimes. Hey, that's *your* angle, isn't it! I tried to help you

save your home and you took the opportunity too make me look like an animal. You're a real prize, aren't you?

ACA *did* generate a lot of interest in the case. I'll say that was a fact. I've had some interesting mail from book writers, film makers, etc. So there's a lot going on. Nobody else has a great passion to present me as a SK; only you. Other people have a tendency to deal with the facts as opposed to your inclination to speculate about unknown and unnamed victims.

4/4/92. You are not to mention my name or work to anyone anywhere. Close up shop on all things GJS. Cease sales, promotions, interviews and conversations on all things GJS… Don't even send out for any new print runs… I am not going to be interviewed… unless the interview concerns the FU and falsified trial evidence… You can either stop… or we can go to war… I'll keep everyone tied up in Court for a long time to come because I have plenty of time to sit here and do litigation. Now are you gonna stop and wait until I'm done in Court or are you gonna fight me? You decide. Just be aware that if you want to fight I won't quit until you are ruined… Better let MN know he can't use KF too. Best course for him is go do something else.

4/12/92. I saw ACA… and we're through. I don't even have to tell you another word, do I? Seeing is enough. I'm not gonna argue legalities with you. I'm just gonna ask you to be a nice lady and pack up everything GJS into some boxes. Seal them and send them to Mom… I want to be nice about this break so there are no evil feelings between us because if I get evil I'm gonna come after you and ruin you. I'm still angry about that ACA presentation and I saw it a week ago. What I should do is come after you. But what I'm gonna do is give you proper warning to cease and desist all things GJS-MQ; and from this day forward don't you ever mention my name again. Are we gonna have a problem with that? You let me know right away because if we are gonna fight I'm coming after your ass fast. If we are gonna have peace that's best and will save us both a lot of trouble. I just want to make it perfectly clear that I will not write another word of fiction for MQ, Paul Dinas or anyone else; not at any price and if you so much as sell one more KF or even mention my name in an interview or the printed word or anything else I'll come after you and hound you into your grave and never quit. *You'll* become my life's work.

How I feel about ACA's presentation transcends mere anger. You've tapped a Black Hole of genuine rage and it's focused on *you*. I do have that hostility compartmentalized enough to act with cool premeditation, and we did have some genuine fun; so let me issue a polite word of caution here… I'm in a state of mind that I won't need much of a push to come after you, so do the conservative and wise thing and go along with me the easy route. Can we do that?

What made me sort of sad was that you could have broken a genuine FU story. Even ACA could have… I invited them to do just that. But no, you chose to insinuate I'm a SK. I do understand that is the more potentially lucrative position. "SK Writes 'How To' Book on Murder." Well, you sure did fuck it up for yourself going that route. You chose to insinuate a lurid lie when truth would have served

you far better. I'm always on your case about that penchant for the negative aspect you seem to relish. No more though. We're finished professionally.

4/16/92. Please contact Mike Newton and have him return to you all the material you've sent him concerning myself and my case. You may send all that down to Mom along with the stuff you have about me now in your possession... Will you do that? Also be advised that I've been made aware that your buddy Hazelwood has published some material referring to me as a serial killer and a sadist. Care to comment? I gave you ample warning about what would occur if you continued to present me to people as a SK.

Thanks to you I've met a number of people from the Satanist underground. To express my appreciation for what you said on ACA I've explained to them about your daughter. They'll probably get in touch with her personally through their people in Georgia. Sondra, if you so much as even mention my name to anyone in any manner whatsoever, I'm going to use every shred of influence at my command to have your kid picked up. She's just right for these people.

What you need to do without any further delay is to get out of my life. I'm going to endure you only long enough to get this matter settled and after that I don't want to have any contact with you ever again either directly or indirectly. I'm not going to argue with you about this. I've made my decision based on what I've seen with my own eyes and heard with my own ears. Just never speak my name to anyone, anywhere ever again. That will suffice. Nothing less. If you want to make an issue of this then the kid is gonna be the one to pay the tab. Am I clear?

Now let's part like reasonable, sensible adults so we have no future conflict at any level. Just do the simple things I've asked and do them as promptly as possible. I truly loved you at one time and do not want to cause you grief so take this opportunity I'm offering you to get out quickly and cleanly. Go fry other fish and make sure my name doesn't come up. Are we in agreement ? Let me know.

4/24/92. I'm poised to sue everyone — articulately. I may not win but I'll break everyone's bank and make the lawyers richer. I can do it and I shall do it if I see it's necessary. Then there is the matter of my being a part of a separate society and our laws are different than your laws, all of which I explained to you in great detail. You seem to think I'm blowing hot air. I'm not. When I put things in gear shit happens. Why? Because I have the necessary criminal connections. I get things done because in my world people exchange services. I want to show you I have the people on call to implement any nastiness I elect to become involved with.

...Pay attention, Girl: I gave you a $GOLDEN$ opportunity to plug in on a unique situation. The FU of a crime/horror writer. Author FU using his art/prose as inculpatory evidence. But you never made that effort. ACA had the same chance... but no... they preferred to spin a web of insinuation that fostered a lie... Shame! Shame! And what's even worse for you is that now you've lost my trust. You led me to believe ACA was a good presentation. It's not, and you are abundantly aware of that. My mail bears out that the viewers were led to believe the book portrays actual acts; not fiction. What your pal FBI-H is now publishing also bears out that he has been influenced by what you've done in a negative manner.

It would now seem I'm down as a SK *and* a sadistic sex-killer. How very interesting. What does he base all that on?

You don't seem to understand when I ask you nice so I need to let you know I have other ways available. I wouldn't kill you. I can make life a real torment for you though. But my preference would be that you come on down here so that we can talk it over and not have this awful thing between us.

You need to rest and put it all to one side and work a real job. There are quite a few very new and important developments in my case and I will not write them out but will, if you come down, tell you about them in person. I'll even assume for the moment you do not realize how destructive to my goals your recent actions are; that you are not acting with malice. I really do want to see you face to face so we can properly communicate about all these things. Maybe if you can see my eyes you'll believe me.

4/26/92. I get amazing mail. Psychologists want to study me so they can learn the secrets of the SK. I ask where they ever got the idea I am an SK. Guess where? ACA. [Smiley-face] Then I have to spend time explaining what tabloid TV is all about: not reality. Then I get letters from people who've read something FBI-H write that says I'm a 'SK-sadist-sex killer.' I guess FBI-H has a list of victims and some M.E. reports that back all that up? Did he get it from ACA, SL or just make it up after reading KF? What do you have to say about that my dear old friend?

Now would be a good time to inquire if you can be re-instated onto my list. Come here and we can talk this over in person, if you wish. I am not going to change my mind about what I've decided but I'd like to have a personal peace between us. Besides I have a lot of neat stuff to tell you about… I won't write it but I'd tell it to you since you are involved, sort of.

5/12/92. Where you seem to have had a problem in the past is that you confuse my fiction with your reality. Let me provide you with an example: I told you early on that I was sufficiently skilled in my art to be able to write fiction that readers would believe is reality. I was even agreeable to show you how this could be done via a KBS program. Then there was the angle where if I lost in Court, we could do a book of "Killer Fact" that would be fiction palmed off as fact because people will believe anything except that which they don't want to believe. As a gesture of my own sincerity I'll start by rescinding my prohibition against further sales of GJS writing. You just go ahead and do the orders that come in to you. I'll do the French interview. You come see me here and we'll talk over a film deal. You / MQ have no rights to any of my work until such a time as we conclude a new agreement between us; so don't go around saying you do. You'd better learn to take me seriously because I do what I say I'll do.

6/19/92. I wrote to you several times offering to meet with you to discuss our differences. You've made no response. My conscience is clear. Under Florida law you've abandoned our Agreement and I've fulfilled my legal obligation by offering you to revise it. You chose not to. The contract is broken and you've no claim; so please do not whore after me about it.

(1) I've sold the true story book. (2) I've sold the true story film of the frame-up. (3) I've sold "The Justice Now Newsletter." Cash in the bank. Sondra, I gave you every chance to go after the true story. You didn't want it. All you want to do is infer that I'm a SK. Fuck that! Other people took what I said seriously and are convinced that I am framed. The TS has been sold to a major publisher. I've got an experienced author on it who is a former journalist. I'm going to warn you one last time: The very next time you say or do anything that causes me problems, and that includes crying to me about what you threw away so recklessly, I am going to encourage my dope addled Satanist pals in Georgia to go pick up your slut daughter and teach her some sex education. Thanks to your pushing the idea that I'm a SK I'm getting plenty of weirdo mail; you've probably gotten some yourself. I know how to pander to weirdos and as you've found out: Yes, there is indeed a Satanic underground... and they do love young girls. My offer is simple: You don't fuck with me; I won't fuck with your kid. Do we have a deal?

I always say nice things about you whenever your name comes up. But I don't like whores and I don't like half-breed teenaged nigger sluts; I know exactly what to do about them. We don't agree. Will never agree. So let's just have peace between us because the alternative is war. You want war? If so, fuck with me; you'll get it in spades. Doubt me? Ask Sadie what happened when Goyo fucked with her and I found out, then ask her what happened to the guy who meddled with Elen. I am sincere. Sincerely good or sincerely bad. It's all up to you.

1993

2/13/93. Hello Whore, the word on the yard is that the Queen of the Sluts was at FSP romancing Danny Rolling. Word also has it that Bobby Lewis is ratting out the Slut's main squeeze to the cops. The entire prison is aware of it: Bobby Lewis and Sondra London are taking down Rolling. Dude name of Williams says the Whore is sexually mesmerizing Danny Boy while her pal, Lewis, pumps him and runs to the cops every time Danny opens his mouth. I was so right about you, Sondra: *whore*. Pure fucking whore. A whore and a rat. The word is that Lewis is digging himself a grave. He'd lie on his own mama for a chance to get out of here... Valentine, you're *mine*. Why you out front licking Rolling's ego? I know what you're up to: *money*. You're gonna get Danny Boy fried while you make a buck off his misery. Right? Well, go for it! Just make sure you keep my name out of this episode. Should I find out that you say I'm a SK or see my name involved in any of this Rollings crap you're at the center of then I'm going to put you and your whoredaughter on my list of unfinished business. Williams don't like you worth shit and he claims to have KKK connections. Me, I like you just fine, always have but *if* you cross the line and attempt to exploit me then I'll be coming for you with something other than love in my heart. I've earned $3,000 this year in out of Court lawsuit settlements. People saying I'm a SK. Say it but have no legal legs to stand on. Don't make the same error and you and I and the kid will be cool. Go do Rolling. I know you'll do him well. You're a pro. I'll give you a reference any time you need one. You are never away from my thoughts, Valentine.

3/8/93. I'm suing lots of people now. I've sued six and already one has settled out of court. More suits are being drafted. Joel Norris is next. That cunt put me in a paperback. What a double-crosser. I *warned* that fucker; now I'm gonna make him pay. I don't make idle threats about lawsuits and stuff. Hey, go kick ass in Court. If you need a deposition... I'll help ya, Whore.

4/19/93. Hi, Babe. Remember me? I remember you. Do you recollect I told you to cease and desist selling my stuff and using my name in an exploitive and negative manner? You are still at it and I am not very happy about it. I told you. I warned you. Really, I did. I gave you every consideration to bow out gracefully. I'm getting lots of mail thanks to you and I'm meeting some real sick types. They send me stuff. *Globe* for one. Lovely. You really played it Queen of the Sluts for them, didn't you? Saw you on Geraldo. Must say you're disgusting, a genuine whore. For the sake of the good times I'm gonna give you one last opportunity to make a clean break. Pack up everything with my name on it and send it to Mom; don't mention my name again in your filthy business of exploiting the victims of crime. Call Mom and settle up with her on the MQ deal from France. I know all about how my work there is being marketed there as *true stories.* I see your name going along with it too. You are a *bad girl.* You also have a slut daughter. Now settle up and keep my name out of your dirty business. I got your address from Danny's pal, a pal who don't like you behind your back. I know where you live and your movements. I'll send some guys to talk things over with you and the kid. I'm at the end of my patience with you.

Do you realize how many nut cases read *Globe*? People who want to write to a real "sadistic sex killer" because they are wannabes. All I need to do is point to you and say 'sic em.' You *know* I'm not a suspect in 34 murders and you *know* Jessup & Place wasn't a sex crime so why are you defaming me with that crap? Now let's get squared away between us otherwise I'm going to do whatever necessary to get you to cease and desist with your exploitation of my name in a defamatory manner and imputing serial murder to me. If you don't respond to good reason, I'll start filing lawsuits. That's an ironclad promise. Now what's your pleasure? I'm open to reason & peace & good sense... or whatever it takes.

10/14/93. I will be meeting with a representative of the New York Times to discuss my criminal charges filed against yourself and Paul Woods with New Scotland Yard for Berne Convention violations under the "Literary Piracy Statutes"... and I'm just getting warmed up, Baby. You have my undivided attention. You are my project for the next 5 years...

10/19/93. Wouldn't it be better if we were friends instead of mean old enemies? I'm agreeable to a peace plan. What's your personal preference, peace or war? You know how I am, no quit in me. I'll stay on you and run you into the earth.

12/5/93. *[Schaefer was barred by the prison administration from writing to Sondra London directly. This letter was addressed to Paul Woods, publisher of* Knockin' on Joe, *a British anthology of prison stories containing Schaefer's* Starke Stories

and an essay about Schaefer by Sondra London. Please note that all of the frivo-
lous lawsuits Schaefer mentions were dismissed, and his attempts to have crimi-
nal charges filed likewise came to naught.]

I made it absolutely clear to Sondra London from the very outset that in my world, the world forced upon me by my circumstances of having been framed for murder, that men live and die by the code of the underworld. We have no lawyers, we operate on a Code of Honor. I told her that if she violated my trust that I would strike back at her according to the dictates of my world, not hers. Sondra elected to violate my friendship and my trust. She has no integrity about her. She is without honor; she is a whore. I spit on her.

I also made it clear to SL that I would never under any circumstances participate in any literary project with other inmates. SL violated that term as well. SL is a liar, a cheat, a fraud and a thief. I am a former street cop who is in open population in perhaps America's most repressive hellhole. I am not in a protective confinement cell: I walk the yard like a man. My closest associate in this slimepit is an Anointed Fourth Prince of the Hand of Death who was a contract killer for the Mafia. He is serving a 125 year minimum mandatory life sentence for crimes too revolting to discuss here. This man has gunned down mobsters from Miami to New York and can give names and dates. He is one of the most honest persons in this prison. All I need to do is ask this gentleman to have SL and her kid murdered and it would be done. SL is alive at this moment because I choose to allow it.

SL has put my name and my work next to that of Robert F. Lewis, who is perhaps the slimiest rat in this prison. Lewis is at the bottom of the heap, a breathing piece of dog feces. Lewis just gave testimony for the State to help put SL's boyfriend, Rolling, on the electric chair. SL is helping Lewis to get her own fiancé executed. SL is less than dog shit, dog vomit. She is vile beyond contempt.

This brings us to the matter of SL's commentary about me. SL is a thief and a liar. Much of what she wrote in KOJ is libelous. I've already sued Robert Ressler concerning what he has done to libelously impute serial murder to me. The case is filed in U.S. District Court. I am suing all persons associated with SL who have libeled me. Suits are already filed against Globe, Michael Newton, Loompanics, Robert Ressler, Joel Norris and others. This is expensive fact, not fiction.

As you have noticed, I am a writer. The other contributors to KOJ are men who, while they do have a point of view, are not men trained as writers. "Starke Stories" are professionally done fiction of superior quality. SL used KOJ as a platform from which she libels me. I am genuinely furious about this situation; I am outraged and I am within an ace of requesting that SL be shot. The scummy whore is to get out of my life because she is dishonest. Ottis Toole has more integrity than Sondra London, you can quote me on that.

I made it clear to SL in April – May 1992 that we were through. I do not lend my good name to advance the cause of persons such as SL, Bobby Lewis and Danny Rolling. You cannot understand what I am saying unless you live an honorable life. You will either grasp this concept or you won't.

Danny Rolling is a confessed sex killer of local college kids. The man is a coward who won't even come out in population. SL took my work and used it to promote this vile scumbag who is valued only as a sideshow freak. DR's draw is

that he is a malignant serial killer. Bobby Lewis is a rat who would be murdered if he came to population. SL knows how I feel about these slimeballs. I am revolted to know my name is associated with them. I cannot adequately express the depth and enormity of my anger about this situation. A person in prison often has nothing except for his reputation. I have a good rep with the people who count, whereas Rolling and Lewis are regarded as shit on one's heel.

I will not have anything whatsoever to do with SL and every time she puts anything into print about me I intend to sue her. I will also sue anyone who publishes anything SL says about me in print which is even borderline libelous. SL is finding out right now that I mean what I say. I am trying my best to have her arrested and jailed.

My work is absolutely unique. It stands alone, and either survives or fails on its own merit. This work does not require a windy introduction full of imputed criminal acts and self-serving justifications for publishing it. I don't require SL to explain my work to the masses or turn on me as a rabid bitch and impute that my work is a product of my personal conduct.

I will not be rebutting SL except to say that she is a liar, deadbeat, thief and whore. Hopefully she'll be dead before this comment is published. Good chance of that happening.

This letter clarifies my position regarding SL.

Sincerely,

Gerard Schaefer

1994

11/11/94. *[From a pleading filed by Plaintiff Schaefer withdrawing his appeal of one of the lawsuits that was dismissed as frivolous.]*

While working in the prison law library Plaintiff was attacked by another inmate and stabbed repeatedly in and about the face, body and hands. Due to the trauma sustained incidental to this attack, Plaintiff is now unable to prosecute his appeal; therefore Plaintiff withdraws the appeal in this case.

Abbreviations used by Schaefer

ACA	A Current Affair (TV show)	KBS	Killer Best Selections aka Killer Bullshit (Ambiguous term)
BD	Bondage & Discipline (Sex perversions)		
BG	Brian Gross (Prison investigator)	KF	Killer Fiction (Book)
		KF or FU	Killer Fact or Frame-Up (Article by London)
BKF	Beyond Killer Fiction (Book)	KS	Killer Serial aka "RC" (Series of stories)
BVM	Blessed Virgin Mary		
CW	Aka "Cas" (Early girlfriend)	LOD	Legion of Decency (Story)
DDK	Detective Dan Kelly (Fictional character)	LP	Lucille Place (Victim's mother)
ES	Elton Schwarz (Defender, married GJS' ex-wife)	MN	Mike Newton (Author)
		MD	Murder Demons (Short story & unwritten true story)
FB	Frita Bandita (Unpublished story about Toole)		
FC	False Confessions (story; also generic term)	MQ	Media Queen (London's publishing business)
FBI-H	Roy Hazelwood (FBI expert in serial killers)	OT	Ottis Toole (Serial killer)
		PK	Patrick Kendrick (Author)
FP	Frieda Powell (Becky)	PP	Publisher's Preface (Article by London)
FS5	Fact Sheet 5 (Magazine)		
FSP	Florida State Prison	RC	Rogue Cop aka "KS" (Series of stories)
FT	Freak Trade (Story & generic commercial perversion)	RD	Rough draft
		RS	Robert Stone (Prosecutor)
FU	Frame-Up (Theory)	SK	Serial killer
G-Wilcox	Goodenough & Wilcox (Double murder)	SL	Sondra London (aka Media Queen)
HLL	Henry Lee Lucas (Serial killer)	SM	Sadomasochism (Sex perversion)
HOD	Hand of Death (Cult)	TS	True story (unwritten)
JN	Joel Norris aka "Beau" (Author)	TSKWLM	The Serial Killer Who Loves Me (Article by London)
JP	Jessup & Place (Double murder)	T/W	Trotter & Wells (Double assault)
		VP	Visitor's Park (at prison)

Killer Verse

Sex Beast

They say I eat little girls… Got a hungry look in my eye
Say I make them scream… & Get off when they die
They call me Sex Beast

The girls will never tell… Those who knew me well
How I made them scream… How I made them yell
They met the Sex Beast

Sexy little prom queens oh so cool… Each one knowing she'd been a fool
Pretty ladies in my hairy paw… Last thing most of them saw
Was the Sex Beast

Long pink tongue licking at her ear… I told her she could disappear
Missing person for eternity… Last thing that girl would see
Was the Sex Beast

She never said a word… When she heard me growl
The last thing she heard… Was the savage howl
Of the Sex Beast

They say I kill little girls… Got that killer look in my eye
Say I make them scream… And watch them die
They call me Sex Beast

Flashing teeth ripping young flesh sweet
Blood splattered from neck to dainty feet
The full moon is the time to feast
So says the Sex Beast
So says the Sex Beast

SUZIE PRIME TRUE CRIME

Hey fuck-slut, little prom queen
What you doing up in North Palm Beach?
Sightseeing, tricking
Scoring your scag?
Say Suzie, where'd you get that bag?
Where's your man, where's your pusher?
Where's your sugar daddy?
How'd you get out of jail?
How'd you make bail?
Suzie prime, true crime
Doing time, earn that dime
Bag, brown scag
Set her free, killing tree
Po-leece fantasy

Suzie Prime, double time
One-two-three
So efficiently
Swinging from the tree
With flying feet
To match the beat
Of dying
That's her fee
For lying
Take her to the tree
That's her fee
For telling
Please don't hang me
She was yelling
Birdie she did sing
Then take a swing
On the rope
No more dope
Just dancing
Fine young thing
Prancing
Spike heels
Rhinestone dress
Now she's just
A stinking mess

Lucille

Lucille!
How'd it feel
Tearing your daughter
From your breast
Driving Suzie from the nest
Junkie daughter pest
The one you laid to rest
No more!
You closed that door
On the teenage whore
Did she stay out late?
Make Mummy wait?
You raised her right
So you swore
Loved her to the core
So you state
Please Lucille
Tell us the date
Suzie met her fate
Did you forget?
To change that date
It's too weird to believe
When did Suzie really leave?
What did you really see?
What's your reality?
What's Lucille's fantasy?
I've heard your lie
No matter how you try
It doesn't fly
Your story's dead
Like Suzie's severed head
Remember
How the doctor said
It's a girl
She was your whole world
So you changed and fed
Sweet little Suzie
But she's not grown
She won't be wed
Your Suzie dreams are dead

GEORGIA PEACH

Pretty Georgia
Sweet peach
Now you're rotting
On the beach
Young girl fled
From her home
For parts unknown
To find her head
Her letter said
Now she's dead
And rotten
Gone but not
Forgotten
By the family
She tried to flee
Running toward
The killing tree
With Suzie
Addicted floozie

Sweet Georgia
Pretty peach
Dead and rotten
On the beach
Body naked
On the sand
Flesh destroyed
By human hand
Were you hanging
From the tree?
Or were you crying
For your life?
Cut to pieces
With the killer's knife?

Pretty Georgia
Do tell
Scream your answers
Up from Hell

MORTAL SIN

Vomit dripping
From her chin
Restitution
For mortal sin

Shapely hips
Painted lips
Salty tears
Making streaks
Down her cheeks
They dribble down
Mixed with snot
Yellow green
Wet sheen
On upper lips
It drips

Frothy bubbles
From her nose
Sticky blood
Between her toes
Hear her squeal
Smell her fear
See her drool
So uncool

NECESSARY BLOOD

Death smell
Evil spell
Salty tears
Streak your cheeks
Its time to die
Now watch you cry
Scared and crying
For your life
By the very sight
Of the killer's knife
Now you're gonna bleed

Real blood
Squirts from your neck
Into the mud
Real blood
Runs out your nose
Onto your lips
Flesh rips
Destroyed
By human hand

At the end
Crawling on your knees
Begging for your life
Oh pretty please
Spare the terror
Of the killer's knife

Now he put you
To the steel
tell me
How's it feel?

Muffled shriek
Caressing sting
Red slime splashes
Over everything
Crimson flow
Between creamy dugs
Here it comes

Necessary blood

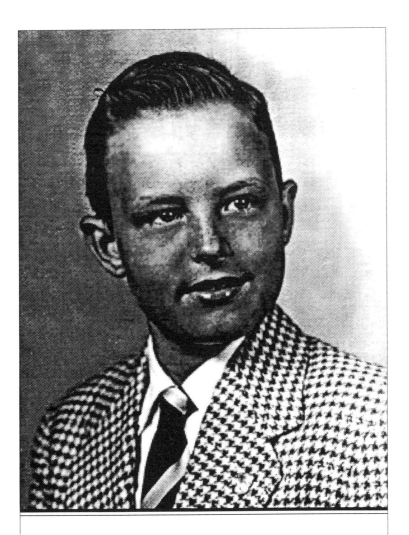

Gerard John Schaefer, shown here at age nine, enjoyed an idyllic childhood. The eldest of three children, he grew up in a comfortable wooded suburb of Atlanta, Georgia, and attended Marist Academy, a parochial school. His mother stayed home caring for the family. His father was a traveling salesman who did well enough to relocate his family to a new home in trendy Ft. Lauderdale, Florida in the fifties, and maintain yacht club and country club memberships throughout Schaefer's adolescence.

Available From Feral House

The Making of a Serial Killer
The Real Story of the Gainesville Murders in the Killer's Own Words
by Danny Rolling and Sondra London; Introduction by Colin Wilson
Rolling, the murderer of five Gainesville college students in 1990, has co-written a remarkable confessional book with Sondra London, the woman who helped produce the book you are now holding. Colin Wilson, an expert on occultism and crime, believes that Roling possessed by the devil while committing his crimes.
$12.95 • 201 pages • illustrated

Death Scenes
A Homicide Detective's Scrapbook
Text by Katherine Dunn
Edited by Sean Tejaratchi
The most remarkable photo-book ever printed, based on the collection of an LAPD detective. Not for the faint of heart. Introduction by *Geek Love*'s Katherine Dunn.
$19.95 • 168 pages • 10 x 8

Cold-Blooded
The Saga of Charles Schmid, the Notorious "Pied Piper of Tucson"
John Gilmore
Schmid, something of a cross between Elvis Presley and Charles Manson, was charismatic, psychopathic and totally bizarre. "Here is a narrative of shadow-life, death and trial that is revealing and shocking and most disturbing." — New York Times
$12.95 • Illustrated with photos • 117 pages

The Bomb
The Classic Novel of Anarchist Violence
Frank Harris
About the infamous Haymarket affair from the point of view of the uncaught man who hurled the bomb. "This book is, in truth, a masterpiece; so intense is the impression that one almost asks, 'Is this a novel or a confession? Did not Frank Harris perhaps throw the bomb?' At least he has thrown one now ... the best novel I have ever read." — Aleister Crowley
$12.95 • 214 pages • Illustrated

The books above can be ordered by check or money order.
Add $2 each for shipping to:

Feral House • 2532 Lincoln Blvd., Suite 359 • Venice, CA, • 90291.

A free catalogue of Feral publications will be sent upon request.